GCSE AQA

Additional Science

Complete Revision and Practice

For the Year 11 exams

Contents

Contents

The Periodic Table

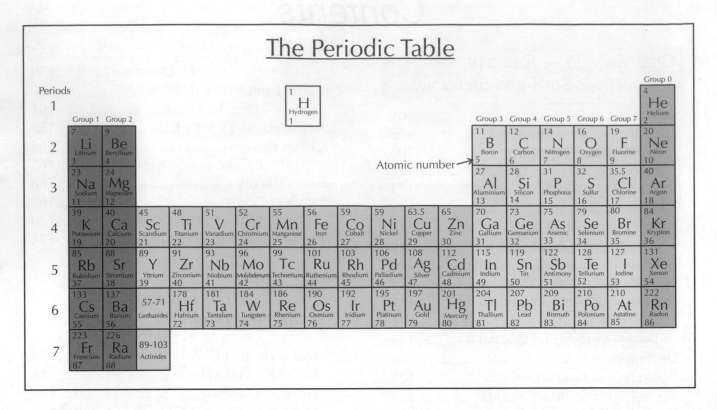

Published by CGP

From original material by Richard Parsons.

Editors:
Katherine Craig, Ceara Hayden, Helena Hayes.

Contributors:
Mike Dagless, James Foster, Barbara Mascetti, John Myers, Adrian Schmit.

ISBN: 978 1 84762 868 8

With thanks to Katie Braid for the proofreading.
With thanks to Anna Lupton for the copyright research.

Data used to construct stopping distance diagram on page 144 from the Highway Code. © Crown Copyright re-produced under the terms of the Click-Use licence.

Pages 190, 191 and 192 contain public sector information published by the Health and Safety Executive and licensed under the Open Government Licence v1.0.

www.cgpbooks.co.uk

Printed by Elanders Ltd, Newcastle upon Tyne.

Clipart from Corel®

The Scientific Process

You need to know a few things about how the world of science works. First up is the <u>scientific process</u> — how a scientist's <u>idea</u> turns into a <u>widely accepted theory</u>.

Scientists come up with **hypotheses** — then **test** them

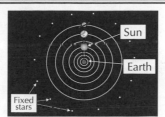

About 500 years ago, we still thought the Solar System looked like this.

1) Scientists try to <u>explain</u> things. Everything.

2) They start by <u>observing</u> something they don't understand — it could be anything, e.g. planets in the sky, a person suffering from an illness, what matter is made of... anything.

3) Then, they come up with a <u>hypothesis</u> — a <u>possible explanation</u> for what they've observed.

4) The next step is to <u>test</u> whether the hypothesis might be <u>right or not</u> — this involves <u>gathering evidence</u> (i.e. <u>data</u> from <u>investigations</u>).

5) The scientist uses the hypothesis to make a <u>prediction</u> — a statement based on the hypothesis that can be <u>tested</u>. They then <u>carry out an investigation</u>.

6) If data from experiments or studies <u>backs up the prediction</u>, you're one step closer to figuring out if the hypothesis is true.

Investigations include lab experiments and studies.

Other scientists will **test** the hypothesis too

1) <u>Other</u> scientists will use the hypothesis to make their <u>own predictions</u>, and carry out their <u>own experiments</u> or studies.

2) They'll also try to <u>reproduce</u> the original investigations to check the results.

3) And if <u>all the experiments</u> in the world back up the hypothesis, then scientists start to think it's <u>true</u>.

4) However, if a scientist somewhere in the world does an experiment that <u>doesn't</u> fit with the hypothesis (and other scientists can <u>reproduce</u> these results), then the hypothesis is in trouble.

5) When this happens, scientists have to come up with a new hypothesis (maybe a <u>modification</u> of the old hypothesis, or maybe a completely <u>new</u> one).

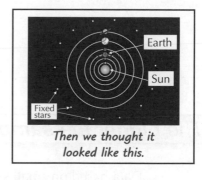

Then we thought it looked like this.

If **evidence** supports a hypothesis, it's **accepted** — **for now**

1) If pretty much every scientist in the world believes a hypothesis to be true because experiments back it up, then it usually goes in the <u>textbooks</u> for students to learn.

Now we think it's more like this.

2) Accepted hypotheses are often referred to as <u>theories</u>.

3) Our <u>currently accepted</u> theories are the ones that have survived this 'trial by evidence' — they've been tested many, many times over the years and survived (while the less good ones have been ditched).

4) However... they never, <u>never</u> become hard and fast, totally indisputable <u>fact</u>. You can never know... it'd only take <u>one</u> odd, totally inexplicable result, and the hypothesising and testing would start all over again.

If you expect me to believe it, then show me the evidence

If scientists think something is true, they need to produce evidence to convince others — it's all part of <u>testing a hypothesis</u>. One hypothesis might survive these tests, while others won't — it's how things progress. And along the way some hypotheses will be disproved — i.e. shown not to be true.

2

Your Data's Got To be Good

Evidence is the key to science — but not all evidence is equally good.
The way evidence is gathered can have a big effect on how trustworthy it is.

Lab experiments and studies are better than rumour

1) Results from experiments in laboratories are great. A lab is the easiest place to control variables so that they're all kept constant (except for the one you're investigating). This makes it easier to carry out a FAIR TEST.

See page 7 for more about fair tests and variables.

2) For things that you can't investigate in the lab (e.g. climate) you conduct scientific studies. As many of the variables as possible are controlled, to make it a fair test.

3) Old wives' tales, rumours, hearsay, "what someone said", and so on, should be taken with a pinch of salt. Without any evidence they're NOT scientific — they're just opinions.

The bigger the sample size the better

1) Data based on small samples isn't as good as data based on large samples.

2) A sample should be representative of the whole population (i.e. it should share as many of the various characteristics in the population as possible) — a small sample can't do that as well.

3) The bigger the sample size the better, but scientists have to be realistic when choosing how big.

4) For example, if you were studying how lifestyle affects people's weight it'd be great to study everyone in the UK (a huge sample), but it'd take ages and cost loads. Studying a thousand people is more realistic.

When it comes to samples, bigger means better

A census is a study which takes into account the entire population — great for collecting loads of data, and properly representative of the whole population, but very difficult and expensive to carry out. A census is conducted in the UK every ten years and is used by the government to plan for the future, but it isn't cheap — the costs of the 2011 census were estimated to be at around £500 million.

2

2

2

Your Data's Got To be Good

When it comes to evidence, <u>reliability</u> and <u>validity</u> are really important.

Evidence Needs to be **Reliable** (**Repeatable** and **Reproducible**)

Evidence is only <u>reliable</u> if it can be <u>repeated</u> (during an experiment) and <u>other scientists can reproduce it too</u> (in other experiments). If it's not reliable, you can't believe it.

RELIABLE means that the data can be <u>repeated, and reproduced by others</u>.

<u>EXAMPLE:</u>

In 1998, a scientist claimed that he'd found a link between the MMR vaccine (for measles, mumps and rubella) and autism.

As a result, many parents stopped their children from having the vaccine — which led to a big rise in the number of children catching measles.

However, no other scientist has been able to repeat the results since — they just weren't reliable. Health authorities have now concluded that the vaccine is safe to use.

Evidence Also Needs to Be **Valid**

VALID means that the data is <u>reliable</u> AND <u>answers the original question</u>.

<u>EXAMPLE: Do power lines cause cancer?</u>

Some studies have found that children who live near <u>overhead power lines</u> are more likely to develop <u>cancer</u>. What they'd actually found was a <u>correlation</u> (relationship) between the variables "<u>presence of power lines</u>" and "<u>incidence of cancer</u>" — they found that as one changed, so did the other.

But this evidence is <u>not enough</u> to say that the power lines <u>cause</u> cancer, as other explanations might be possible.

For example, power lines are often near <u>busy roads</u>, so the areas tested could contain <u>different levels</u> of <u>pollution</u> from traffic.

So these studies don't show a definite link and so don't <u>answer the original question</u>.

RRR — Reliable means Repeatable and Reproducible...

The scientific community won't accept someone's data if it can't be repeated by anyone else. It may sound like a really fantastic new theory, but if there's no other support for it, it just isn't reliable.

Bias and Issues Created by Science

Even the world of science isn't without its problems. <u>Bias</u> can get the better of even the most accomplished scientists — which is why it's important for you to <u>recognise</u> it when it rears its ugly head.

Scientific *evidence* can be *presented* in a *biased way*

1) People who want to make a point can sometimes <u>present data</u> in a <u>biased way</u>, e.g. they overemphasise a relationship in the data. (Sometimes <u>without knowing</u> they're doing it.)

2) And there are all sorts of reasons <u>why</u> people might <u>want</u> to do this — for example...

- They want to keep the <u>organisation</u> or <u>company</u> that's <u>funding the research</u> happy. (If the results aren't what they'd like they might not give them any more money to fund further research.)
- <u>Governments</u> might want to persuade voters, other governments, journalists, etc.
- <u>Companies</u> might want to show off their products or make impressive safety claims.
- <u>Environmental campaigners</u> might want to persuade people to behave differently.

Things can affect *how seriously evidence* is *taken*

1) If an investigation is done by a team of <u>highly-regarded scientists</u> it's sometimes taken <u>more seriously</u> than evidence from <u>less well known scientists</u>.

2) But having experience, authority or a fancy qualification <u>doesn't</u> necessarily mean the evidence is <u>good</u> — the only way to tell is to look at the evidence scientifically (e.g. is it reliable, valid, etc.).

3) Also, some evidence might be <u>ignored</u> if it could create <u>political problems</u>, or <u>emphasised</u> if it <u>helps a particular cause</u>.

<u>EXAMPLE: GLOBAL WARMING</u>

Some governments were <u>pretty slow</u> to accept the fact that human activities are causing <u>global warming</u>, despite all the <u>evidence</u>. This is because accepting it means they've got to <u>do something about it</u>, which <u>costs money</u> and could <u>hurt their economy</u>. This could <u>lose</u> them a lot of <u>votes</u>.

Trust me — I've got a BSc and a PhD

It's easy to believe people in authority, but you have to ignore that fact and look at the evidence. Spotting biased evidence can be difficult — ask yourself 'Does the scientist (or the person writing about it) stand to gain something (or lose something)?' If they do, it's possible that it could be biased.

Bias and Issues Created by Science

No area of science is without issues of some kind — whether it's the matter of finding the money to <u>fund research</u>, <u>environmental problems</u> or even <u>ethical issues</u>, there's always plenty of room for <u>controversy</u>.

Scientific developments are *great*, but they can *raise issues*

Scientific <u>knowledge is increased</u> by doing experiments. And this knowledge leads to <u>scientific developments</u>, e.g. new technologies or new advice. These developments can create <u>issues</u> though. For example:

Economic issues: Society <u>can't</u> always <u>afford</u> to do things scientists recommend (e.g. investing heavily in alternative energy sources) without <u>cutting back elsewhere</u>.

Social issues: Decisions based on scientific evidence affect <u>people</u> — e.g. should fossil fuels be taxed more highly (to invest in alternative energy)? Should alcohol be banned (to prevent health problems)? <u>Would the effect on people's lifestyles be acceptable...</u>

Environmental issues: <u>Nuclear power stations</u> can provide us with a reliable source of <u>electricity</u>, but disposing of the <u>waste</u> can lead to <u>environmental issues</u>.

Ethical issues: There are a lot of things that scientific developments have made possible, but <u>should we do them</u>? E.g. develop better nuclear weapons.

Where science goes, controversy follows

<u>Nuclear energy</u> is one area of science that raises a lot of issues — <u>economic</u> (is it too expensive? Is it a viable energy option?), <u>social</u> (will it affect people living nearby?), <u>environmental</u> (will nuclear waste pollute the surrounding area?) and <u>ethical</u> (should we use the technology to develop weapons?).

Science Has Limits

Science can give us <u>amazing things</u> — cures for diseases, space travel, heated toilet seats...
But science has its <u>limitations</u> — there are questions that it just can't answer.

Some questions are **unanswered** by science — so far

1) We <u>don't understand everything</u>. And we <u>never will</u>. We'll find out <u>more</u>,
for sure — as more hypotheses are suggested, and more experiments are done.
But there'll <u>always</u> be things we don't know.

> EXAMPLES:
> - Today we don't know as much as we'd like about the <u>impacts</u> of <u>global warming</u>.
>   How much will <u>sea level rise</u>? And to what extent will <u>weather patterns change</u>?
> - We also don't know anywhere near as much as we'd like about the <u>Universe</u>.
>   Are there other <u>life forms</u> out there? And what is the Universe <u>made of</u>?

2) These are complicated questions. At the moment scientists don't all agree on the
answers because there <u>isn't enough</u> reliable and valid <u>evidence</u>.

3) But <u>eventually</u>, we probably <u>will</u> be able to answer these questions once and for all...
All we need is <u>more evidence</u>.

4) But by then there'll be loads of <u>new</u> questions to answer.

Other questions are **unanswerable** by science

1) Then there's the other type... questions that all the experiments in the world <u>won't</u> help us answer
— the "<u>Should we be doing this at all?</u>" type questions. There are always two sides...

2) Take <u>space exploration</u>. It's <u>possible</u> to do it — but does that mean we <u>should</u>?

3) Different people have <u>different opinions</u>.

For example...
Some people say it's a <u>good idea</u>... it <u>increases our knowledge</u> about the
Universe, we <u>develop new technologies</u> that can be useful on Earth too,
it <u>inspires young people</u> to take an interest in science, etc.

Other people say it's a <u>bad idea</u>... the vast sums of <u>money</u> it costs should
be spent on <u>more urgent problems</u>, like providing clean drinking water
and curing diseases in poor countries. Others say that we should
concentrate research efforts on understanding our <u>own planet</u> better first.

4) The question of whether something is <u>morally</u> or <u>ethically</u> right or wrong <u>can't be answered</u> by
more <u>experiments</u> — there is <u>no "right" or "wrong" answer</u>.

5) The best we can do is get a <u>consensus</u> from society — a <u>judgement</u> that <u>most people</u> are more or
less happy to live by. <u>Science</u> can provide <u>more information</u> to help people make this judgement,
and the judgement might <u>change</u> over time. But in the end it's up to <u>people</u> and their <u>conscience</u>.

Science doesn't have all the answers

Science <u>can't</u> tell you whether you <u>should</u> or <u>shouldn't</u> do something. That kind of thing is up to you
and society to decide. There are tons of questions that science <u>might be able to answer</u> in the future
— like how much sea level might rise due to global warming, or what the Universe is made of.

Designing Investigations

You need to know a lot about <u>investigations</u> for your <u>controlled assessment</u> and <u>all your exams</u>. Investigations include <u>experiments</u> and <u>studies</u>. The next nine pages take you from start to finish. Enjoy.

Investigations *produce evidence* to *support* or *disprove* a *hypothesis*

1) Scientists <u>observe</u> things and come up with <u>hypotheses</u> to explain them (see page 1).

2) To figure out whether a hypothesis might be correct or not you need to do an <u>investigation</u> to gather some <u>evidence</u>.

3) The first step is to use the hypothesis to come up with a <u>prediction</u> — a statement about what you <u>think will happen</u> that you can <u>test</u>.

Sometimes the words 'hypothesis' and 'prediction' are used interchangeably.

4) For example, if your <u>hypothesis</u> is:

> "Tooth cavities are caused by eating too much sugary food."

Then your <u>prediction</u> might be:

> "People who eat more sugary food will have more tooth cavities."

5) Investigations are used to see if there are <u>patterns</u> or <u>relationships</u> <u>between two variables</u>. For example, to see if there's a pattern or relationship between the variables 'having tooth cavities' and 'consumption of sugary food'.

See page 3 for more on reliability and validity.

6) The investigation has to be a <u>FAIR TEST</u> to make sure the evidence is <u>reliable</u> and <u>valid</u>...

To make an investigation a *fair test* you have to *control the variables*

1) In a lab experiment you usually <u>change one variable</u> and <u>measure</u> how it affects the <u>other variable</u>.

> EXAMPLE: you might change only the angle of a slope and measure how it affects the time taken for a toy car to travel down it.

2) To make it a fair test <u>everything else</u> that could affect the results should <u>stay the same</u> (otherwise you can't tell if the thing you're changing is causing the results or not — the data won't be reliable or valid).

> EXAMPLE continued: you need to keep the slope length the same, otherwise you won't know if any change in the time taken is caused by the change in angle, or the change in length.

3) The variable you CHANGE is called the INDEPENDENT variable.
4) The variable you MEASURE is called the DEPENDENT variable.
5) The variables that you KEEP THE SAME are called CONTROL variables.

> EXAMPLE continued:
> Independent variable = angle of slope
> Dependent variable = time taken
> Control variable = length of slope

Designing Investigations

Before you start collecting data, it's useful to know the sort of results you might get so you can design your experiment to be as good as it can be. That's why scientists use <u>trial runs</u> and <u>preliminary experiments</u>.

Trial runs help decide the range and interval of variable values

1) It's a good idea to do a <u>trial run</u> first
— a <u>quick version</u> of your experiment.

SLOPE EXAMPLE FROM
PREVIOUS PAGE CONTINUED:

• You might do trial runs at 20, 40, 60 and 80°. If the time taken is too short to accurately measure at 80°, you might narrow the range to 20-60°.

• If using 20° intervals gives you a big change in time taken you might decide to use 10° intervals, e.g. 20, 30, 40, 50°...

2) Trial runs are used to figure out the <u>range</u> of variable values used in the proper experiment (the upper and lower limit). For example, if you <u>can't</u> accurately measure the change in the dependent variable at the upper values in the trial run, you might <u>narrow</u> the range in the proper experiment.

3) And trial runs can be used to figure out the <u>interval</u> (gaps) between the values too. The intervals can't be too small (otherwise the experiment would take ages), or too big (otherwise you might miss something).

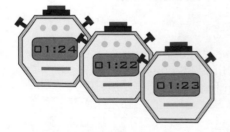

4) Trial runs can also help you figure out <u>how many times</u> the experiment has to be <u>repeated</u> to get reliable results. E.g. if you repeat it three times and the <u>results</u> are all <u>similar</u>, then three repeats is enough.

You won't get a trial run at the exam, so get learning

Always use trial runs to help you <u>plan</u> your investigation so you can make it as <u>effective as possible</u>. A trial run can give you an idea of <u>what kind of values you're looking for</u>.

Designing Investigations

Not all investigations can be conducted within the laboratory. Sometimes there are <u>extra variables</u> that you can't control. That doesn't mean you can ignore them though — it means it's time for a <u>control group</u>.

It can be **hard** to **control the variables** in a **study**

1) It's important that a study is a <u>fair test</u>, just like a lab experiment.

2) It's a lot trickier to control the variables in a study than it is in a lab experiment though (see page 7). Sometimes you can't control them all, but you can use a <u>control group</u> to help.

3) This is a group of whatever you're studying (people, plants, lemmings, etc.) that's kept under the <u>same conditions</u> as the group in the experiment, but doesn't have anything done to it.

EXAMPLE: PESTICIDES

If you're studying the effect of pesticides on crop growth, pesticide is applied to one field but <u>not to another field</u> (the control field).

Both fields are planted with the <u>same crop</u>, and are in the <u>same area</u> (so they get the same weather conditions). The control field is there to try and account for variables like the weather, which don't stay the same all the time, but could <u>affect the results</u>.

Investigations can be **hazardous**

1) A <u>hazard</u> is something that can <u>potentially cause harm</u>. Hazards include:

- <u>Microorganisms</u>, e.g. some bacteria can make you ill.
- <u>Chemicals</u>, e.g. sulfuric acid can burn your skin and alcohols catch fire easily.
- <u>Fire</u>, e.g. an unattended Bunsen burner is a fire hazard.
- <u>Electricity</u>, e.g. faulty electrical equipment could give you a shock.

2) Scientists need to <u>manage the risk</u> of hazards by doing things to reduce them. For example:

You can find out about potential hazards by looking in textbooks, doing some internet research, or asking your teacher.

- If you're working with <u>sulfuric acid</u>, always wear gloves and safety goggles. This will reduce the risk of the acid coming into contact with your skin and eyes.
- If you're using a <u>Bunsen burner</u>, stand it on a heat proof mat. This will reduce the risk of starting a fire.

Collecting Data

After designing an investigation you'll need to get your hands mucky and <u>collect some data</u>.

*Your data should be **reliable**, **accurate** and **precise***

1) To <u>improve</u> reliability you need to <u>repeat</u> the readings and calculate the <u>mean</u> (average). You need to repeat each reading at least <u>three times</u>.

2) To make sure your results are reliable you can cross check them by taking a <u>second set of readings</u> with <u>another instrument</u> (or a <u>different observer</u>).

3) Checking your results match with <u>secondary sources</u>, e.g. other studies, also increases the reliability of your data.

4) Your data also needs to be <u>ACCURATE</u>. Really accurate results are those that are <u>really close</u> to the <u>true answer</u>.

5) Your data also needs to be <u>PRECISE</u>. Precise results are ones where the data is <u>all really close</u> to the <u>mean</u> (i.e. not spread out).

Repeat	Data set 1	Data set 2
1	12	11
2	14	17
3	13	14
Mean	13	14

Data set 1 is more precise than data set 2.

*Your **equipment** has to be **right for the job***

1) The measuring equipment you use has to be <u>sensitive enough</u> to measure the changes you're looking for.

> For example, if you need to measure changes of 1 ml you need to use a measuring cylinder that can measure in 1 ml steps — it'd be no good trying with one that only measures 10 ml steps.

2) The <u>smallest change</u> a measuring instrument can <u>detect</u> is called its <u>RESOLUTION</u>.

> E.g. some mass balances have a resolution of 1 g, some have a resolution of 0.1 g, and some are even more sensitive.

3) Also, equipment needs to be <u>calibrated</u> so that your data is <u>more accurate</u>.

> E.g. mass balances need to be set to zero before you start weighing things.

For good data, remember RAP — Reliable, Accurate and Precise

Weirdly, data can be really <u>precise</u> but <u>not very accurate</u>, e.g. a fancy piece of lab equipment might give results that are precise, but if it's not calibrated properly those results won't be accurate. Likewise, data can be accurate <u>without</u> being precise. For example, an experiment might tell you that the speed of sound in air is in the range of 300 m/s to 350 m/s. This is accurate (because it's true) but it's not at all precise.

Collecting Data

All experimental data have some errors in them. A good scientist doesn't ignore errors, but instead finds out why they are there and tries to minimise them.

You need to look out for errors and anomalous results

1) The results of your experiment will always vary a bit because of random errors — tiny differences caused by things like human errors in measuring.

2) You can reduce their effect by taking many readings and calculating the mean.

3) If the same error is made every time, it's called a systematic error. For example, if you measured from the very end of your ruler instead of from the 0 cm mark every time, all your measurements would be a bit small.

4) Just to make things more complicated, if a systematic error is caused by using equipment that isn't zeroed properly it's called a zero error. For example, if a mass balance always reads 1 gram before you put anything on it, all your measurements will be 1 gram too heavy.

5) You can compensate for some systematic errors if you know about them though, e.g. if your mass balance always reads 1 gram before you put anything on it you can subtract 1 gram from all your results.

6) Sometimes you get a result that doesn't seem to fit in with the rest at all. These results are called anomalous results.

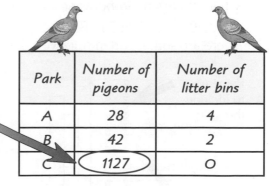

Park	Number of pigeons	Number of litter bins
A	28	4
B	42	2
C	1127	0

7) You should investigate them and try to work out what happened. If you can work out what happened (e.g. you measured something totally wrong) you can ignore them when processing your results.

Avoid zero errors — always zero your equipment

It's not enough just to identify which results are anomalous — you should provide a reason for why they are there. Otherwise, they might not be anomalous results at all, they could just a be a result that you are missing due to bias in your experiment. One scientist's anomaly could be another's discovery.

Processing and Presenting Data

After you've collected your data you'll have <u>lots of info</u> that you have to <u>make some kind of sense of</u>. You need to <u>process</u> and <u>present</u> it so you can look for <u>patterns</u> and <u>relationships</u> in it.

Data needs to be organised

1) Tables are dead useful for <u>organising data</u>.

2) When you draw a table <u>use a ruler</u>, make sure <u>each column</u> has a <u>heading</u> (including the <u>units</u>) and keep it neat and tidy.

3) Annoyingly, tables aren't very useful for showing <u>patterns</u> or <u>relationships</u> in data. You need to use some kind of graph for that.

You might have to process your data

1) When you've done repeats of an experiment you should always calculate the <u>mean</u> (average). To do this <u>ADD TOGETHER</u> all the data values and <u>DIVIDE</u> by the total number of values in the sample.

2) You might also need to calculate the <u>range</u> (how spread out the data is). To do this find the <u>LARGEST</u> number and <u>SUBTRACT</u> the <u>SMALLEST</u> number from it.

Ignore anomalous results when calculating these.

EXAMPLE

Test tube	Repeat 1 (g)	Repeat 2 (g)	Repeat 3 (g)	Mean (g)	Range (g)
A	28	37	32	(28 + 37 + 32) ÷ 3 = 32.3	37 − 28 = 9
B	47	51	60	(47 + 51 + 60) ÷ 3 = 52.7	60 − 47 = 13
C	68	72	70	(68 + 72 + 70) ÷ 3 = 70.0	72 − 68 = 4

If your data comes in categories, present it in a bar chart

1) If the independent variable is <u>categoric</u> (comes in distinct categories, e.g. blood types, metals) you should use a <u>bar chart</u> to display the data.

2) You also use them if the independent variable is <u>discrete</u> (the data can be counted in chunks, where there's no in-between value, e.g. number of people is discrete because you can't have half a person).

3) There are some <u>golden rules</u> you need to follow for <u>drawing</u> bar charts:

Remember to include the <u>units</u>.

If you've got more than one set of data <u>include a key</u>.

Ice Cream Sales in Malmesbury and Chippenham

Malmesbury
Chippenham

Draw it nice and <u>big</u> (covering at least half of the graph paper).

Number sold (thousands)

Chocolate   Mint   Strawberry   Lemon
Ice cream flavour

<u>Label both axes</u>.

Leave a <u>gap between</u> different categories.

Bar charts — perfect for discrete variables

The stuff on this page might all seem a bit basic, but it's <u>easy marks</u> in the exams. Examiners are a bit picky when it comes to bar charts — if you don't draw them properly they won't be happy. Also, <u>double check</u> any mean or range <u>calculations</u> you do, just to be sure they're correct.

Presenting Data

If your data is *continuous*, plot a *line graph*

1) If the independent variable is <u>continuous</u> (numerical data that can have any value within a range, e.g. length, volume, temperature) you should use a <u>line graph</u> to display the data.

2) Here are the <u>rules</u> for <u>drawing</u> line graphs:

Remember to include the <u>units</u>.

Put the <u>dependent</u> variable (the thing you measure) on the <u>y-axis</u> (the <u>vertical</u> one).

<u>Label both axes</u>.

If you've got more than one set of data <u>include a key</u>.

Draw it nice and <u>big</u> (covering at least half of the graph paper).

Put the <u>independent</u> variable (the thing you change) on the <u>x-axis</u> (the <u>horizontal</u> one).

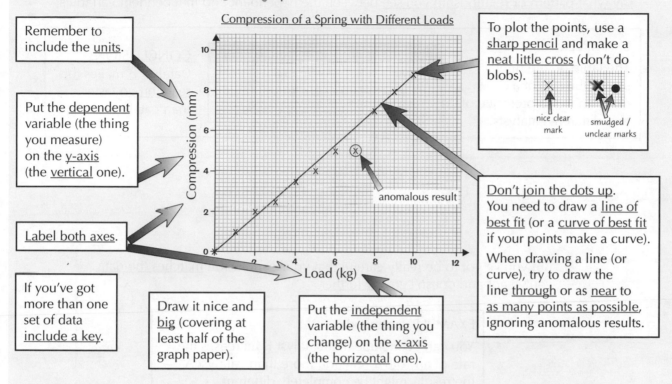

Compression of a Spring with Different Loads

anomalous result

To plot the points, use a <u>sharp pencil</u> and make a <u>neat little cross</u> (don't do blobs).

nice clear mark

smudged / unclear marks

<u>Don't join the dots up</u>. You need to draw a <u>line of best fit</u> (or a <u>curve of best fit</u> if your points make a curve).

When drawing a line (or curve), try to draw the line <u>through</u> or as <u>near</u> to <u>as many points as possible</u>, ignoring anomalous results.

3) Line graphs are used to <u>show the relationship</u> between two variables (just like other graphs).

4) Data can show <u>three</u> different types of correlation (relationship):

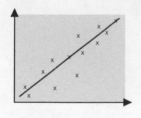

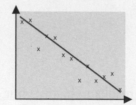

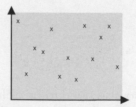

<u>POSITIVE</u> correlation — as one variable <u>increases</u> the other <u>increases</u>.

<u>NEGATIVE</u> correlation — as one variable <u>increases</u> the other <u>decreases</u>.

<u>NO</u> correlation — there's <u>no relationship</u> between the two variables.

5) You need to be able to describe the following relationships on line graphs too:

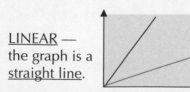

<u>LINEAR</u> — the graph is a <u>straight line</u>.

<u>DIRECTLY PROPORTIONAL</u> — the graph is a <u>straight line</u> where both variables increase (or decrease) in the <u>same ratio</u>.

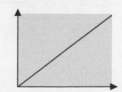

There's a positive correlation between revision and boredom

...but there's also a positive correlation between <u>revision</u> and getting a <u>better mark in the exam</u>. Cover the page and write down the <u>rules</u> you need to remember when <u>drawing graphs</u>.

Drawing Conclusions

You're nearly there now — the next step is to draw a conclusion. Here's what you need to do...

You can **only conclude** what the data shows and **NO MORE**

1) Drawing conclusions might seem pretty straightforward — you just look at your data and say what pattern or relationship you see between the dependent and independent variables.

EXAMPLE:

The table on the right shows the rate of a reaction in the presence of two different catalysts.

Catalyst	Rate of reaction (cm³/s)
A	13.5
B	19.5
No catalyst	5.5

CONCLUSION:
Catalyst B makes this reaction go faster than catalyst A.

2) But you've got to be really careful that your conclusion matches the data you've got and doesn't go any further.

EXAMPLE continued:

You can't conclude that catalyst B increases the rate of any other reaction more than catalyst A — the results might be completely different.

3) You also need to be able to use your results to justify your conclusion (i.e. back up your conclusion with some specific data).

EXAMPLE continued:

The rate of this reaction was 6 cm³/s faster using catalyst B compared with catalyst A.

I conclude that this page is a bit dull...

In the exams you could be given a conclusion and asked whether some data supports it — so make sure you understand how far conclusions can go. Remember, in a conclusion you can only say things that you can actually support with data. If you've got no evidence, it's just your opinion. Correlation and cause are also important in conclusions — luckily that's what the next page is about.

Drawing Conclusions

Sometimes, drawing a conclusion is really <u>straightforward</u>. But it can be easy to make a conclusion that <u>seems</u> to be supported by your evidence, but <u>actually isn't</u>. This page explains how to avoid these pitfalls.

Correlation DOES NOT mean cause

1) If two things are correlated (i.e. there's a relationship between them) it <u>doesn't</u> necessarily mean that a change in one variable is <u>causing</u> the change in the other — this is <u>really important, don't forget it</u>.

2) There are <u>three possible reasons</u> for a correlation:

1 CHANCE

1) Even though it might seem a bit weird, it's possible that two things show a correlation in a study purely because of <u>chance</u>.

2) For example, one study might find a correlation between people's hair colour and how good they are at frisbee. But other scientists don't get a correlation when they investigate it — the results of the first study are just a fluke.

2 LINKED BY A 3rd VARIABLE

1) A lot of the time it may <u>look</u> as if a change in one variable is causing a change in the other, but it <u>isn't</u> — a <u>third variable links</u> the two things.

2) For example, there's a correlation between water temperature and shark attacks. This obviously isn't because warmer water makes sharks crazy. Instead, they're linked by a third variable — the number of people swimming (more people swim when the water's hotter, and with more people in the water you get more shark attacks).

3 CAUSE

1) Sometimes a change in one variable does <u>cause</u> a change in the other.

2) For example, there's a correlation between exposure to radiation and thyroid cancer. This is because radiation can cause cancer.

3) You can only conclude that a correlation is due to cause when you've <u>controlled all the variables</u> that could, just could, be affecting the result. (For the radiation example above this would include things like age and exposure to other things that cause cancer).

Some correlations are more complicated than they first seem

If there is one thing to take away from this page it's that <u>correlation does not imply causation</u>. This is a <u>really important</u> idea in science — you could link pretty much anything to anything else if you try hard enough. For example, there's a <u>correlation</u> between the rise in atmospheric CO_2 levels and the rise in obesity — which could lead you to conclude that obesity is <u>caused</u> by atmospheric CO_2. But it might be that both atmospheric CO_2 levels and obesity levels have risen with the <u>number of cars sold</u>.

Controlled Assessment (ISA) — Section One

Controlled Assessment involves doing an experiment and answering two question papers on it under exam conditions. First up, planning your experiment.

There are two sections in the Controlled Assessment

Part one: planning

Before you do the Section 1 question paper you'll be given time to do some research into the topic that's been set — you'll need to develop a hypothesis/prediction and come up with two different methods to test it.

In your research, you should use a variety of different sources (e.g. the internet, textbooks etc.). You'll need to be able to outline both methods and say which one is best (and why it's the best one) and describe your preferred method in detail.

You're allowed to write notes about your two methods on one side of A4 and have them with you for both question papers.

In Section 1, you could be asked things like:

1) What your hypothesis/prediction is.

2) What variables you're going to control (and how you're going to control them).

3) What measurements you're going to take.

4) What range and interval of values you will use for the independent variable.

5) How you'd figure out the range and interval using a trial run (sometimes called a 'preliminary investigation' in the question papers). See page 8 for more.

6) How many times you're going to repeat the experiment — a minimum of three is a good idea.

7) What equipment you're going to use (and why that equipment is right for the job).

There's lots of help on all of these things on pages 7-11.

8) How to carry out the experiment, i.e. what you do first, what you do second...

9) What hazards are involved in doing the experiment, and how to reduce them.

10) What table you'll draw to put your results in. See page 12 for how to draw one that examiners will love.

When you've done the planning and completed the first question paper you'll actually do the experiment. Then you'll have to present your data. Make sure you use the right type of graph, and you draw it properly — see pages 12-13 for help.

After that it's onto the Section 2 question paper (see next page).

When you fail to plan, you're planning to fail

That might be an Everest-sized list of stuff, but it's all important. No need to panic at the sight of it though — as long as you've learnt everything on the previous few pages, you should be fine.

Controlled Assessment (ISA) — Section Two

Once you've planned your experiment and got some data, it's time to move on to the second part of the controlled assessment — coming up with some <u>conclusions</u>.

Part two: *drawing conclusions and evaluating*

For the Section 2 question paper you have to do these things for <u>your experiment</u>:

1) <u>Analyse</u> and <u>draw conclusions</u> from your results. For this you need to <u>describe the relationship</u> between the variables in <u>detail</u> — see page 13 for how to do this.

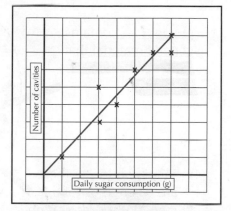

> E.g. 'I found that there is a relationship between eating sugary foods and having tooth cavities. The more sugary foods you eat the more tooth cavities you'll have. For example, my results showed...'.

2) Say whether your results <u>back up the hypothesis/prediction</u>, and give reasons <u>why</u> or <u>why not</u>.

> E.g. 'My results did not back up the prediction. The prediction was that eating more sugary food has no effect on the number of tooth cavities you have. But I found the opposite to be true in my investigation'.

3) <u>Evaluate</u> your experiment. For this you need to <u>suggest ways you could improve your experiment</u>.

- Comment on your <u>equipment</u> and <u>method</u>, e.g. could you have used more <u>accurate</u> equipment?

- Make sure you <u>explain how</u> the improvements would give you <u>better data</u> next time.

- <u>Refer to your results</u>. E.g. 'My data wasn't accurate enough because the mass balance I used only measured in 1 g steps. I could use a more sensitive one next time (e.g. a mass balance that measures in 0.5 g steps) to get more accurate data'.

4) You'll also be <u>given some secondary data</u> (data collected by someone else) from an experiment on the same topic and asked to <u>analyse it</u>. This just involves doing what you did for your data with the secondary data, e.g. draw conclusions from it.

If that's controlled assessment, I'd hate to see uncontrolled assessment

Don't panic when you're given some secondary data — just because someone else collected it doesn't mean it's any better than the data you have collected yourself so look at it with an <u>unbiased eye</u>. Remember to check for <u>anomalies</u> and <u>trends</u>, and make sure you only make conclusions based on what the data says and <u>no more</u>.

Cells

<u>All</u> living things are made of <u>cells</u>. When someone first peered down a microscope at a slice of cork and drew the <u>boxes</u> they saw, little did they know that they'd seen the <u>building blocks</u> of <u>every organism on the planet</u>.

Most **Animal Cells** Have Certain **Features** in **Common**

Most <u>human cells</u>, like most <u>animal</u> cells, have the following parts — make sure you know them all:

1) <u>Nucleus</u> — contains <u>genetic material</u> that <u>controls the activities</u> of the cell.

2) <u>Cytoplasm</u> — gel-like substance where most of the <u>chemical reactions</u> happen. It contains <u>enzymes</u> (see page 38) that control these chemical reactions.

3) <u>Cell membrane</u> — holds the cell together and controls what goes <u>in</u> and <u>out</u>.

4) <u>Mitochondria</u> — these are where most of the reactions for <u>respiration</u> take place (see page 43). Respiration releases <u>energy</u> that the cell needs to work.

5) <u>Ribosomes</u> — these are where <u>proteins</u> are made in the cell.

Plant Cells have Some **Extra Features**

Plant cells usually have <u>all the bits</u> that <u>animal</u> cells have, plus a few <u>extra</u> things that animal cells <u>don't</u> have:

1) Rigid <u>cell wall</u> — made of <u>cellulose</u>. It <u>supports</u> the cell and strengthens it.

2) <u>Chloroplasts</u> — these are where <u>photosynthesis</u> occurs, which makes food for the plant (see page 26). They contain a <u>green</u> substance called <u>chlorophyll</u>.

3) <u>Permanent vacuole</u> — contains <u>cell sap</u>, a weak solution of sugar and salts.

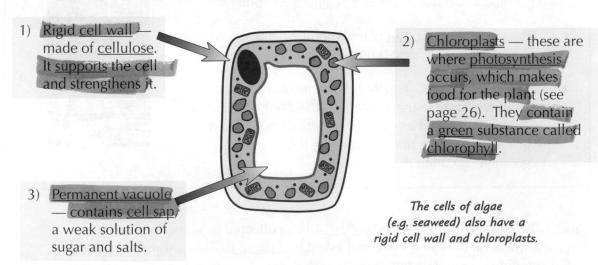

The cells of algae (e.g. seaweed) also have a rigid cell wall and chloroplasts.

There's quite a bit to learn in biology — but that's life, I guess...

On this page are a <u>typical animal cell</u> and a <u>typical plant cell</u> with all the typical bits you need to know. But not all plant or animal cells are the same — they have different <u>structures</u> and <u>produce</u> different substances depending on the <u>job</u> they do.

Cells

You also need to know about <u>yeast</u> and <u>bacterial cells</u>...

*Yeast is a **Single-Celled** Organism*

1) Yeast is a <u>microorganism</u>.

2) A yeast cell has a <u>nucleus</u>, <u>cytoplasm</u>, and a <u>cell membrane</u> surrounded by a <u>cell wall</u>.

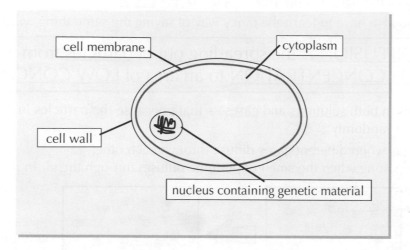

cell membrane

cytoplasm

cell wall

nucleus containing genetic material

*Bacterial Cells Have **No Nucleus***

1) Bacteria are also <u>single-celled</u> microorganisms.

2) A bacterial cell has <u>cytoplasm</u> and a <u>cell membrane</u> surrounded by a <u>cell wall</u>.

3) The <u>genetic material</u> floats in the cytoplasm because bacterial cells don't have a <u>nucleus</u>.

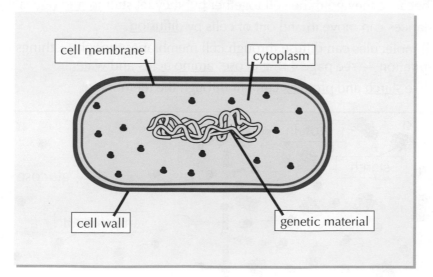

cell membrane

cytoplasm

cell wall

genetic material

Both yeast and bacteria are single-celled microorganisms

On this page are a typical <u>yeast cell</u> and a typical <u>bacterial cell</u>. Make sure you know their structures. Copy out the diagrams, without looking at the book, and see if you can remember all the labels.

Diffusion

Particles <u>move about randomly</u>, and after a bit they end up <u>evenly spaced</u>.

Don't Be Put Off by the **Fancy Word**

1) "<u>Diffusion</u>" is simple. It's just the <u>gradual movement</u> of particles from places where there are <u>lots</u> of them to places where there are <u>fewer</u> of them.

2) That's all it is — just the <u>natural tendency</u> for stuff to <u>spread out</u>.

3) Unfortunately you also have to learn the fancy way of saying the same thing, which is this:

> <u>DIFFUSION</u> is the <u>spreading out</u> of <u>particles</u> from an area of <u>HIGH CONCENTRATION</u> to an area of <u>LOW CONCENTRATION</u>

4) Diffusion happens in both <u>solutions</u> and <u>gases</u> — that's because the particles in these substances are free to <u>move about</u> randomly.

5) The <u>simplest type</u> is when different <u>gases</u> diffuse through each other.
This is what's happening when the smell of perfume diffuses through the air in a room:

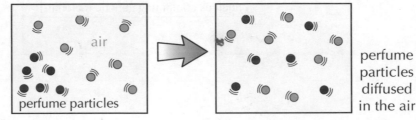

perfume particles

perfume particles diffused in the air

6) The <u>bigger</u> the <u>difference</u> in concentration, the <u>faster</u> the diffusion rate.

Cell Membranes Are Kind of Clever...

1) They're clever because they <u>hold</u> the cell together <u>but</u> they let stuff <u>in and out</u> as well.

2) Dissolved substances can move in and out of cells by <u>diffusion</u>.

3) Only very <u>small</u> molecules can <u>diffuse</u> through cell membranes though — things like <u>oxygen</u> (needed for respiration — see page 43), <u>glucose</u>, <u>amino acids</u> and <u>water</u>.

4) <u>Big</u> molecules like <u>starch</u> and <u>proteins</u> can't fit through the membrane:

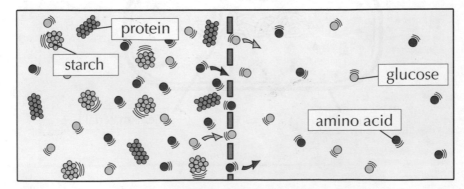

protein

starch

glucose

amino acid

5) Just like with diffusion in air, particles flow through the cell membrane from where there's a <u>high concentration</u> (a lot of them) to where there's a <u>low concentration</u> (not such a lot of them).

6) They're only moving about <u>randomly</u> of course, so they go <u>both</u> ways — but if there are a lot <u>more</u> particles on one side of the membrane, there's a <u>net</u> (overall) movement <u>from</u> that side.

Specialised Cells

Page 18 shows the structure of some typical cells. However, most cells are <u>specialised</u> for their specific function, so their structure can vary...

1) *Palisade Leaf Cells* Are Adapted for *Photosynthesis*

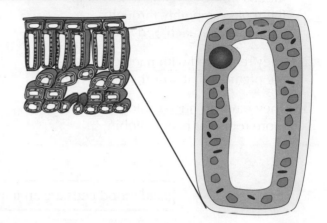

1) Packed with <u>chloroplasts</u> for <u>photosynthesis</u>. More of them are crammed at the <u>top</u> of the cell — so they're nearer the <u>light</u>.

2) <u>Tall</u> shape means a lot of <u>surface area</u> exposed down the side for <u>absorbing CO_2</u> from the air in the leaf.

3) <u>Thin</u> shape means that you can pack loads of them in at the top of a leaf.

> Palisade leaf cells are grouped together at the top of the leaf where most of the <u>photosynthesis</u> happens.

2) *Guard Cells* Are Adapted to *Open and Close Pores*

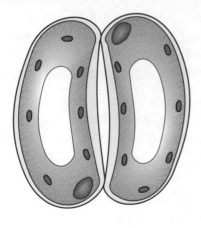

1) Special kidney shape which <u>opens</u> and <u>closes</u> the <u>stomata</u> (pores) in a leaf.

2) When the plant has <u>lots</u> of water the guard cells fill with it and go plump and <u>turgid</u>. This makes the stomata <u>open</u> so <u>gases</u> can be exchanged for <u>photosynthesis</u>.

3) When the plant is <u>short</u> of water, the guard cells lose water and become <u>flaccid</u>, making the stomata <u>close</u>. This helps stop too much water vapour <u>escaping</u>.

4) <u>Thin</u> outer walls and <u>thickened</u> inner walls make the opening and closing work.

5) They're also <u>sensitive to light</u> and <u>close at night</u> to save water without losing out on photosynthesis.

> Guard cells are therefore adapted to their function of allowing <u>gas exchange</u> and <u>controlling water loss</u> within a <u>leaf</u>.

Specialised Cells

3) *Red Blood Cells* Are Adapted to *Carry Oxygen*

1) <u>Concave</u> shape gives a big <u>surface area</u> for absorbing <u>oxygen</u>. It also helps them pass <u>smoothly</u> through <u>capillaries</u> to reach body cells.

2) They're packed with <u>haemoglobin</u> — the pigment that absorbs the oxygen.

3) They have <u>no nucleus</u>, to leave even more room for haemoglobin.

Red blood cells are an important part of the <u>blood</u>.

4) *Sperm* and *Egg* Cells Are Specialised for *Reproduction*

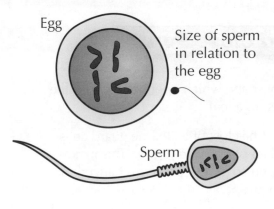

Egg

Size of sperm in relation to the egg

Sperm

1) The main functions of an <u>egg cell</u> are to carry the female DNA and to <u>nourish</u> the developing embryo in the early stages. The egg cell contains huge <u>food reserves</u> to feed the embryo.

2) When a <u>sperm</u> fuses with the egg, the egg's <u>membrane</u> instantly <u>changes</u> its structure to stop any more sperm getting in. This makes sure the offspring end up with the <u>right amount</u> of DNA.

3) The function of a <u>sperm</u> is basically to get the <u>male DNA</u> to the <u>female DNA</u>. It has a <u>long tail</u> and a <u>streamlined head</u> to help it <u>swim</u> to the egg. There are a lot of <u>mitochondria</u> in the cell to provide the <u>energy</u> needed.

4) Sperm also carry <u>enzymes</u> in their heads to digest through the egg cell membrane.

Sperm and eggs are very important cells in <u>reproduction</u>.

Cells have the same basic bits but are specialised for their function

These cells all have all the bits shown on page 18, even though they look completely different and do <u>totally different jobs</u>. Apart from red blood cells — which, for example, don't have a nucleus.

Cell Organisation

How, you might wonder, does having all these specialised cells mean you end up with a working human... the answer's organisation.

Large Multicellular Organisms are Made Up of Organ Systems

1) As you know from the previous pages, specialised cells carry out a particular function.

2) The process by which cells become specialised for a particular job is called differentiation.

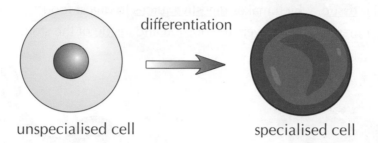

differentiation

unspecialised cell   specialised cell

3) Differentiation occurs during the development of a multicellular organism.

4) These specialised cells form tissues, which form organs, which form organ systems (see page 24).

5) Large multicellular organisms (e.g. humans) have different systems inside them for exchanging and transporting materials.

Similar Cells are Organised into Tissues

1) A tissue is a group of similar cells that work together to carry out a particular function.

2) It can include more than one type of cell.

3) In mammals (like humans), examples of tissues include:

- Muscular tissue, which contracts (shortens) to move whatever it's attached to.
- Glandular tissue, which makes and secretes chemicals like enzymes and hormones.
- Epithelial tissue, which covers some parts of the body, e.g. the inside of the gut.

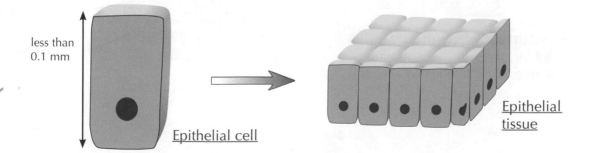

less than 0.1 mm

Epithelial cell

Epithelial tissue

Cell Organisation

We left off at <u>tissues</u> on the previous page — now you need to know how they're organised...

Tissues are Organised into Organs

1) An <u>organ</u> is a group of <u>different tissues</u> that work together to perform a certain <u>function</u>.

2) For example, the <u>stomach</u> is an organ made of these tissues:

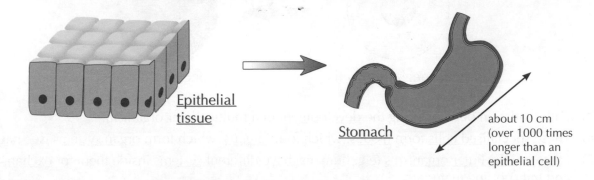

- <u>Muscular tissue</u>, which moves the stomach wall to <u>churn up the food</u>.
- <u>Glandular tissue</u>, which makes <u>digestive juices</u> to digest food.
- <u>Epithelial tissue</u>, which covers the <u>outside</u> and <u>inside</u> of the stomach.

<u>Epithelial</u>
<u>tissue</u>

<u>Stomach</u>

about 10 cm
(over 1000 times
longer than an
epithelial cell)

Organs are Organised into Organ Systems

An <u>organ system</u> is a <u>group of organs</u> working together to perform a particular <u>function</u>. For example, the <u>digestive system</u> (found in humans and mammals) <u>breaks down food</u> and is made up of these organs:

1) <u>Glands</u> (e.g. the <u>pancreas</u> and <u>salivary glands</u>), which produce <u>digestive juices</u>.

2) The <u>stomach</u> and <u>small intestine</u>, which <u>digest</u> food.

3) The <u>liver</u>, which produces <u>bile</u>.

4) The <u>small intestine</u>, which <u>absorbs</u> soluble <u>food</u> molecules.

5) The <u>large intestine</u>, which <u>absorbs water</u> from undigested food, leaving <u>faeces</u>.

The digestive system <u>exchanges materials</u> with the <u>environment</u> by <u>taking in nutrients</u> and <u>releasing substances</u> such as bile.

There's more on the digestive system on pages 40-41.

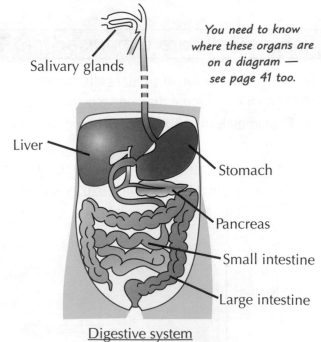

You need to know where these organs are on a diagram — see page 41 too.

Salivary glands

Liver

Stomach

Pancreas

Small intestine

Large intestine

<u>Digestive system</u>

Remember — cells, tissues, organs, organ systems...

OK, so from the last couple of pages you know that <u>cells</u> are organised into <u>tissues</u>, the tissues into <u>organs</u>, the organs into <u>organ systems</u> and the organ systems into a whole <u>organism</u>.

Warm-Up and Exam Questions

So, hopefully you've read the last seven pages. But could you cope if a question on cells or diffusion came up in the exam? With amazing new technology we can simulate that very situation....

Warm-Up Questions

1) Give three ways in which animal cells are different from plant cells.
2) Define diffusion.
3) a) What is the function of a red blood cell?
   b) Describe two ways in which a red blood cell is adapted to its function.
4) Name the process by which cells become specialised for a particular job. *— differentiation*
5) What is an organ system?
6) Name five organs that are part of the human digestive system.

Exam Questions

1   The diagram shows a palisade cell from a leaf.

(a)   Which label points to a chloroplast?

(1 mark)

(b)   Name the green substance present in chloroplasts.

(1 mark)

(c)   Apart from having chloroplasts, suggest **one** other way in which a palisade cell is adapted for photosynthesis.

(1 mark)

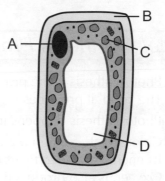

2   Below are three diagrams showing cells surrounded by glucose.

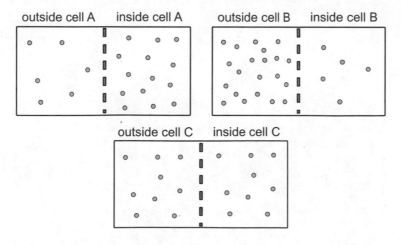

(a)   Into which cell, **A**, **B** or **C**, will there be a net movement of glucose? Explain your answer.

(2 marks)

(b)   Other than glucose, name **one** molecule that can diffuse through cell membranes into cells.

(1 mark)

Plant Structure and Photosynthesis

Take a good look at the <u>photosynthesis equation</u> below — you <u>must learn</u> it.

Plant Cells Are Organised Into *Tissues* And *Organs* Too

<u>Plants</u> are made of <u>organs</u> like <u>stems</u>, <u>roots</u> and <u>leaves</u>. These organs are made of <u>tissues</u>.
For example, <u>leaves</u> are made of:

- <u>Mesophyll tissue</u> — this is where most of the <u>photosynthesis</u> in a plant occurs.
- <u>Xylem</u> and <u>phloem</u> — they <u>transport</u> things like <u>water</u>, <u>mineral ions</u> and <u>sucrose</u> around the plant.
- <u>Epidermal tissue</u> — this <u>covers</u> the whole plant.

The <u>leaf diagram</u> at the bottom of the page shows where these tissues are in a plant.

Learn the *Equation* for *Photosynthesis*:

Carbon dioxide + water $\xrightarrow[\text{chlorophyll}]{\text{sunlight}}$ glucose + oxygen

Photosynthesis Produces Glucose *Using* Sunlight

1) <u>Photosynthesis</u> is the process that produces '<u>food</u>' in plants and algae.
   The 'food' it produces is <u>glucose</u>.

2) Photosynthesis happens inside the <u>chloroplasts</u>.

3) Chloroplasts contain a green substance called <u>chlorophyll</u>, which absorbs <u>sunlight</u> and uses
   its energy to convert <u>carbon dioxide</u> (from the air) and <u>water</u> (from the soil) into <u>glucose</u>.
   <u>Oxygen</u> is also produced as a by-product.

4) Photosynthesis happens in the <u>leaves</u> of all <u>green plants</u> — this is largely what the leaves are for.
   Below is a cross-section of a leaf showing the <u>four</u> raw materials needed for <u>photosynthesis</u>.

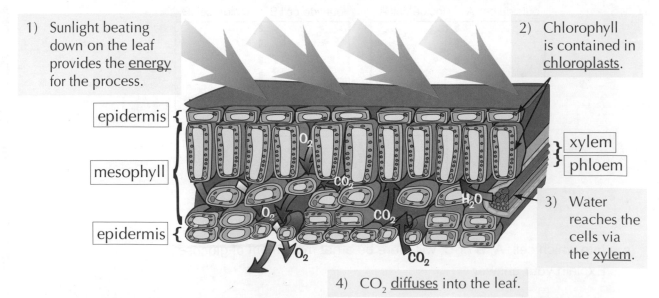

1) Sunlight beating down on the leaf provides the <u>energy</u> for the process.

2) Chlorophyll is contained in <u>chloroplasts</u>.

epidermis

mesophyll

epidermis

xylem
phloem

3) Water reaches the cells via the <u>xylem</u>.

4) CO_2 <u>diffuses</u> into the leaf.

'Photo' means light and 'synthesis' means putting together...

...so photosynthesis is 'putting together <u>glucose</u>'. See, it's not too bad. But you must learn the <u>equation</u>.

The Rate of Photosynthesis

The rate of photosynthesis is affected by the intensity of light, the volume of CO_2, and the temperature. Plants also need water for photosynthesis, but when a plant is so short of water that it becomes the limiting factor in photosynthesis, it's already in such trouble that this is the least of its worries.

The **Limiting Factor** Depends on the Conditions

Any of these three factors can become the limiting factor. This just means that it's stopping photosynthesis from happening any faster.

Which factor is limiting at a particular time depends on the environmental conditions:

- at night it's pretty obvious that light is the limiting factor,
- in winter it's often the temperature,
- if it's warm enough and bright enough, the amount of CO_2 is usually limiting.

You can do experiments to work out the ideal conditions for photosynthesis in a particular plant. The easiest type to use is a water plant like Canadian pondweed — you can easily measure the amount of oxygen produced in a given time to show how fast photosynthesis is happening (remember, oxygen is made during photosynthesis).

You could either count the bubbles given off, or if you want to be a bit more accurate you could collect the oxygen in a gas syringe.

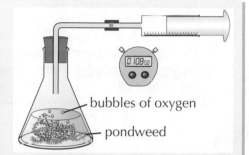

bubbles of oxygen

pondweed

Not Enough **Light** Slows Down the Rate of Photosynthesis

1) Light provides the energy needed for photosynthesis.

2) As the light level is raised, the rate of photosynthesis increases steadily — but only up to a certain point.

3) Beyond that, it won't make any difference because then it'll be either the temperature or the CO_2 level which is the limiting factor.

4) In the lab you can change the light intensity by moving a lamp closer to or further away from your plant.

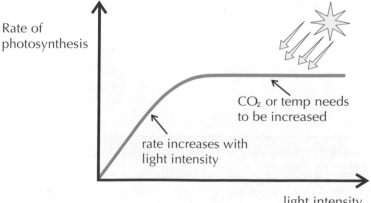

Rate of photosynthesis

CO_2 or temp needs to be increased

rate increases with light intensity

light intensity

5) But if you just plot the rate of photosynthesis against "distance of lamp from the beaker", you get a weird-shaped graph. To get a graph like the one above you either need to measure the light intensity at the beaker using a light meter or do a bit of nifty maths with your results.

The Rate of Photosynthesis

Too Little **Carbon Dioxide** Also Slows it Down

1) CO_2 is one of the <u>raw materials</u> needed for photosynthesis.

2) As with light intensity the amount of <u>CO_2</u> will only increase the rate of photosynthesis up to a point. After this the graph <u>flattens out</u> showing that CO_2 is no longer the <u>limiting factor</u>.

3) As long as <u>light</u> and <u>CO_2</u> are in plentiful supply then the factor limiting photosynthesis must be <u>temperature</u>.

4) There are loads of different ways to control the amount of CO_2. One way is to dissolve different amounts of <u>sodium hydrogencarbonate</u> in the water, which <u>gives off</u> CO_2.

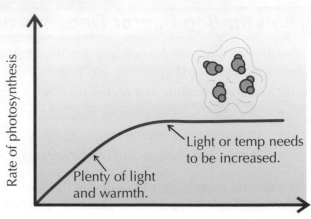

Light or temp needs to be increased.

Plenty of light and warmth.

% level of CO_2

The **Temperature** has to be Just Right

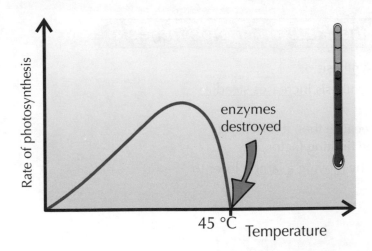

enzymes destroyed

45 °C Temperature

1) Usually, if the temperature is the <u>limiting factor</u> it's because it's <u>too low</u> — the <u>enzymes</u> needed for photosynthesis work more <u>slowly</u> at low temperatures.

2) But if the plant gets <u>too hot</u>, the enzymes it needs for photosynthesis and its other reactions will be <u>damaged</u>.

3) This happens at about <u>45 °C</u> (which is pretty hot for outdoors, although <u>greenhouses</u> can get that hot if you're not careful).

4) Experimentally, the best way to control the temperature of the flask is to put it in a <u>water bath</u>.

In all these experiments, you have to try and keep all the variables <u>constant</u> apart from the one you're investigating, so it's a <u>fair test</u>:

* use a <u>bench lamp</u> to control the intensity of the light (careful not to <u>block the light</u> with anything)
* keep the flask in a <u>water bath</u> to help keep the temperature constant
* you <u>can't</u> really do anything about the CO_2 levels — you just have to use a <u>large flask</u>, and do the experiments as <u>quickly</u> as you can, so that the plant doesn't use up too much of the CO_2 in the flask. If you're using sodium hydrogencarbonate make sure it's changed each time.

The Rate of Photosynthesis

Growing plants outdoors can be <u>very difficult</u>, especially on a <u>large scale</u> — it's almost impossible to control the weather and other conditions. But there's a way around that...

You can **Artificially Create** the **Ideal Conditions** for **Farming**

1) The most common way to artificially create the <u>ideal environment</u> for plants is to grow them in a <u>greenhouse</u>.

2) Greenhouses help to <u>trap</u> the Sun's <u>heat</u>, and make sure that the <u>temperature</u> doesn't become <u>limiting</u>. In winter a farmer or gardener might use a <u>heater</u> as well to keep the temperature at the ideal level. In summer it could get <u>too hot</u>, so they might use <u>shades</u> and <u>ventilation</u> to cool things down.

3) <u>Light</u> is always needed for photosynthesis, so commercial farmers often supply <u>artificial light</u> after the Sun goes down to give their plants more quality photosynthesis time.

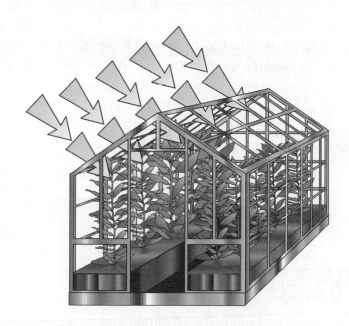

Greenhouses are used to grow plants, including food crops, flowers and tobacco plants.

4) Farmers and gardeners can also increase the level of <u>carbon dioxide</u> in the greenhouse. A fairly common way is to use a <u>paraffin heater</u> to heat the greenhouse. As the paraffin burns, it makes carbon dioxide as a <u>by-product</u>.

5) Keeping plants <u>enclosed</u> in a greenhouse also makes it easier to keep them free from <u>pests</u> and <u>diseases</u>. The farmer can add <u>fertilisers</u> to the soil as well, to provide all the <u>minerals</u> needed for healthy growth.

6) Sorting all this out <u>costs money</u> — but if the farmer can keep the conditions <u>just right</u> for photosynthesis, the plants will grow much <u>faster</u> and a <u>decent crop</u> can be harvested much more <u>often</u>, which can then be <u>sold</u>. It's important that a farmer supplies just the <u>right amount</u> of heat, light, etc. — enough to make the plants grow well, but <u>not</u> more than the plants <u>need</u>, as this would just be <u>wasting money</u>.

Greenhouses control the growing environment

Farmers use greenhouses to make sure crops get the right amount of carbon dioxide, light and heat. They can alter the conditions using paraffin heaters, artificial light and ventilation. This ensures nothing becomes a limiting factor for photosynthesis, which means a good crop is produced.

BIOLOGY 2A — CELLS, ORGANS AND POPULATIONS

How Plants Use Glucose

Once plants have made the glucose, there are various ways they can use it.

1) For **Respiration**

1) Plants manufacture glucose in their leaves.
2) They then use some of the glucose for respiration (see page 43).
3) This releases energy which enables them to convert the rest of the glucose into various other useful substances, which they can use to build new cells and grow.
4) To produce some of these substances they also need to gather a few minerals from the soil.

2) Making **Cell Walls**

Glucose is converted into cellulose for making strong cell walls (see page 18), especially in a rapidly growing plant.

Algae also use glucose to make cellulose for cell walls, fats and oils for storage, and amino acids for proteins.

3) Making **Proteins**

Glucose is combined with nitrate ions (absorbed from the soil) to make amino acids, which are then made into proteins.

4) Stored in **Seeds**

Glucose is turned into lipids (fats and oils) for storing in seeds. Sunflower seeds, for example, contain a lot of oil — we get cooking oil and margarine from them. Seeds also store starch (see below).

5) Stored as **Starch**

1) Glucose is turned into starch and stored in roots, stems and leaves, ready for use when photosynthesis isn't happening, like in the winter.
2) Starch is insoluble which makes it much better for storing than glucose — a cell with lots of glucose in would draw in loads of water and swell up.
3) Potato and parsnip plants store a lot of starch underground over the winter so a new plant can grow from it the following spring. We eat the swollen storage organs.

All life depends on photosynthesis

Plants are pretty crucial in ensuring the flow of energy through nature. They are able to use the Sun's energy to make glucose, the energy source that humans and other animals need for respiration. Make sure you know the photosynthesis equation inside out — look back at p.26 if you don't.

Warm-Up and Exam Questions

So, here we go again — another set of questions to test your knowledge. But don't roll your eyes, I promise they'll be really, really enjoyable. OK, don't hold me to that, but make sure you do them...

Warm-Up Questions

1) Name four factors that are needed for photosynthesis.
2) What is meant by a limiting factor for the rate of photosynthesis?
3) Sketch a graph to show how the rate of photosynthesis varies with increasing CO_2.
4) Give one way in which a farmer could increase the level of CO_2 in his greenhouse.
5) Name the process that converts glucose into energy in plants.

Exam Questions

1   Photosynthesis makes glucose.   The glucose may then be converted to other substances. Some of these substances are listed below:

        starch   **cellulose**   **amino acids**

Match each of these substances to its correct function from the list below.
• Making cell walls.
• Making proteins.
• Storing energy.

(3 marks)

2   The diagram shows part of the structure of a leaf as it looks under a microscope.

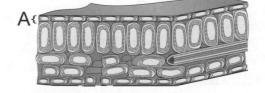

(a)   Name the tissue labelled **A**.

(1 mark)

(b)   Name **two** other tissues that can be found in a leaf.

(2 marks)

3   The table shows the rate of photosynthesis of a plant at different temperatures.

Temperature (°C)	Rate of photosynthesis (arbitrary units)
0	0
10	17
20	35
30	67
40	82
50	0

(a)   Explain the difference between:

(i)   the rates of photosynthesis at 10 °C and at 20 °C.

(1 mark)

(ii)   the rates of photosynthesis at 40 °C and at 50 °C.

(1 mark)

(b)   A student said that the optimum temperature for photosynthesis in this plant was 40 °C. Comment on this statement.

(2 marks)

Exam Questions

4   Jane did an experiment to see how the rate of photosynthesis depends on light intensity.
    The diagram shows her apparatus.

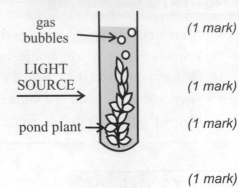

   (a)   How can Jane measure the rate of photosynthesis?

(1 mark)

   (b)   In this experiment:

      (i)   what is the dependent variable?

(1 mark)

      (ii)   what is the independent variable?

(1 mark)

   (c)   State **one** factor that should be kept constant
      during this experiment.

(1 mark)

5   The graph shows how a plant's rate of
    photosynthesis varies with the light intensity.

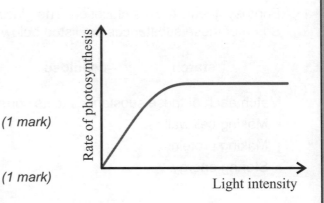

   (a)   Label a point at which light intensity is
      the limiting factor for photosynthesis.

(1 mark)

   (b)   What else can limit a plant's
      rate of photosynthesis?

(1 mark)

6   The diagram shows a variegated leaf —
    it's partly green and partly white.

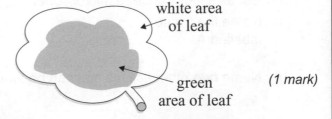

   (a)   What substance is present in the green
      parts of the leaf but not the white parts?

(1 mark)

Abisola did an experiment in which part of the
leaf was covered with black paper, as shown:
The leaf was then exposed to light for four hours and was then tested for starch.

   (b)   (i)   Copy and complete the diagram below by shading in the part(s) of the
         leaf that you would expect to contain **starch**.

(1 mark)

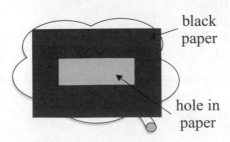

      (ii)   Explain your answer to part (b)(i).

(2 marks)

Distribution of Organisms

Don't worry — you're nearly at the end of this section. But first you need to get your head around some ecology. These next few pages are all about investigating the distribution of organisms...

The **Environment Varies**, So **Organisms Live** in **Different Places**

1) A habitat is the place where an organism lives, e.g. a playing field.

2) The distribution of an organism is where an organism is found, e.g. in a part of the playing field.

3) Where an organism is found is affected by environmental factors such as:

- Temperature.
- Availability of water.
- Availability of oxygen and carbon dioxide.
- Availability of nutrients.
- Amount of light.

4) An organism might be more common in one area than another due to differences in environmental factors between the two areas. For example, in a field, you might find that daisies are more common in the open, than under trees, because there's more light available in the open.

5) There are a couple of ways to study the distribution of an organism. You can:

- measure how common an organism is in two sample areas (e.g. using quadrats) and compare them.
- study how the distribution changes across an area, e.g. by placing quadrats along a transect (p. 34).

Use **Quadrats** to **Study** The **Distribution** of **Small** Organisms

A quadrat is a square frame enclosing a known area, e.g. 1 m². To compare how common an organism is in two sample areas, just follow these simple steps:

A quadrat

1 m

1 m

1) Place a 1 m² quadrat on the ground at a random point within the first sample area. E.g. divide the area into a grid and use a random number generator to pick coordinates.

2) Count all the organisms within the quadrat.

3) Repeat steps 1 and 2 as many times as you can.

4) Work out the mean number of organisms per quadrat within the first sample area.

- For example, Anna counted the number of daisies in 7 quadrats within her first sample area and recorded the following results: 18, 20, 22, 23, 23, 23, 25

- Here the MEAN is: $\dfrac{\text{TOTAL number of organisms}}{\text{NUMBER of quadrats}} = \dfrac{154}{7} = \underline{22}$ daisies per quadrat.

- You also need to know about the MODE, which is the MOST COMMON value. In this example it's 23.

- And the MEDIAN is the MIDDLE value, when they're in order of size. In this example it's 23 also.

5) Repeat steps 1 to 4 in the second sample area.

6) Finally compare the two means. E.g. you might find 2 daisies per m² in the shade, and 22 daisies per m² (lots more) in the open field.

Count all the organisms in a quadrat, but first remember to...

...put down your quadrat in a random place before you start counting. Even chucking the quadrat over your shoulder is better than putting it down on the first big patch of organisms that you see.

Distribution of Organisms

I'm afraid you need to know a bit more about the <u>distribution of organisms</u>...

In the Exam You Might Have to Work Out **Population Size**

To work out the <u>population size</u> of an organism in one sample area:

1) Work out the <u>mean number of organisms per m²</u>.
   (If your quadrat has an area of 1 m², this is the <u>same</u> as the mean
   number of organisms per quadrat, worked out on the previous page.)

2) Then multiply the <u>mean</u> by the <u>total area</u> (in m²) of the habitat.

> E.g. if the area of an open field is <u>800 m²</u>, and there are <u>22 daisies per m²</u>,
> then the size of the daisy population is <u>22 x 800 = 17 600</u>.

Transects Show How Organisms are **Distributed Along a Line**

You can use lines called <u>transects</u> to help find out how organisms (like plants) are <u>distributed</u> across
an area — e.g. if an organism becomes <u>more or less common</u> as you move from a hedge towards the
middle of a field. Here's what to do:

1) <u>Mark out a line</u> in the area you want to study using a tape measure.

2) Then <u>collect data</u> along the line.

3) You can do this by just <u>counting</u> all the organisms you're interested in that <u>touch</u> the line.

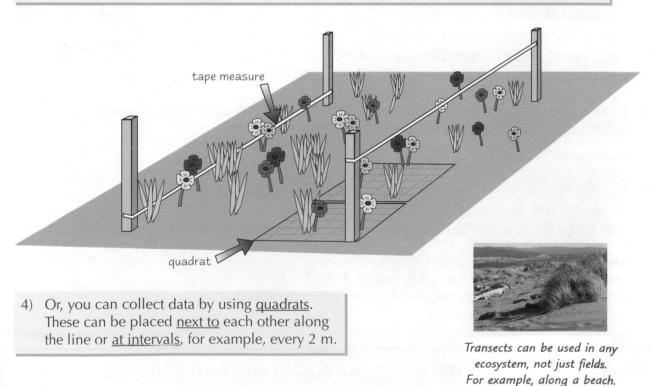

tape measure

quadrat

4) Or, you can collect data by using <u>quadrats</u>.
   These can be placed <u>next to</u> each other along
   the line or <u>at intervals</u>, for example, every 2 m.

*Transects can be used in any
ecosystem, not just fields.
For example, along a beach.*

Distribution of Organisms

When **Collecting Environmental Data** You Need to Think About...

1) Reliability

1) <u>Quadrats</u> and <u>transects</u> are <u>pretty good tools</u> for finding out how an organism is distributed.

2) But, you have to work hard to make sure your results are <u>reliable</u> — which means making sure they are <u>repeatable</u> and <u>reproducible</u>.

3) To make your results <u>more</u> reliable you need to:

> • Take a <u>large sample size</u>, e.g. use as many quadrats and transects as possible in your sample area. Bigger samples are more representative of the whole population.
>
> • Use <u>random</u> samples, e.g. randomly put down or mark out your quadrat or transect. If all your samples are in <u>one spot</u>, and everywhere else is <u>different</u>, the results you get won't be <u>reproducible</u>.

2) Validity

1) For your results to be <u>valid</u> they must be <u>reliable</u> (see above) and <u>answer the original question</u>.

2) To answer the original question, you need to <u>control all the variables</u>.

3) The question you want to answer is whether a <u>difference in distribution</u> between two sample areas is <u>due</u> to a <u>difference in one environmental factor</u>.

4) If you've controlled all the <u>other variables</u> that could be affecting the distribution, you'll know whether a <u>difference in distribution</u> is caused by the <u>environmental factor</u> or not.

5) If you <u>don't</u> control the other variables you <u>won't know</u> whether any correlation you've found is because of <u>chance</u>, because of the <u>environmental factor</u> you're looking at or because of a <u>different variable</u> — the study <u>won't</u> give you <u>valid data</u>.

Look back at page 33 for the different environmental factors that can affect distribution. E.g. some types of buttercups are more common in moist areas.

Your investigation needs to be reliable and valid

Take a look back at <u>How Science Works</u> (page 3) to remind yourself all about <u>reliability</u> and <u>validity</u>. If you get a question in the exam about how to make an investigation using <u>quadrats</u> or <u>transects</u> more reliable, think about the <u>sample size</u> and whether samples have been taken <u>randomly</u>.

Warm-Up and Exam Questions

It's finally the end of the section, but before you go on to the next one a few questions need answering.

Warm-Up Questions

1) What do we mean by the 'distribution of an organism'?
2) What is a quadrat?
3) Claire used a 1 m² quadrat to count the number of buttercups in a sample area.
   She placed the quadrat nine times. Here are her results: 2, 15, 4, 6, 8, 3, 11, 10, 9.
   Work out the median number of buttercups per quadrat in her sample area.
4) What is the name of a line used to measure the distribution of organisms across an area?

Exam Questions

1 Paul investigated the distribution of dandelions.
He counted the number of dandelions in 10 quadrats in five different fields.
His quadrat measured 1 m². Paul's results are shown in the table below.

Field	Mean number of dandelions per quadrat
A	10
B	35
C	21
D	37
E	21

(a) What is the mode of Paul's data?

(1 mark)

(b) (i) A week later Paul repeated his experiment in a sixth field, Field F.
His results for each quadrat are shown below:

6   15   9   14   20   5   3   11   10   7

Using this data, estimate the mean number of dandelions per m² in Field F.

(2 marks)

(ii) Field F measures 90 m by 120 m.
Estimate the number of dandelions in the whole of Field F.

(2 marks)

(c) Paul's friend Anna also investigated the number of dandelions
in the same six fields. Anna also used a 1 m² quadrat.
She counted the number of dandelions in 20 quadrats per field.

Which investigation, Paul's or Anna's, is likely to produce more reliable data?
Give a reason for your answer.

(1 mark)

Revision Summary for Biology 2a

And where do you think you're going? It's no use just reading through and thinking you've got it all —
this stuff will only stick in your head if you've learnt it <u>properly</u>. And that's what these questions are for.
I won't pretend they'll be easy — they're not meant to be, but all the information's in the section
somewhere. Have a go at all the questions, then if there are any you can't answer, go back, look stuff up
and try again. Enjoy...

1) Name five parts of a cell that both plant and animal cells have.
2) Name three features of a yeast cell.
3) Where is the genetic material found in:
   a) bacterial cells
   b) animal cells?
4) Name three substances that can diffuse through cell membranes, and two that can't.
5) Give one way that a guard cell is adapted for controlling water loss.
6) Give three ways that a sperm cell is adapted for swimming to an egg cell.
7) What is a tissue? What is an organ?
8) Give three examples of tissues in the human stomach, and say what job they do.
9) Name one organ system found in the human body.
10) Give an example of a plant tissue and a plant organ.
11) Write down the equation for photosynthesis.
12) What is the green substance in leaves that absorbs sunlight?
13) Name the three factors that can limit the rate of photosynthesis.
14) You carry out an experiment where you change the light intensity experienced by a piece of
    Canadian pondweed by changing the distance between the pondweed and a lamp supplying it
    with light. Write down three important things which must be kept constant for this experiment
    to be a fair test.
15) Explain why it's important that a plant doesn't get too hot.
16) Describe three things that a gardener could do to make sure she grows a good crop of tomatoes
    in her greenhouse.
17) Why is glucose turned into starch when plants need to store it for later?
18) Write down four other ways that plants can use the glucose produced by photosynthesis.
19) What is a habitat?
20) Give five environmental factors that can affect the distribution of organisms.
21) Briefly describe how you could find out how common an organism is in two sample areas
    using quadrats.
22) Describe one way of using a transect to find out how an organism is distributed across an area.

Enzymes

Chemical reactions are what make you work. And enzymes are what make them work.

Enzymes Are Catalysts Produced by Living Things

1) Living things have thousands of different chemical reactions going on inside them all the time.

2) These reactions need to be carefully controlled — to get the right amounts of substances.

3) You can usually make a reaction happen more quickly by raising the temperature.
This would speed up the useful reactions but also the unwanted ones too... not good.
There's also a limit to how far you can raise the temperature inside a living creature before its cells start getting damaged.

4) So... living things produce enzymes that act as biological catalysts. Enzymes reduce the need for high temperatures and we only have enzymes to speed up the useful chemical reactions in the body.

> A CATALYST is a substance which INCREASES the speed of a reaction, without being CHANGED or USED UP in the reaction.

5) Enzymes are all proteins and all proteins are made up of chains of amino acids.
These chains are folded into unique shapes, which enzymes need to do their jobs (see below).

6) As well as catalysts, proteins act as structural components of tissues (e.g. muscles), hormones and antibodies.

Enzymes Have Special Shapes So They Can Catalyse Reactions

1) Chemical reactions usually involve things either being split apart or joined together.

2) Every enzyme has a unique shape that fits onto the substance involved in a reaction.

3) Enzymes are really picky — they usually only catalyse one reaction.

4) This is because, for the enzyme to work, the substance has to fit its special shape.
If the substance doesn't match the enzyme's shape, then the reaction won't be catalysed.

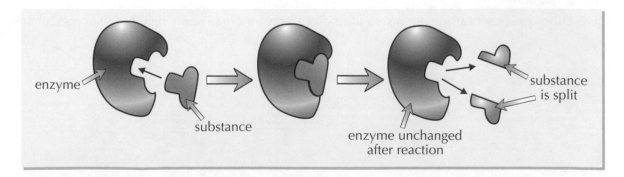

enzyme   substance   enzyme unchanged after reaction   substance is split

Enzymes speed up chemical reactions

Just like you've got to have the correct key for a lock, you've got to have the right substance for an enzyme. If the substance doesn't fit, the enzyme won't catalyse the reaction...

Enzymes

Enzymes are clearly very clever, but they're <u>not</u> very versatile. They need just the right <u>conditions</u> if they're going to work properly.

Enzymes *Need the* Right Temperature...

1) Changing the <u>temperature</u> changes the rate of an enzyme-catalysed reaction.

2) Like with any reaction, a higher temperature <u>increases</u> the rate at first.

3) But if it gets <u>too hot</u>, some of the <u>bonds</u> holding the enzyme together <u>break</u>. This destroys the enzyme's <u>special shape</u> and so it won't work any more. It's said to be <u>denatured</u>.

4) Enzymes in the <u>human body</u> normally work best at around <u>37 °C</u>.

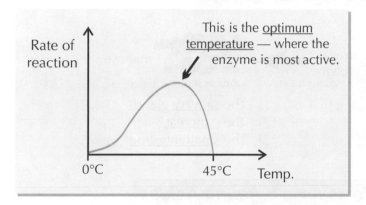

Rate of reaction

This is the <u>optimum temperature</u> — where the enzyme is most active.

0°C   45°C   Temp.

...and the Right pH

1) The <u>pH</u> also affects enzymes. If it's too high or too low, the pH interferes with the <u>bonds</u> holding the enzyme together.

2) This changes the shape and <u>denatures</u> the enzyme.

3) All enzymes have an <u>optimum pH</u> that they work best at. It's often <u>neutral pH 7</u>, but <u>not always</u> — e.g. <u>pepsin</u> is an enzyme used to break down <u>proteins</u> in the <u>stomach</u>. It works best at <u>pH 2</u>, which means it's well-suited to the <u>acidic conditions</u> there.

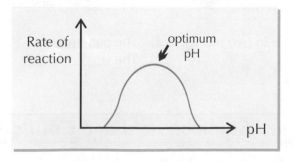

Rate of reaction

optimum pH

pH

Most enzymes catalyse just one reaction

The <u>optimum temperature</u> for most human enzymes is around <u>normal body temperature</u>. And <u>stomach enzymes</u> work best at <u>low pH</u>, but the enzymes in your <u>small intestine</u> like <u>high pH</u>.

Enzymes and Digestion

Not all enzymes work inside body cells — some work <u>outside</u> cells. For example, the enzymes used in <u>digestion</u> are produced by cells and then <u>released</u> into the <u>gut</u> to <u>mix</u> with <u>food</u>.

Digestive Enzymes Break Down Big Molecules into Smaller Ones

1) <u>Starch</u>, <u>proteins</u> and <u>fats</u> are big molecules.
   They're too big to pass through the walls of the digestive system.

2) <u>Sugars</u>, <u>amino acids</u>, <u>glycerol</u> and <u>fatty acids</u> are much smaller molecules.
   They can pass easily through the walls of the digestive system.

3) The <u>digestive enzymes</u> break down the big molecules into the smaller ones.

Amylase Converts Starch into Sugars

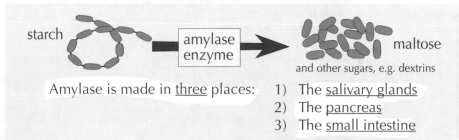

starch → amylase enzyme → maltose and other sugars, e.g. dextrins

Amylase is made in <u>three</u> places:
1) The <u>salivary glands</u>
2) The <u>pancreas</u>
3) The <u>small intestine</u>

Protease Converts Proteins into Amino Acids

proteins → protease enzymes → amino acids

Protease is made in <u>three</u> places:
1) The <u>stomach</u> (it's called <u>pepsin</u> there)
2) The <u>pancreas</u>
3) The <u>small intestine</u>

Lipase Converts Lipids into Glycerol and Fatty Acids

lipid → lipase enzymes → glycerol and fatty acids

Lipase is made in <u>two</u> places:
1) The <u>pancreas</u>
2) The <u>small intestine</u>

Remember, lipids are fats and oils.

Bile Neutralises the Stomach Acid and Emulsifies Fats

1) Bile is <u>produced</u> in the <u>liver</u>. It's <u>stored</u> in the <u>gall bladder</u> before it's released into the <u>small intestine</u>.

2) The <u>hydrochloric acid</u> in the stomach makes the pH <u>too acidic</u> for enzymes in the small intestine to work properly. Bile is <u>alkaline</u> — it <u>neutralises</u> the acid and makes conditions <u>alkaline</u>. The enzymes in the small intestine <u>work best</u> in these alkaline conditions.

3) It <u>emulsifies</u> fats. In other words it breaks the fat into <u>tiny droplets</u>. This gives a much <u>bigger surface area</u> of fat for the enzyme lipase to work on — which makes its digestion <u>faster</u>.

Enzymes and Digestion

So now you know what the enzymes do, here's a nice <u>big picture</u> of the <u>whole</u> of the digestive system.

The **Breakdown** of Food is Catalysed by **Enzymes**

1) Enzymes used in the digestive system are produced by specialised cells in <u>glands</u> and in the <u>gut lining</u>.

2) Different enzymes catalyse the <u>breakdown</u> of different food molecules.

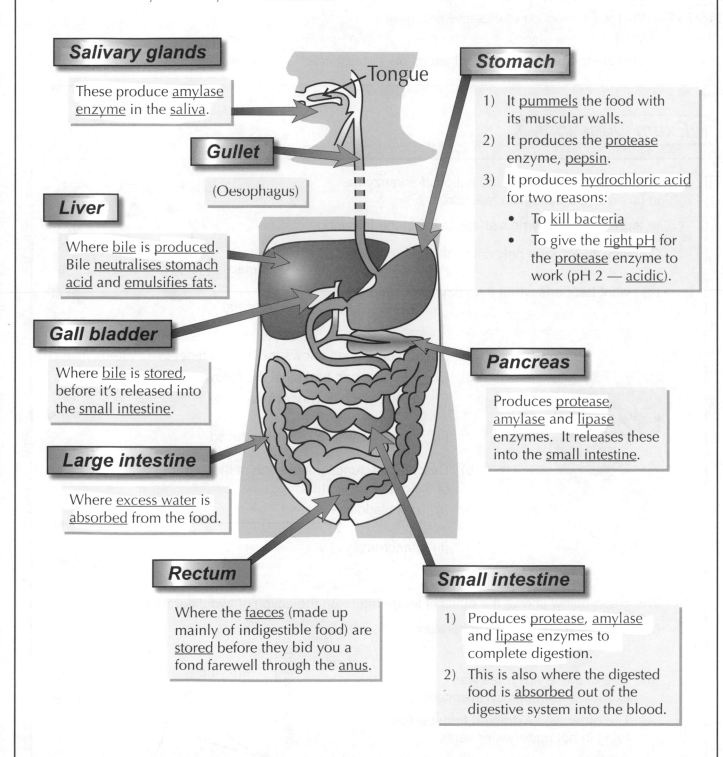

Salivary glands

These produce <u>amylase enzyme</u> in the <u>saliva</u>.

Tongue

Gullet

(Oesophagus)

Liver

Where <u>bile</u> is <u>produced</u>. Bile <u>neutralises stomach acid</u> and <u>emulsifies fats</u>.

Gall bladder

Where <u>bile</u> is <u>stored</u>, before it's released into the <u>small intestine</u>.

Large intestine

Where <u>excess water</u> is <u>absorbed</u> from the food.

Rectum

Where the <u>faeces</u> (made up mainly of indigestible food) are <u>stored</u> before they bid you a fond farewell through the <u>anus</u>.

Stomach

1) It <u>pummels</u> the food with its muscular walls.
2) It produces the <u>protease</u> enzyme, <u>pepsin</u>.
3) It produces <u>hydrochloric acid</u> for two reasons:
    * To <u>kill bacteria</u>
    * To give the <u>right pH</u> for the <u>protease</u> enzyme to work (pH 2 — <u>acidic</u>).

Pancreas

Produces <u>protease</u>, <u>amylase</u> and <u>lipase</u> enzymes. It releases these into the <u>small intestine</u>.

Small intestine

1) Produces <u>protease</u>, <u>amylase</u> and <u>lipase</u> enzymes to complete digestion.
2) This is also where the digested food is <u>absorbed</u> out of the digestive system into the blood.

That's nine different bits of the digestive system you need to know
Did you know that the whole of your digestive system is actually a big hole that goes right through your body? It just gets loads of food, digestive juices and enzymes piled into it...

Warm-Up and Exam Questions

Doing well in exams isn't just about remembering all the facts, although that's important. You have to get used to the way the exams are phrased and make sure you always read the question carefully.

Warm-Up Questions

1) Enzymes are sometimes referred to as 'biological catalysts'. What is a catalyst?
2) What is meant by the optimum pH of an enzyme?
3) What is the function of digestive enzymes?
4) Which enzyme digests: (a) starch (b) protein (c) lipids?
5) What are the products of the digestion of: (a) starch (b) protein (c) lipids?

Exam Questions

1   The diagram represents the action of an enzyme in catalysing a biological reaction.

In terms of the enzyme's shape, explain the following:

(a) why an enzyme only catalyses one reaction.
(1 mark)

(b) what happens when the enzyme is denatured.
(1 mark)

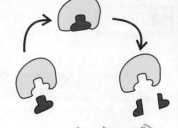

2   The diagram on the left shows the human digestive system.

(a) Copy the diagram and label the following parts:

(i)   a part which is very acidic
(1 mark)

(ii) the place where bile is produced
(1 mark)

(b) Describe the functions of each of these parts of the digestive system:

(i)   gall bladder
(1 mark)

(ii) pancreas
(2 marks)

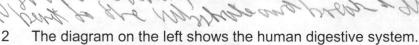

3   The graph below shows the effect of temperature on the action of two different enzymes.

(a) What is the optimum temperature for enzyme **A**?
(1 mark)

(b) One of these enzymes was extracted from human liver cells.

The other was extracted from bacteria living in hot underwater vents.

Suggest which enzyme came from the bacteria. Give a reason for your answer.
(1 mark)

Enzymes and Respiration

Many chemical reactions inside cells are controlled by enzymes — including the ones in respiration.

Respiration is NOT "Breathing In and Out"

Respiration involves many reactions, all of which are catalysed by enzymes. These are really important reactions, as respiration releases the energy that the cell needs to do just about everything.

1) Respiration is not breathing in and breathing out, as you might think.

2) Respiration is the process of releasing energy from the breakdown of glucose — and it goes on in every cell in your body.

3) It happens in plants too. All living things respire. It's how they release energy from their food.

> RESPIRATION is the process of RELEASING ENERGY
> FROM GLUCOSE, which goes on IN EVERY CELL.

Aerobic Respiration Needs Plenty of Oxygen

1) Aerobic respiration is respiration using oxygen. It's the most efficient way to release energy from glucose. (You can also have anaerobic respiration, which happens without oxygen, but that doesn't release nearly as much energy — see page 45.)

2) Aerobic respiration goes on all the time in plants and animals.

3) Most of the reactions in aerobic respiration happen inside mitochondria (see page 18).

4) You need to learn the overall word equation:

> Glucose + oxygen $\Longrightarrow$ carbon dioxide + water + ENERGY

Respiration Releases Energy for All Kinds of Things

You need to learn these four examples of what the energy released by aerobic respiration is used for:

1) To build up larger molecules from smaller ones (like proteins from amino acids).

2) In animals, to allow the muscles to contract (which in turn allows them to move about).

3) In mammals and birds the energy is used to keep their body temperature steady (unlike other animals, mammals and birds keep their bodies constantly warm).

4) In plants, to build sugars, nitrates and other nutrients into amino acids, which are then built up into proteins.

Respiration releases energy from glucose

So... respiration — that's a pretty important thing. Cyanide is a really nasty toxin that stops respiration by stopping enzymes involved in the process from working — so it's pretty poisonous (it can kill you). Your brain, heart and liver are affected first because they have the highest energy demands... nice.

Exercise

When you exercise, your body quickly adapts so that your muscles get <u>more oxygen and glucose</u> to supply <u>energy</u>.

Exercise *Increases* the *Heart Rate*

1) Muscles are made of <u>muscle cells</u>. These use <u>oxygen</u> to <u>release energy</u> from <u>glucose</u> (<u>aerobic respiration</u> — see page 43), which is used to <u>contract</u> the muscles.

2) An <u>increase</u> in muscle activity requires <u>more glucose and oxygen</u> to be supplied to the muscle cells. Extra carbon dioxide needs to be <u>removed</u> from the muscle cells. For this to happen the blood has to flow at a <u>faster</u> rate.

3) This is why physical activity:

- <u>increases</u> your <u>breathing rate</u> and makes you breathe <u>more deeply</u> to meet the demand for <u>extra oxygen</u>.

- <u>increases</u> the speed at which the <u>heart pumps</u>.

An unfit person's heart rate goes up a lot more during exercise than a fit person, and they take longer to recover.

Glycogen is Used During Exercise

1) Some <u>glucose</u> from food is <u>stored</u> as <u>glycogen</u>.

2) Glycogen's mainly stored in the liver, but each <u>muscle</u> also has its own store.

3) During vigorous exercise muscles use glucose <u>rapidly</u>, so some of the stored glycogen is converted back to <u>glucose</u> to provide more energy.

Glucose is stored as glycogen in the liver and muscles

I bet you're exhausted after reading this page. But nonetheless, you need to know about the changes that happen in your body when you exercise — your <u>breathing rate increases</u>, your <u>breathing depth increases</u> and your <u>heart rate increases</u> too. All this helps plenty of glucose and oxygen to get to your muscles, and carbon dioxide to be taken away, which is just what you need to keep them working.

Exercise and Anaerobic Respiration

If your body can't get enough oxygen or glucose to your muscles, it has a back-up plan ready...

Anaerobic Respiration is Used if There's Not Enough Oxygen

1) When you do vigorous exercise and your body can't supply enough oxygen to your muscles, they start doing anaerobic respiration instead of aerobic respiration.

2) "Anaerobic" just means "without oxygen".
It's the incomplete breakdown of glucose, which produces lactic acid.

$$glucose \rightarrow energy + lactic\ acid$$

3) This is NOT the best way to convert glucose into energy because lactic acid builds up in the muscles, which gets painful. It also causes muscle fatigue — the muscles get tired and they stop contracting efficiently.

4) Another downside is that anaerobic respiration does not release nearly as much energy as aerobic respiration — but it's useful in emergencies.

5) The advantage is that at least you can keep on using your muscles for a while longer.

Anaerobic Respiration Leads to an Oxygen Debt

1) After resorting to anaerobic respiration, when you stop exercising you'll have an "oxygen debt".

2) In other words you have to "repay" the oxygen that you didn't get to your muscles in time, because your lungs, heart and blood couldn't keep up with the demand earlier on.

3) This means you have to keep breathing hard for a while after you stop, to get more oxygen into your blood. Blood flows through your muscles to remove the lactic acid by oxidising it to harmless CO_2 and water.

4) While high levels of CO_2 and lactic acid are detected in the blood (by the brain), the pulse and breathing rate stay high to try and rectify the situation.

These rowers have finished rowing, but they're still breathing hard to replace their oxygen debt.

Oxygen debt needs to be repaid

Yeast also respire anaerobically, but they produce ethanol (and carbon dioxide). So perhaps it's just as well humans produce lactic acid instead — or after a bit of vigorous exercise we'd all be drunk.

Uses of Enzymes

Some <u>microorganisms</u> produce enzymes which pass <u>out</u> of their cells and catalyse reactions outside them (e.g. to <u>digest</u> the microorganism's <u>food</u>). These enzymes have many <u>uses</u> in the <u>home</u> and in <u>industry</u>.

Enzymes Are Used in **Biological Detergents**

1) <u>Enzymes</u> are the '<u>biological</u>' ingredients in biological detergents and washing powders.

2) They're mainly <u>protein-digesting</u> enzymes (<u>proteases</u>) and <u>fat-digesting</u> enzymes (<u>lipases</u>).

3) Because the enzymes break down <u>animal</u> and <u>plant</u> matter, they're ideal for removing <u>stains</u> like <u>food</u> or <u>blood</u>.

4) Biological detergents are also <u>more effective</u> at working at <u>low temperatures</u> (e.g. 30 °C) than other types of detergents.

Enzymes Are Used to **Change Foods**

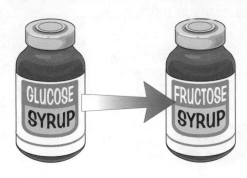

1) The <u>proteins</u> in some <u>baby foods</u> are '<u>pre-digested</u>' using protein-digesting enzymes (<u>proteases</u>), so they're easier for the baby to digest.

2) Carbohydrate-digesting enzymes (<u>carbohydrases</u>) can be used to turn <u>starch syrup</u> into <u>sugar syrup</u>.

3) <u>Glucose syrup</u> can be turned into <u>fructose syrup</u> using an <u>isomerase</u> enzyme. Fructose is <u>sweeter</u>, so you can use <u>less</u> of it — good for slimming foods and drinks.

Using Enzymes in **Industry** Takes a Lot of **Control**

Enzymes are <u>really useful</u> in industry. They <u>speed up</u> reactions without the need for <u>high temperatures</u> and <u>pressures</u>. You need to know the <u>advantages</u> and <u>disadvantages</u> of using them, so here are a few to get you started:

ADVANTAGES:

1) They're <u>specific</u>, so they only catalyse the <u>reaction</u> you <u>want</u> them to.

2) Using lower temperatures and pressures means a <u>lower cost</u> as it <u>saves energy</u>.

3) Enzymes work for a <u>long time</u>, so after the <u>initial cost</u> of buying them, you can <u>continually</u> use them.

4) They are <u>biodegradable</u> and therefore cause less <u>environmental pollution</u>.

DISADVANTAGES:

1) Some people can develop <u>allergies</u> to the enzymes (e.g. in biological washing powders).

2) Enzymes can be <u>denatured</u> by even a <u>small</u> increase in temperature. They're also susceptible to <u>poisons</u> and changes in <u>pH</u>. This means the conditions in which they work must be <u>tightly controlled</u>.

3) Enzymes can be <u>expensive</u> to produce.

4) <u>Contamination</u> of the enzyme with other substances can affect the reaction.

From baby food to washing powder — enzymes make life easier

There's no denying that <u>enzymes</u> are <u>useful</u>, but they're also quite <u>picky</u> — e.g. tiny changes in pH can stop them working. Make sure you know both the <u>advantages</u> and <u>disadvantages</u> of using enzymes.

Warm-Up and Exam Questions

You know the drill by now — work your way through the warm-up questions, then the exam questions. After all, plenty of practice is the only way to make sure that you're well-prepared for the exams.

Warm-Up Questions

1) Define respiration.
2) State three changes that take place in the body during vigorous exercise.
3) What substance, stored in the liver and muscles, is broken down during exercise to release glucose?
4) Explain why proteases are used in some baby food.
5) What type of enzymes are used to turn starch syrup into sugar syrup?

Exam Questions

1   In the human body, respiration may be aerobic or anaerobic at different times.
   (a) Explain why the body uses anaerobic respiration during vigorous exercise.

   (2 marks)

   (b) Write down the word equation for anaerobic respiration.

   (1 mark)

   (c) Give **two** disadvantages of anaerobic respiration.

   (2 marks)

2   Enzymes are used in the food industry to turn glucose syrup into fructose syrup.
   (a) Name the enzyme used to turn glucose syrup into fructose syrup.

   (1 mark)

   (b) Explain why this process is carried out.

   (2 marks)

3   The graph below shows the rate of oxygen use by a person before, during and after a period of exercise.

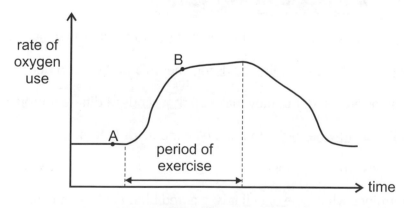

   (a) Why is the rate of oxygen consumption higher at **B** than at **A**?

   (1 mark)

   (b) Suggest why oxygen use remains high, even after the period of exercise ends.

   (1 mark)

DNA

The first step in understanding genetics is getting to grips with DNA.

Chromosomes Are Really Long Molecules of DNA

1) <u>DNA</u> stands for <u>d</u>eoxyribose <u>n</u>ucleic <u>a</u>cid.

2) It contains all the <u>instructions</u> to put an organism together and <u>make it work</u>.

3) It's found in the <u>nucleus</u> of animal and plant cells, in really <u>long molecules</u> called <u>chromosomes</u>.

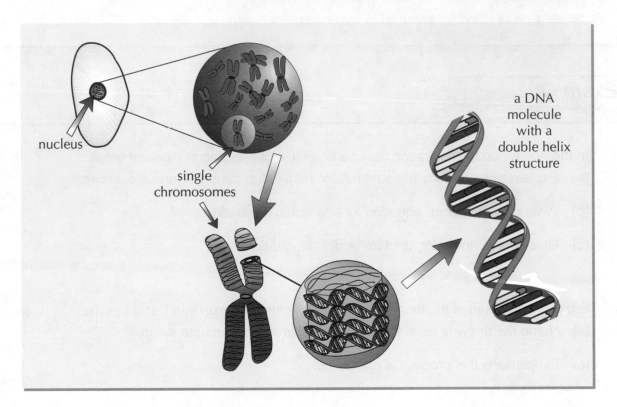

nucleus

single chromosomes

a DNA molecule with a double helix structure

A Gene Codes for a Specific Protein

1) A <u>gene</u> is a <u>section</u> of DNA. It contains the <u>instructions</u> to make a <u>specific protein</u>.

2) Cells make <u>proteins</u> by stringing <u>amino acids</u> together in a particular order.

3) Only <u>20</u> amino acids are used, but they make up <u>thousands</u> of different <u>proteins</u>.

4) Genes simply tell cells <u>in what order</u> to put the amino acids together.

5) DNA also determines what <u>proteins</u> the cell <u>produces</u>, e.g. haemoglobin, keratin.

6) That in turn determines what <u>type of cell</u> it is, e.g. red blood cell, skin cell.

Your genes make you different from everyone else

You've got to make sure you know exactly what <u>chromosomes</u> and <u>genes</u> are. If you don't get that sorted out first, then anything else you read about them later on won't make a lot of sense.

DNA Fingerprinting

Now this is interesting — you can use <u>DNA</u> to <u>catch criminals</u> or to <u>identify</u> the <u>father</u> of a child.

Everyone has Unique DNA...   *...except identical twins and clones*

1) Almost everyone's DNA is <u>unique</u>. The only exceptions are <u>identical twins</u>, where the two people have identical DNA, and <u>clones</u>.

2) <u>DNA fingerprinting</u> (or genetic fingerprinting) is a way of <u>cutting up</u> a person's DNA into small sections and then <u>separating</u> them.

3) Every person's genetic fingerprint has a <u>unique</u> pattern (unless they're identical twins or clones of course). This means you can <u>tell people apart</u> by <u>comparing samples</u> of their DNA.

DNA fingerprinting is used in...

1) Forensic Science

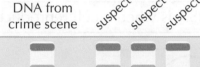

DNA (from hair, skin flakes, blood, semen etc.) taken from a <u>crime scene</u> is compared with a DNA sample taken from a suspect.

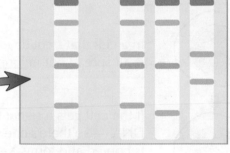

In the diagram, suspect 1's DNA has the same pattern as the DNA from the crime scene — so suspect 1 was probably at the crime scene.

2) Paternity Testing

To see if a man is the father of a particular child.

- Some people would like there to be a national <u>genetic database</u> of everyone in the country. That way, DNA from a crime scene could be checked against <u>everyone</u> in the country to see whose it was.

- But others think this is a big <u>invasion of privacy</u>, and they worry about how <u>safe</u> the data would be and what <u>else</u> it might be used for.

- There are also <u>scientific problems</u> — <u>false positives</u> can occur if <u>errors</u> are made in the procedure or if the data is <u>misinterpreted</u>.

Forensic science is useful, but some people have concerns

In the exam you might have to interpret data on <u>DNA fingerprinting for identification</u>. They could give you the results of a <u>paternity test</u> — the DNA fingerprint of a child, its mother and some possible fathers. Remember, <u>half</u> of the child's DNA will <u>match</u> the <u>mother's DNA</u> and <u>half</u> will match the <u>father's DNA</u>.

Cell Division — Mitosis

In order to <u>survive</u> and <u>grow</u>, our cells have got to be able to <u>divide</u>. And that means our <u>DNA</u> as well...

Mitosis Makes New Cells for Growth and Repair

1) <u>Body cells</u> normally have <u>two copies</u> of each <u>chromosome</u> — one from the organism's 'mother', and one from its 'father'. So, humans have two copies of chromosome 1, two copies of chromosome 2, etc.

2) The diagram shows the <u>23 pairs of chromosomes</u> from a human cell. The 23rd pair are a bit different — see page 55.

3) When a body cell <u>divides</u> it needs to make new cells <u>identical</u> to the <u>original</u> cell — with the <u>same number</u> of chromosomes.

4) This type of cell division is called <u>mitosis</u>. It's used when plants and animals want to <u>grow</u> or to <u>replace</u> cells that have been <u>damaged</u>.

> "<u>MITOSIS</u> is when a cell reproduces itself <u>by splitting</u> to form <u>two identical offspring</u>."

In a cell that's not dividing, the DNA is all spread out in <u>long strings</u>.

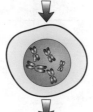

If the cell gets a signal to <u>divide</u>, it needs to <u>duplicate</u> its DNA — so there's one copy for each new cell. The DNA is copied and forms <u>X-shaped</u> chromosomes. Each 'arm' of the chromosome is an <u>exact duplicate</u> of the other.

The left arm of the chromosome has the same DNA as the right arm.

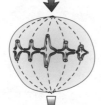

The chromosomes then <u>line up</u> at the centre of the cell and <u>cell fibres</u> pull them apart. The <u>two arms</u> of each chromosome go to <u>opposite ends</u> of the cell.

<u>Membranes</u> form around each of the sets of chromosomes. These become the <u>nuclei</u> of the two new cells.

Lastly, the <u>cytoplasm</u> divides.

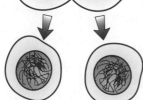

You now have <u>two new cells</u> containing exactly the same DNA — they're <u>identical</u>.

Asexual Reproduction Also Uses Mitosis

1) Some organisms also <u>reproduce</u> by mitosis, e.g. strawberry plants form runners in this way, which become new plants.

2) This is an example of <u>asexual</u> reproduction.

3) The offspring have exactly the <u>same genes</u> as the parent — so there's <u>no variation</u>.

Cell Division — Meiosis

Mitosis makes identical cells, but there's another type of cell division which doesn't — it's meiosis...

Gametes Have Half the Usual Number of Chromosomes

1) During sexual reproduction, two cells called gametes (sex cells) combine to form a new individual.

2) Gametes only have one copy of each chromosome. This is so that you can combine one sex cell from the 'mother' and one sex cell from the 'father' and still end up with the right number of chromosomes in body cells. For example, human body cells have 46 chromosomes. The gametes have 23 chromosomes each, so that when an egg and sperm combine, you get 46 chromosomes again.

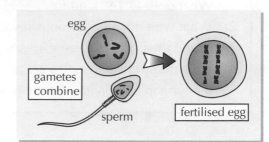

3) The new individual will have a mixture of two sets of chromosomes, so it will inherit features from both parents. This is how sexual reproduction produces variation.

Meiosis Involves Two Divisions

To make new cells which only have half the original number of chromosomes, cells divide by meiosis. In humans, it only happens in the reproductive organs (e.g. ovaries and testes).

"MEIOSIS produces cells which have half the normal number of chromosomes."

chromosome pair

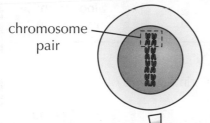

As with mitosis, before the cell starts to divide, it duplicates its DNA — one arm of each chromosome is an exact copy of the other arm.

In the first division in meiosis (there are two divisions) the chromosome pairs line up in the centre of the cell.

The pairs are then pulled apart, so each new cell only has one copy of each chromosome. Some of the father's chromosomes (shown in blue) and some of the mother's chromosomes (shown in red) go into each new cell.

In the second division the chromosomes line up again in the centre of the cell. It's a lot like mitosis. The arms of the chromosomes are pulled apart.

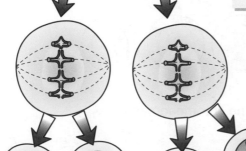

You get four gametes each with only a single set of chromosomes in it.

After two gametes join at fertilisation, the cell grows by repeatedly dividing by mitosis.

Warm-Up and Exam Questions

It's time to see how much you picked up about DNA and cell division, with the help of a few questions...

Warm-Up Questions

1) What does DNA stand for?
2) What type of cell division is involved in the regeneration of body parts?
3) Name the organs where gametes are formed.
4) How many chromosomes are there in a human liver cell?
5) If a human cell divides by meiosis, how many chromosomes do the new cells each have?

Exam Questions

1 Describe how a cell divides to form gametes.

(3 marks)

2 Mr X and Mr Y are both suspects
in a burglary. A blood stain has been
found on a crowbar at the crime scene.
The police carry out a DNA fingerprint
on Mr X, Mr Y and the blood from the
crime scene.

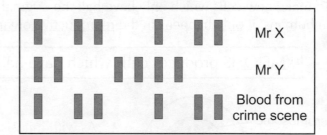

The diagram shows part of the test results.

(a) Do the results suggest that either of the suspects were at the crime scene?
Explain your answer.

(1 mark)

(b) A police officer investigating the burglary says that no two people have
exactly the same genetic fingerprint. Is he correct? Explain your answer.

(2 marks)

3 (a) The diagram below shows the chromosomes of a
cell that is about to divide by meiosis.

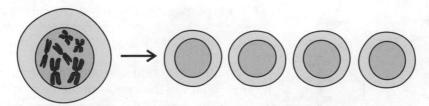

(i) Copy and complete the diagram to show the chromosomes
in the daughter cells.

(2 marks)

(ii) How is the genetic content of the new cells different from the original cell?

(1 mark)

(b) State **three** ways in which meiosis is different from mitosis.

(3 marks)

Stem Cells

Most cells have specific features that make them particularly suited to the job that they do. But stem cells are a bit like a blank canvas — they have the potential to turn into other types of cells. And because of that, they're very important little cells...

Embryonic Stem Cells Can Turn into ANY Type of Cell

1) You know that <u>differentiation</u> is the process by which a cell <u>changes</u> to become <u>specialised</u> for its job (see page 23).

2) In most <u>animal</u> cells, the ability to differentiate is <u>lost</u> at an early stage, but lots of <u>plant</u> cells <u>don't</u> ever lose this ability.

3) Some cells are <u>undifferentiated</u>. They can develop into <u>different types of cell</u> depending on what <u>instructions</u> they're given. These cells are called <u>STEM CELLS</u>.

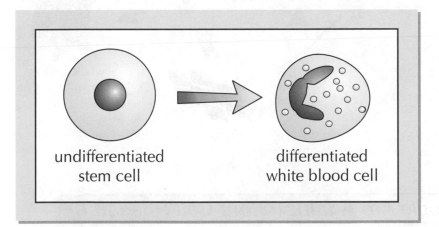

undifferentiated
stem cell

differentiated
white blood cell

4) Stem cells are found in early <u>human embryos</u>. They're <u>exciting</u> to doctors and medical researchers because they have the potential to turn into <u>any</u> kind of cell at all. This makes sense if you think about it — <u>all</u> the <u>different types</u> of cell found in a human being have to come from those <u>few cells</u> in the early embryo.

5) Adults also have stem cells, but they're only found in certain places, like <u>bone marrow</u>. These aren't as <u>versatile</u> as embryonic stem cells — they can't turn into <u>any</u> cell type at all, only certain ones.

Stem cells are pretty versatile little cells...

Your cells are pretty highly <u>specialised</u> for the jobs that they do — think how different a red blood cell is from any other cell. But you can trace <u>all</u> cells back to undifferentiated <u>stem cells</u> in the embryo.

Stem Cells

Stem cell research has exciting possibilities, but it's also pretty <u>controversial</u>.

Stem Cells May Be Able to **Cure** Many **Diseases**

1) Medicine <u>already</u> uses adult stem cells to cure <u>disease</u>. For example, people with some <u>blood diseases</u> (e.g. <u>sickle cell anaemia</u>) can be treated by <u>bone marrow transplants</u>. Bone marrow contains <u>stem cells</u> that can turn into <u>new blood cells</u> to replace the faulty old ones.

2) Scientists can also <u>extract</u> stem cells from very early human embryos and <u>grow</u> them.

3) These embryonic stem cells could be used to <u>replace faulty cells</u> in sick people — you could make <u>beating heart muscle cells</u> for people with <u>heart disease</u>, <u>insulin-producing cells</u> for people with <u>diabetes</u>, <u>nerve cells</u> for people <u>paralysed by spinal injuries</u>, and so on.

4) To get cultures of <u>one specific type</u> of cell, researchers try to <u>control</u> the differentiation of the stem cells by changing the environment they're growing in. So far, it's still a bit hit and miss — lots more <u>research</u> is needed.

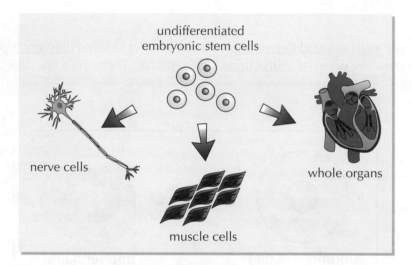

Some People Are **Against Stem Cell Research**

1) Some people are <u>against</u> stem cell research because they feel that human embryos <u>shouldn't</u> be used for experiments since each one is a <u>potential human life</u>.

2) Others think that curing patients who <u>already exist</u> and who are <u>suffering</u> is more important than the rights of <u>embryos</u>.

3) One fairly convincing argument in favour of this point of view is that the embryos used in the research are usually <u>unwanted ones</u> from <u>fertility clinics</u> that would probably just be <u>destroyed</u> if they weren't used for research. But of course, campaigners for the rights of embryos usually want this banned too.

4) These campaigners feel that scientists should concentrate more on finding and developing <u>other sources</u> of stem cells, so people could be helped <u>without</u> having to use embryos.

5) In some countries stem cell research is <u>banned</u>, but it's allowed in the UK as long as it follows <u>strict guidelines</u>.

Alternative sources of stem cells would avoid the controversy

Research has been done into getting stem cells from <u>other sources</u> — for example, some scientists think it might be possible to get cells from <u>umbilical cords</u> to behave like embryonic stem cells.

X and Y Chromosomes

Now for a couple of very important little chromosomes...

Your **Chromosomes** Control Whether You're **Male** or **Female**

1) There are 22 matched pairs of chromosomes in every human body cell.

2) The 23rd pair are labelled XX or XY.

3) They're the two chromosomes that decide whether you turn out male or female.

> All men have an X and a Y chromosome: XY
> The Y chromosome causes male characteristics.

> All women have two X chromosomes: XX
> The XX combination allows
> female characteristics to develop.

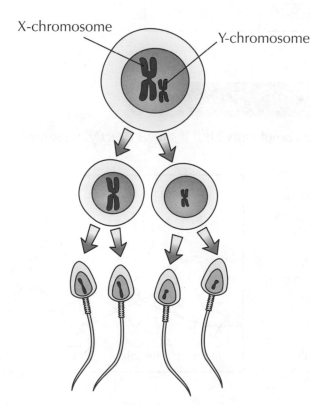

X-chromosome   Y-chromosome

When making sperm, the X and Y chromosomes are drawn apart in the first division in meiosis. There's a 50% chance each sperm cell gets an X chromosome and a 50% chance it gets a Y chromosome.

A similar thing happens when making eggs. But the original cell has two X chromosomes, so all the eggs have one X chromosome.

The Y chromosome is physically smaller than the X chromosome

It's possible for people to have one X and two Y chromosomes, or even three X chromosomes, in their cells. But you don't really need to know this — just remember that it's XX for girls and XY for boys.

X and Y Chromosomes

You can work out the <u>probability</u> of offspring being male or female by using a <u>genetic diagram</u>.

Genetic Diagrams *Show the* Possible Combinations *of Gametes*

1) To find the <u>probability</u> of getting a boy or a girl, you can draw a <u>genetic diagram</u>.

2) Put the <u>possible gametes</u> from <u>one</u> parent down the side, and those from the <u>other</u> parent along the top.

3) Then in each middle square you <u>fill in</u> the letters from the top and side that line up with that square. The <u>pairs of letters</u> in the middle show the possible combinations of the gametes.

4) There are <u>two XX results</u> and <u>two XY results</u>, so there's the same probability of getting a boy or a girl.

5) Don't forget that this <u>50:50 ratio</u> is only a <u>probability</u> at each pregnancy. If you had four kids they <u>could</u> all be <u>boys</u>.

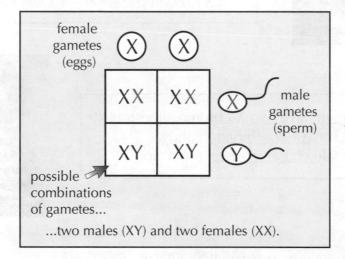

There's More Than One Type *of Genetic Diagram*

The other type of genetic diagram looks a bit more complicated, but it shows exactly the same thing.

1) At the top are the <u>parents</u>.

2) The middle circles show the <u>possible gametes</u> that are formed. One gamete from the female combines with one gamete from the male (during fertilisation).

3) The criss-cross lines show <u>all</u> the <u>possible</u> ways the X and Y chromosomes <u>could</u> combine.

4) The <u>possible combinations</u> of the offspring are shown in the bottom circles.

5) Remember, only <u>one</u> of these possibilities would <u>actually happen</u> for any one offspring.

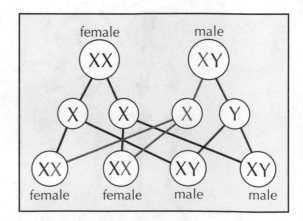

These diagrams aren't as scary as they look...

Most genetic diagrams you'll see in exams concentrate on a <u>gene</u>, instead of a <u>chromosome</u>. But the principle's the same. Don't worry — there are loads of other examples on the following pages.

Warm-Up and Exam Questions

There's only one way to do well in the exam — learn the facts and then practise lots of exam questions to see what it'll be like on the big day. We couldn't have made it easier for you — so do it.

Warm-Up Questions

1) What does cell 'differentiation' mean?
2) Give one example of a condition that could be treated with embryonic stem cells.
3) What combination of X and Y chromosomes does: a) a male have?   b) a female have?

Exam Questions

1   Read the passage below about stem cell research.

> Stem cell research has been widely debated over the past few years. Adult stem cells have already been used to cure disorders, and it is thought that embryonic stem cells have the potential to treat many more disorders.
>
> One of the most controversial issues surrounds the technique used to create embryonic stem cells. Current legislation in the UK means that production of stem cells by human reproductive cloning is illegal. Research can only be carried out on embryos produced in the laboratory and surplus embryos created for use in *in vitro* fertilisation (IVF).

(a) What are stem cells?

(2 marks)

(b) Describe how stem cells could be used to treat disorders.

(1 mark)

(c) Explain why embryonic stem cells have the potential to treat more disorders than adult stem cells.

(1 mark)

(d) Give **one** place where adult stem cells are found in the body.

(1 mark)

(e) *In this question you will be assessed on the quality of your English, the organisation of your ideas and your use of appropriate specialist vocabulary.*

Discuss why some people are in favour of using embryos to create stem cells for research, while others are against the idea.

(6 marks)

2   Karen and Frank have four children. They are all girls.
Karen discovers that she is pregnant. What is the probability
that the new baby will be a boy? Explain your answer.

(2 marks)

The Work of Mendel

Gregor Mendel was pretty much the <u>founder of genetics</u>. Here's a whole page on him.

Mendel Did Genetic Experiments with Pea Plants

1) <u>Gregor Mendel</u> was an Austrian monk who trained in <u>mathematics</u> and <u>natural history</u> at the University of Vienna. On his garden plot at the monastery, Mendel noted how <u>characteristics</u> in <u>plants</u> were <u>passed on</u> from one generation to the next.

2) The results of his research were published in <u>1866</u> and eventually became the <u>foundation</u> of modern <u>genetics</u>.

3) These diagrams show two <u>crosses for height</u> in <u>pea plants</u> that Mendel carried out...

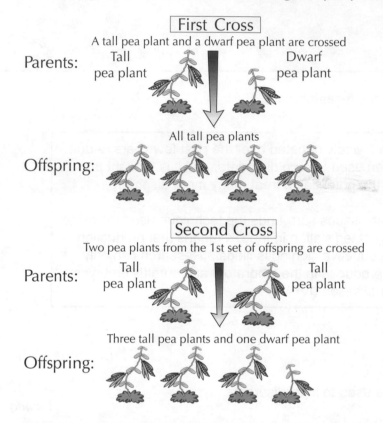

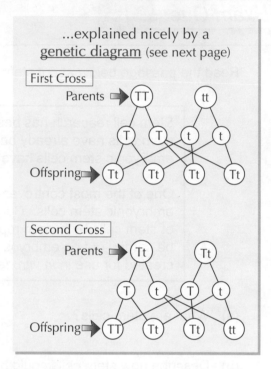

Mendel had shown that the height characteristic in pea plants was determined by separately inherited "<u>hereditary units</u>" passed on from each parent. The ratios of tall and dwarf plants in the offspring showed that the unit for tall plants, <u>T</u>, was <u>dominant</u> over the unit for dwarf plants, <u>t</u>.

Mendel Reached Three Important Conclusions

Mendel reached these three important conclusions about <u>heredity in plants</u>:

1) Characteristics in plants are determined by "<u>hereditary units</u>".
2) Hereditary units are passed on from both parents, <u>one unit</u> from <u>each parent</u>.
3) Hereditary units can be <u>dominant</u> or <u>recessive</u> — if an individual has <u>both</u> the dominant and the recessive unit for a characteristic, the <u>dominant</u> characteristic will be expressed.

We now know that the "hereditary units" are, of course, <u>genes</u>.

But in Mendel's time <u>nobody</u> knew anything about genes or DNA, and so the <u>significance</u> of his work was not to be realised until <u>after his death</u>.

Genetic Diagrams

When a single gene controls the inheritance of a characteristic, you can work out the odds of getting it...

Genetic Diagrams Show the Possible Genes of Offspring

1) Alleles are different versions of the same gene.

2) In genetic diagrams letters are usually used to represent alleles.

3) If an organism has two alleles for a particular gene the same, then it's HOMOZYGOUS. If its two alleles for a particular gene are different, then it's HETEROZYGOUS.

Remember, gametes only have one allele, but all the other cells in an organism have two.

4) If the two alleles are different, only one can determine what characteristic is present. The allele for the characteristic that's shown is called the dominant allele (use a capital letter for dominant alleles — e.g. 'C'). The other one is called recessive (and you show these with small letters — e.g. 'c').

5) For an organism to display a recessive characteristic, both its alleles must be recessive (e.g. cc). But to display a dominant characteristic the organism can be either CC or Cc, because the dominant allele overrules the recessive one if the plant/animal/other organism is heterozygous.

You Need to be Able to Interpret, Explain and Construct Them

Imagine you're cross-breeding hamsters, some with normal hair and a mild disposition and others with wild scratty hair and a leaning towards crazy acrobatics.

Let's say that the gene which causes the crazy nature is recessive, so we use a small "b" for it, whilst normal (boring) behaviour is due to a dominant gene, so we represent it with a capital "B".

1) A crazy hamster must have the genotype bb. However, a normal hamster could have two possible genotypes — BB or Bb.

2) Here's what happens if you breed from two homozygous hamsters:

Genotype means what alleles you have. Phenotype means the actual characteristic.

Parents' phenotypes:	Normal	Crazy
Parents' genotypes:	BB	bb
Gametes' genotypes:	B B	b b
Offspring's genotypes:	Bb Bb	Bb Bb
Offspring's phenotypes:	All the offspring are normal (boring).	

3) If two of these offspring now breed, you'll get the next generation:

When you cross two parents to look at just one characteristic, it's called a monohybrid cross.

Parents' phenotypes:	Normal	Normal
Parents' genotypes:	Bb	Bb
Gametes' genotypes:	B b	B b
Offspring's genotypes:	BB Bb	Bb bb
Offspring's phenotypes:	Normal Normal	Normal Crazy

4) This gives a 3:1 ratio of normal to crazy offspring in this generation. Remember that "results" like this are only probabilities — they don't say definitely what'll happen.

Genetic Disorders

It's not just characteristics that are passed on — some <u>disorders</u> are inherited. You need to <u>learn these two</u>.

Cystic Fibrosis is Caused by a Recessive Allele

<u>Cystic fibrosis</u> is a <u>genetic disorder</u> of the <u>cell membranes</u>. It <u>results</u> in the body producing a lot of thick sticky <u>mucus</u> in the <u>air passages</u> and in the <u>pancreas</u>.

1) The allele which causes cystic fibrosis is a <u>recessive allele</u>, 'f', carried by about <u>1 person in 25</u>.

2) Because it's recessive, people with only <u>one copy</u> of the allele <u>won't</u> have the disorder — they're known as <u>carriers</u>.

3) For a child to have the disorder, <u>both parents</u> must be either <u>carriers</u> or <u>sufferers</u>.

4) There's a <u>1 in 4 chance</u> of a child having the disorder if <u>both</u> parents are <u>carriers</u>:

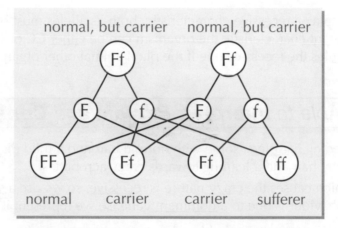

Polydactyly is Caused by a Dominant Allele

<u>Polydactyly</u> is a <u>genetic disorder</u> where a baby's born with <u>extra fingers or toes</u>. It doesn't usually cause any other problems so <u>isn't life-threatening</u>.

1) The disorder is caused by a <u>dominant allele</u>, 'D', and so can be inherited if just <u>one parent</u> carries the defective allele.

2) The <u>parent</u> that <u>has</u> the defective allele will be a <u>sufferer</u> too since the allele is dominant.

3) As the genetic diagram shows, there's a <u>50% chance</u> of a child having the disorder if <u>one</u> parent has the D allele.

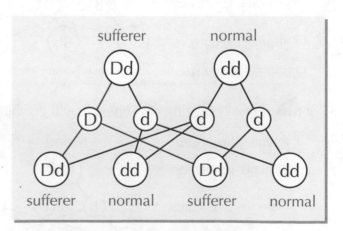

That's four genetic diagrams in two pages — get scribbling...

Genetic diagrams look pretty confusing at first, but they're really <u>not</u>. The important thing to get clear in your head is whether the <u>characteristic</u> is caused by a <u>dominant</u> or <u>recessive allele</u>.

Screening for Genetic Disorders

In vitro fertilisation (IVF) is quite widely used now by people who have problems conceiving naturally. Part of the process involves screening for genetic disorders, but some people are unhappy about this.

Embryos Can Be Screened for Genetic Disorders

1) During *in vitro* fertilisation (IVF), embryos are fertilised in a laboratory, and then implanted into the mother's womb. More than one egg is fertilised, so there's a better chance of the IVF being successful.

2) Before being implanted, it's possible to remove a cell from each embryo and analyse its genes.

3) Many genetic disorders could be detected in this way, such as cystic fibrosis.

4) Embryos with 'good' alleles would be implanted into the mother — the ones with 'bad' alleles destroyed.

There is a huge debate raging about embryonic screening. Here are some arguments for and against it.

Against Embryonic Screening

1) There may come a point where everyone wants to screen their embryos so they can pick the most 'desirable' one, e.g. they want a blue-eyed, blond-haired, intelligent boy.

2) The rejected embryos are destroyed — they could have developed into humans.

3) It implies that people with genetic problems are 'undesirable' — this could increase prejudice.

4) Screening is expensive.

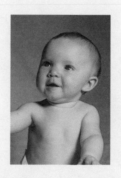

For Embryonic Screening

1) It will help to stop people suffering.

2) There are laws to stop it going too far. At the moment parents cannot even select the sex of their baby (unless it's for health reasons).

3) During IVF, most of the embryos are destroyed anyway — screening just allows the selected one to be healthy.

4) Treating disorders costs the Government (and the taxpayers) a lot of money.

Many people think that embryonic screening isn't justified for genetic disorders that don't affect a person's health, such as polydactyly (see page 60).

Embryonic screening — it's a tricky one...

In the exam you may be asked to compare the issues for and against embryonic screening for different disorders. Make sure you can apply the pros and cons above to different disorders and you'll be fine.

More Genetic Diagrams

In the exam they could ask about the inheritance of <u>any</u> kind of characteristic that's controlled by a <u>single gene</u>, because the principle's <u>always the same</u>. So here's a bit more on genetic diagrams...

You Should be able to **Predict** and **Explain** the Outcomes of Crosses

If you've got your head round all this, you should be able to draw a <u>genetic diagram</u> and <u>work out</u> the outcomes of crosses between individuals for each <u>possible combination</u> of <u>dominant</u> and <u>recessive alleles</u> of a gene. But it'll make it easier for you if you've seen all the different types before. So get ready for a couple of pages of examples...

All the Offspring are **Normal**

Let's take another look at the <u>crazy hamster</u> example from page 59:

In this cross, a hamster with <u>two dominant alleles</u> (BB) is crossed with a hamster with <u>two recessive alleles</u> (bb). <u>All</u> the offspring are normal (boring).

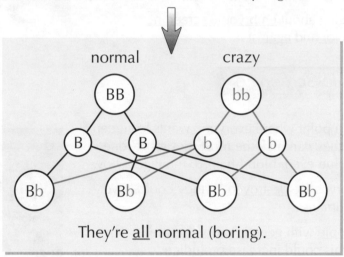

They're <u>all</u> normal (boring).

But, if you crossed a hamster with <u>two dominant alleles</u> (BB) with a hamster with <u>a dominant</u> and <u>a recessive allele</u> (Bb), you would also get <u>all</u> normal (boring) offspring.

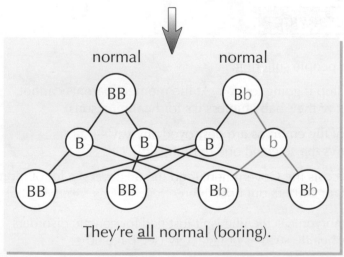

They're <u>all</u> normal (boring).

To find out <u>which</u> it was you'd have to <u>breed the offspring together</u> and see what kind of <u>ratio</u> you got that time — then you'd have a good idea. If it was <u>3:1</u>, it's likely that you originally had BB and bb.

More Genetic Diagrams

One more example of a genetic cross diagram coming up on this page. Then a little bit about another type of genetic diagram that you need to know how to interpret — called a family tree...

There's a *1:1 Ratio* in the Offspring

1) A cat with <u>long hair</u> was bred with another cat with <u>short hair</u>.

2) The long hair is caused by a <u>dominant</u> allele 'H', and the short hair by a <u>recessive</u> allele 'h'.

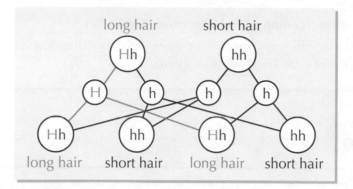

3) They had 8 kittens — 4 with long hair and 4 with short hair.

4) This is a <u>1:1</u> ratio — it's what you'd expect when a parent with only <u>one dominant allele</u> (Hh) is crossed with a parent with <u>two recessive alleles</u> (hh).

You Need to be Able to *Interpret Family Trees*

Knowing how inheritance works can help you to interpret a <u>family tree</u> — this is one for <u>cystic fibrosis</u>.

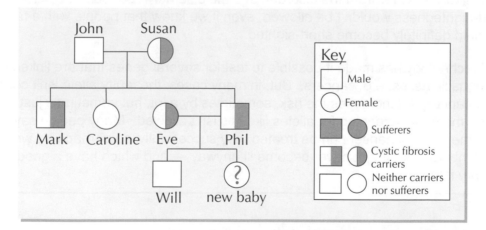

1) From the family tree, you can tell that the allele for cystic fibrosis <u>isn't</u> dominant because plenty of the family <u>carry</u> the allele but <u>aren't sufferers</u>.

2) There is a <u>25%</u> chance that the new baby will be a sufferer and a <u>50%</u> chance that it will be a carrier, as both of its parents are carriers but not sufferers. The case of the new baby is just the same as the genetic diagram on page 60 — so the baby could be <u>normal</u> (FF), a <u>carrier</u> (Ff) or a <u>sufferer</u> (ff).

It's enough to make you go cross-eyed...

If you see a <u>family tree</u> showing the inheritance of a <u>dominant allele</u>, it <u>won't</u> have any <u>carriers</u> on it (everyone who carries the allele is a sufferer). A good way to work out a family tree is to write the <u>genotype</u> of each person onto it — try copying the one above and writing the genotypes on for practice.

Warm-Up and Exam Questions

There's no better preparation for exam questions than doing... err... practice exam questions. Hang on, what's this I see...

Warm-Up Questions

1) What are alleles?
2) Explain how it's possible to be a carrier of cystic fibrosis without knowing.
3) What is polydactyly?
4) What is meant by the **screening** of embryos produced by IVF?
5) What offspring ratio would you expect if a parent with only one dominant allele is crossed with a parent with two recessive alleles?

Exam Questions

1 Read this passage about embryo screening.

Embryo screening already happens in the UK for genetic disorders like cystic fibrosis. A genetic test can be done during IVF treatment — so that doctors can select a healthy embryo to implant in the mother. The other embryos are discarded.

At the moment, regulations say that embryo screening is only allowed when there is "a significant risk of a serious genetic condition being present in the embryo." In other words, it is only allowed when a child of the person carrying the faulty allele would be likely to suffer from the disorder, and the disorder is serious. So screening for short-sightedness wouldn't be allowed, even if we knew that people with a faulty allele would definitely become short-sighted.

Medical technology has made it possible to test for several genes that are linked to very serious illnesses, e.g. cancers. But, in many cases, the faulty allele isn't certain to cause cancer — it increases the risk, sometimes by a lot, but sometimes just slightly. So, at the moment, screening for alleles like this isn't allowed. Many people say this is right. Some kinds of cancer can be treated very successfully, so perhaps it's wrong to destroy embryos that might never become ill anyway — and which have a good chance of recovery if they do.

(a) Could embryos be screened for polydactyly under the current regulations? Explain your answer.

(1 mark)

(b) Cancer is a serious illness that kills thousands of people each year in the UK. Why is cancer not included in embryo screening?

(3 marks)

(c) Give **one** reason why a person might be opposed to screening embryos for genetic conditions.

(1 mark)

Exam Questions

2   In one of Gregor Mendel's experiments, he crossed thoroughbred purple-flowered pea plants with thoroughbred white-flowered plants. The first generation of offspring were all purple-flowered.

    (a)   In Mendel's experiment, which characteristic is recessive?

(1 mark)

    (b)   Using the symbols **F** and **f** to represent the alleles for purple and white, write down the combination of alleles (genetic make-up) of each of the following:

       (i)   the original purple-flowered parent plant

(1 mark)

       (ii)   the original white-flowered parent plant

(1 mark)

       (iii) the first generation of purple-flowered offspring

(1 mark)

3   Cystic fibrosis is a disease caused by recessive alleles.

          F = the normal allele
          f = the faulty allele that leads to cystic fibrosis

The genetic diagram below shows the possible inheritance of cystic fibrosis from one couple.

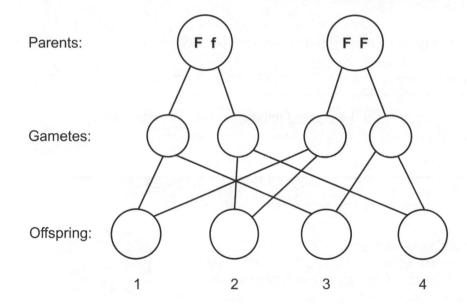

    (a)   Copy and complete the genetic diagram.

(2 marks)

    (b)   Which of the possible offspring will be sufferers and which will be unaffected?

(1 mark)

    (c)   (i)   What proportion of the possible offspring are homozygous?

(1 mark)

         (ii)   Which of the possible offspring are carriers of the disease?

(1 mark)

Fossils and Extinction

Fossils can be really useful — if they're <u>well preserved</u>, they can show you what creatures that have been dead for millions of years might have <u>looked</u> like.

Fossils are the **Remains** of *Plants and Animals*

Fossils are the <u>remains</u> of organisms from <u>many years ago</u>, which are found in <u>rocks</u>.
Fossils provide the <u>evidence</u> that organisms lived ages ago.

Fossils form in rocks in one of <u>three</u> ways:

1) From **Gradual Replacement** by **Minerals**

Most fossils happen this way...

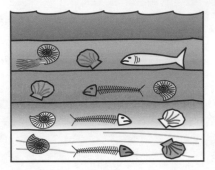

1) Things like <u>teeth</u>, <u>shells</u>, <u>bones</u> etc., which <u>don't decay</u> easily, can last a long time when <u>buried</u>.

2) They're eventually <u>replaced by minerals</u> as they decay, forming a <u>rock-like substance</u> shaped like the original hard part.

3) The surrounding sediments also turn to rock, but the fossil stays <u>distinct</u> inside the rock and eventually someone <u>digs it up</u>.

2) From **Casts** and **Impressions**

1) Sometimes, fossils are formed when an organism is <u>buried</u> in a <u>soft</u> material like clay. The clay later <u>hardens</u> around it and the organism decays, leaving a <u>cast</u> of itself.

> An animal's <u>burrow</u> or a plant's <u>roots</u> can be preserved as casts.

2) Things like footprints can be <u>pressed</u> into these materials when soft, leaving an <u>impression</u> when it hardens.

3) From **Preservation** in Places Where **No Decay** Happens

1) In <u>amber</u> (a clear yellow 'stone' made from fossilised resin) and <u>tar pits</u> there's no <u>oxygen</u> or <u>moisture</u> so <u>decay microbes</u> can't survive.

2) In <u>glaciers</u> it's too <u>cold</u> for the <u>decay microbes</u> to work.

3) <u>Peat bogs</u> are too <u>acidic</u> for <u>decay microbes</u>.

Fossils give us information about ancient animals and plants

It's amazing that <u>fossils</u> of organisms can still exist millions of years after they died. You need to know the <u>three ways</u> that fossils form — cover the page and scribble them down till you're sure you've got it.

Fossils and Extinction

Fossils can also help us to work out how life on Earth has <u>evolved</u>. Evolution leads to the development of lots of <u>different species</u>. But not every species is still around today...

No One Knows How Life Began...

Fossils show how many of today's species have <u>evolved</u> (changed and developed) over millions of years. But where did the <u>first</u> living thing come from...

1) There are various <u>hypotheses</u> suggesting how life first came into being, but no one really <u>knows</u>.

2) Maybe the first life forms came into existence in a primordial <u>swamp</u> (or under the <u>sea</u>) here on <u>Earth</u>. Maybe simple organic molecules were brought to Earth on <u>comets</u> — these could have then become more <u>complex</u> organic molecules, and eventually very simple <u>life forms</u>.

3) These hypotheses can't be supported or disproved because there's a <u>lack</u> of <u>valid</u> and <u>reliable</u> evidence.   *Validity and reliability are explained on page 3.*

4) There's a lack of evidence because scientists believe many early organisms were <u>soft-bodied</u>, and soft tissue tends to decay away <u>completely</u>. So the fossil record is <u>incomplete</u>.

5) Plus, fossils that did form millions of years ago may have been <u>destroyed</u> by <u>geological activity</u>, e.g. the movement of tectonic plates may have crushed fossils already formed in the rock.

Extinction Happens if You Can't Evolve Quickly Enough

The fossil record contains many species that <u>don't exist any more</u> — these species are said to be <u>extinct</u>. <u>Dinosaurs</u> and <u>mammoths</u> are extinct animals, with only <u>fossils</u> to tell us they existed at all.

Species become extinct for these reasons:

1) The <u>environment changes</u> too quickly (e.g. destruction of habitat).

2) A <u>new predator</u> kills them all (e.g. humans hunting them).

3) A <u>new disease</u> kills them all.

4) They can't <u>compete</u> with another (new) species for <u>food</u>.

5) A <u>catastrophic event</u> happens that kills them all (e.g. a volcanic eruption or a collision with an asteroid).

6) A <u>new species</u> develops (this is called speciation — see page 68).

Dodos are now extinct. Humans not only hunted them, but introduced other animals which ate all their eggs, and we destroyed the forest where they lived — they really didn't stand a chance...

Species evolve — or become extinct...

We don't really know how life on Earth began — there are plenty of hypotheses, but we won't really know unless we find valid and reliable evidence. I'm afraid that's just science for you...

Speciation

If you've been wondering how a <u>new species</u> can spring up, this is the page for you.

Speciation is the Development of a New Species

1) A species is a group of <u>similar organisms</u> that can <u>reproduce</u> to give <u>fertile offspring</u>.

2) <u>Speciation</u> is the development of a <u>new species</u>.

3) Speciation occurs when <u>populations</u> of the <u>same species</u> become so <u>different</u> that they can <u>no longer breed</u> together to produce <u>fertile offspring</u>.

Isolation and Natural Selection Lead to Speciation

<u>ISOLATION</u> is where <u>populations</u> of a species are <u>separated</u>.

1) Isolation can happen due to a <u>physical barrier</u>. E.g. floods and earthquakes can cause barriers that <u>geographically isolate</u> some individuals from the main population.

2) <u>Conditions</u> on either side of the barrier will be <u>slightly different</u>, e.g. they may have <u>different climates</u>.

3) Because the environment is <u>different</u> on each side, <u>different characteristics</u> will become more common in each population due to <u>natural selection</u>:

- Each population shows <u>variation</u> because they have a wide range of <u>alleles</u>.
- In each population, individuals with characteristics that make them better adapted to their environment have a <u>better chance of survival</u> and so are more likely to <u>breed</u> successfully.
- So the <u>alleles</u> that control the <u>beneficial characteristics</u> are more likely to be <u>passed on</u> to the <u>next generation</u>.

4) Eventually, individuals from the different populations will have <u>changed</u> so much that they <u>won't</u> be able to <u>breed</u> with one another to produce fertile offspring.

5) The two groups will have become <u>separate species</u>:

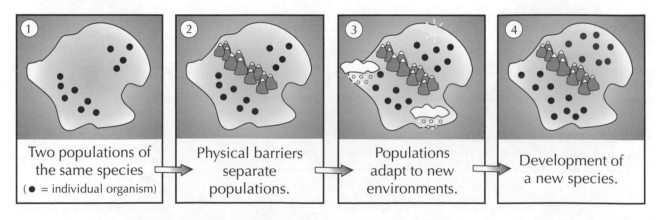

| Two populations of the same species (● = individual organism) | Physical barriers separate populations. | Populations adapt to new environments. | Development of a new species. |

A new species can develop when populations become separated

So <u>speciation</u> happens if two or more populations of the same species change so much that they can <u>no longer breed together</u> to produce <u>fertile offspring</u>. It can be caused by populations becoming <u>separated</u> from each other. Now then, time to learn this page before moving on to more questions...

Warm-Up and Exam Questions

You need to test your knowledge with a few warm-up questions, followed by some exam questions...

Warm-Up Questions

1) What are fossils?
2) Give an example of something that can be preserved as a cast.
3) Some fossils of early organisms did form in ancient rocks.
   Explain why many of these fossils have not survived to the present day.
4) What is an extinct species?
5) What does the term 'isolation' mean in the context of speciation?

Exam Questions

1   The fossils of an extinct species of insect is found preserved inside a piece of amber.

   (a)   Explain why the remains of the insect have been preserved
         so well inside the amber.

(2 marks)

   (b)   This particular species of insect became extinct because a catastrophic
         event wiped out every member of the species at once.

         Give **one** example of the kind of catastrophic
         event that could wipe out a species.

(1 mark)

2   The picture on the right shows what scientists
     believe the dinosaur **Stegosaurus** looked like.

   (a)   Fossils of Stegosaurus teeth have been discovered.

         Briefly explain how the fossils of the Stegosaurus
         teeth were formed.

(2 marks)

   (b)   Scientists cannot be completely sure what Stegosaurus
         looked like because of a lack of evidence.

         Suggest why there is not enough evidence to
         show exactly what Stegosaurus looked like.

(1 mark)

3   Two different species of birds are found on two nearby islands.
     The two species were originally just one species living on one of the islands.

     Suggest an explanation for how the two different bird species developed.

(5 marks)

Revision Summary for Biology 2b

Wow, that was quite a long section. First there was all the stuff about enzymes and then came all the genetics bits. And just to finish off, some questions. Use these to find out what you know about it all — and what you don't. Then look back and learn the bits you don't know.
Then try the questions again, and again...

1) State four functions of proteins in living cells.

2) Explain why an enzyme-catalysed reaction stops when the reaction mixture is heated above a certain temperature.

3) In which three places in the body is amylase produced?

4) Where in the body is bile: a) produced?   b) stored?   c) used?

5) Explain why the stomach produces hydrochloric acid.

6) Write down the word equation for aerobic respiration.

7) Give two examples of how an animal uses the energy released by aerobic respiration.

8) What is anaerobic respiration? Which acid does anaerobic respiration produce in humans?

9) Explain how you repay an oxygen debt.

10) Give two kinds of enzyme that would be useful in a biological washing powder.

11) Discuss the advantages and disadvantages of using enzymes in industry.

12) Explain how DNA controls the activities of a cell.

13) Explain how DNA fingerprinting is used in forensic science.

14) What is mitosis used for in the human body? Describe the four steps in mitosis.

15) Name the other type of cell division that isn't mitosis.

16) Which chromosome in the human body causes male characteristics?

17) Copy and complete the diagrams to show what happens to the X and Y chromosomes during reproduction.

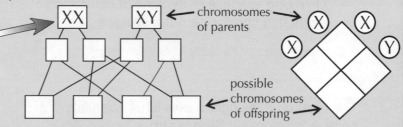

18) List three important conclusions that Mendel reached following his experiments with pea plants.

19) The significance of Mendel's work was not realised until 1900, 16 years after Mendel died. Suggest why the importance of the work wasn't understood at the time.

20) What is meant by an organism being heterozygous? What about homozygous?

21) Describe the basic difference between a recessive allele and a dominant one.

22) What is cystic fibrosis?

23) If both parents carry the recessive allele for cystic fibrosis, what is the probability of their child being a carrier?

24)*Blue colour in a plant is carried on a recessive allele, b. The dominant allele, B, gives white flowers. In the first generation after a cross, all the flowers are white. These are bred together and the result is a ratio of 54 white : 19 blue. What were the alleles of the flowers used in the first cross?

25) Name the three ways that fossils can form.

26) Give three reasons why some species become extinct.

27) What is speciation?

* Answers on page 243.

Atoms and Compounds

Just to refresh your memory, atoms contain <u>three</u> types of particle — <u>protons</u>, <u>neutrons</u> and <u>electrons</u>.

Atomic number *and* mass number *describe an atom*

These two numbers tell you how many of each kind of particle an atom has.

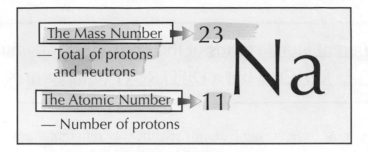

1) The <u>atomic number</u> tells you how many <u>protons</u> there are.

2) Atoms of the <u>same</u> element all have the <u>same</u> number of <u>protons</u> — so atoms of <u>different</u> elements will have <u>different</u> numbers of <u>protons</u>.

3) To get the number of <u>neutrons</u>, just <u>subtract</u> the <u>atomic number</u> from the <u>mass number</u>. Electrons aren't counted in the mass number because their <u>relative mass</u> is very small.

PARTICLE	MASS
Proton	1
Neutron	1
Electron	very small

Compounds are **chemically bonded**

1) Compounds are formed when <u>atoms</u> of <u>two or more</u> elements are <u>chemically combined</u> together. For example, carbon dioxide is a <u>compound</u> formed from a <u>chemical reaction</u> between carbon and oxygen.

2) It's difficult to <u>separate</u> the two original elements out again.

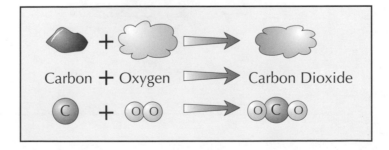

Atomic number = number of protons

If you look at a periodic table you can find the <u>atomic number</u> and <u>mass number</u> of any element. You can then use these to find out the number of <u>protons</u>, <u>neutrons</u> or <u>electrons</u> in that element.

Isotopes

This page is all to do with the stuff inside the nucleus...

Isotopes *are the same except for an extra* **neutron** *or two*

A favourite exam question: "Explain what is meant by the term isotope".
LEARN the definition:

> Isotopes are: different atomic forms of the same element, which have the
> SAME number of PROTONS but a DIFFERENT number of NEUTRONS.

1) The upshot is: isotopes must have the same atomic number but different mass numbers.

2) If they had different atomic numbers, they'd be different elements altogether.

3) Carbon-12 and carbon-14 are a very popular pair of isotopes.

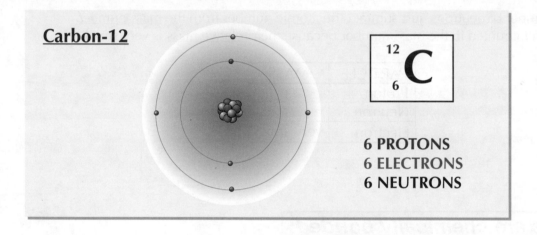

Carbon-12

$^{12}_{6}\text{C}$

6 PROTONS
6 ELECTRONS
6 NEUTRONS

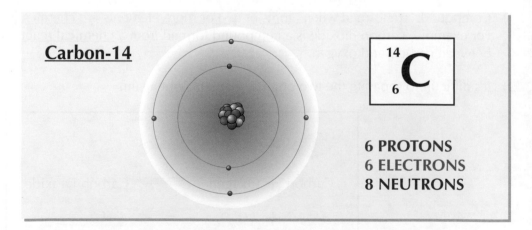

Carbon-14

$^{14}_{6}\text{C}$

6 PROTONS
6 ELECTRONS
8 NEUTRONS

Will this be in your exam — isotope so...

Carbon-14 is unstable. It makes up about one ten-millionth of the carbon in living things. When things die, the C-14 is trapped inside the dead material, and it gradually decays into nitrogen. So by measuring the proportion of C-14 found in some old wood you can calculate how long ago it was living wood.

Ionic Bonding

Ionic bonding is one of the ways atoms can form compounds.

Ionic bonding — *transferring* electrons

In ionic bonding, atoms lose or gain electrons to form charged particles (called ions) which are then strongly attracted to one another (because of the attraction of opposite charges, + and –).

A shell with just one electron is well keen to get rid...

1) All the atoms over at the left-hand side of the periodic table, e.g. sodium, potassium, calcium etc. have just one or two electrons in their outer shell (highest energy level).

2) And they're pretty keen to get shot of them, because then they'll only have full shells left, which is how they like it. (They try to have the same electronic structure as a noble gas.)

3) So given half a chance they do get rid, and that leaves the atom as an ion instead.

4) Now ions aren't the kind of things that sit around quietly watching the world go by. They tend to leap at the first passing ion with an opposite charge and stick to it like glue.

A nearly full shell is well keen to get that extra electron...

1) On the other side of the periodic table, the elements in Group 6 and Group 7, such as oxygen and chlorine, have outer shells which are nearly full.

2) They're obviously pretty keen to gain that extra one or two electrons to fill the shell up.

3) When they do, of course, they become ions and before you know it, pop, they've latched onto the atom (ion) that gave up the electron a moment earlier.

The reaction of sodium and chlorine is a classic case:

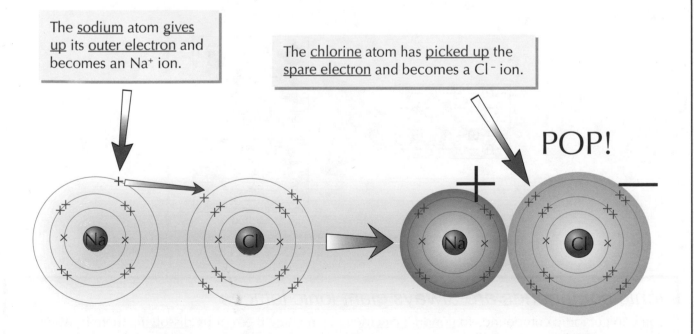

The sodium atom gives up its outer electron and becomes an Na⁺ ion.

The chlorine atom has picked up the spare electron and becomes a Cl⁻ ion.

POP!

Ionic Bonding

Ionic bonds produce <u>giant ionic structures</u>.

Ionic compounds have a regular lattice structure

1) <u>Ionic compounds</u> always have <u>giant ionic lattices</u>.

2) The ions form a closely packed <u>regular lattice</u> arrangement.

3) There are very strong <u>electrostatic forces of attraction</u> between <u>oppositely charged</u> ions, in <u>all directions</u>.

4) A single crystal of <u>sodium chloride</u> (salt) is <u>one giant ionic lattice</u>, which is why salt crystals tend to be cuboid in shape. The <u>Na$^+$</u> and <u>Cl$^-$ ions</u> are held together in a regular lattice.

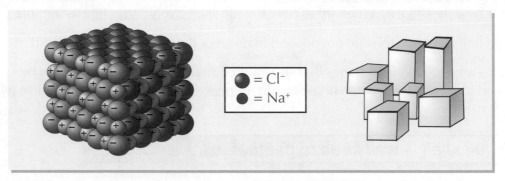

= Cl$^-$
= Na$^+$

Ionic compounds all have similar properties

1) They all have <u>high melting points</u> and <u>high boiling points</u> due to the <u>strong attraction</u> between the ions. It takes a large amount of <u>energy</u> to overcome this attraction. When ionic compounds <u>melt</u>, the ions are <u>free to move</u> and they'll <u>carry electric current</u>.

2) They do <u>dissolve easily</u> in water though. The ions <u>separate</u> and are all <u>free to move</u> in the solution, so they'll <u>carry electric current</u>.

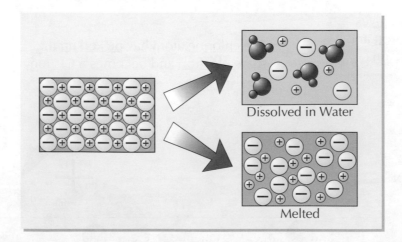

Dissolved in Water

Melted

Ionic compounds are always giant ionic lattices

You can get ionic compounds to <u>conduct electricity</u> by <u>melting</u> them or by <u>dissolving</u> them in water. Dissolving them is easier though as it takes a lot of energy to melt an ionic compound. Either way, it's the free ions that carry the electric current.

Ions

Make sure you've really got your head around the idea of ionic bonding before you start on this page.

Groups *1 & 2* and *6 & 7* are the most likely to form *ions*

1) Remember, atoms that have <u>lost</u> or <u>gained</u> an electron (or electrons) are <u>ions</u>.

2) Ions have the <u>electronic structure</u> of a <u>noble gas</u>.

3) The elements that most readily form ions are those in <u>Groups 1</u>, <u>2</u>, <u>6 and 7</u>.

4) <u>Group 1 and 2 elements</u> are <u>metals</u> and they <u>lose</u> electrons to form <u>positive ions</u>.

5) For example, <u>Group 1</u> elements (the <u>alkali metals</u>) form ionic compounds with <u>non-metals</u> where the metal ion has a 1$^+$ charge. E.g. K^+Cl^-.

6) <u>Group 6 and 7 elements</u> are <u>non-metals</u>. They <u>gain</u> electrons to form <u>negative ions</u>.

7) For example, <u>Group 7</u> elements (the <u>halogens</u>) form ionic compounds with the <u>alkali metals</u> where the halide ion has a 1$^-$ charge. E.g. Na^+Cl^-.

8) The <u>charge</u> on the <u>positive ions</u> is the <u>same</u> as the <u>group number</u> of the element:

POSITIVE IONS		NEGATIVE IONS	
Group 1	Group 2	Group 6	Group 7
Li^+ Na^+ K^+	Be^{2+} Mg^{2+} Ca^{2+}	O^{2-}	F^- Cl^-

9) Any of the positive ions above can <u>combine</u> with any of the negative ions to form an <u>ionic compound</u>.

10) Only elements at <u>opposite sides</u> of the periodic table will form ionic compounds, e.g. Na and Cl, where one of them becomes a <u>positive ion</u> and one becomes a <u>negative ion</u>.

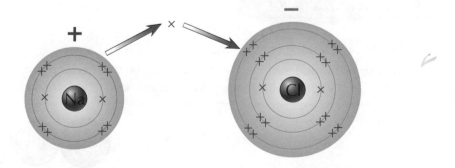

Remember, the + and − charges we talk about, e.g. Na^+ for sodium, just tell you <u>what type of ion the atom WILL FORM</u> in a chemical reaction. In sodium <u>metal</u> there are <u>only neutral sodium atoms, Na</u>. The Na^+ ions <u>will only appear</u> if the sodium metal <u>reacts</u> with something like water or chlorine.

Formulas of Ionic Compounds

You need to be able to write down the right <u>chemical formulas</u> for ionic compounds.

Look at **charges** to work out the **formula** of an **ionic compound**

1) Ionic compounds are made up of a <u>positively charged</u> part and a <u>negatively charged</u> part.

2) The <u>overall charge</u> of <u>any compound</u> is <u>zero</u>.

3) So all the <u>negative charges</u> in the compound must <u>balance</u> all the <u>positive charges</u>.

4) You can use the charges on the <u>individual ions</u> present to work out the formula for the ionic compound:

Sodium chloride

Sodium chloride contains Na^+ (+1) and Cl^- (–1) ions.

(+1) + (–1) = 0. The charges are balanced with one of each ion, so the formula for sodium chloride = NaCl.

NaCl

Magnesium chloride

Magnesium chloride contains Mg^{2+} (+2) and Cl^- (–1) ions.

Because a chloride ion only has a 1⁻ charge we will need <u>two</u> of them to balance out the 2⁺ charge of a magnesium ion. This gives us the formula $MgCl_2$.

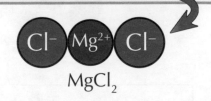

$MgCl_2$

The formula for exam success = revision...

The main thing to remember is that in compounds the <u>total charge must always add up to zero</u>. But, you won't be able to work out a formula if you don't know the <u>charges</u> of the ions involved. So, if you haven't already, learn the charges in the table on the previous page.

Electronic Structure of Ions

This page has some lovely drawings of the <u>electronic structures</u> of ions.
It's your job to make sure you can do drawings just like them in the exam.

Show the electronic structure of **simple** ions with **diagrams**

A useful way of representing ions is by <u>drawing</u> out their electronic structure. Just use a big <u>square bracket</u> and a + or − to show the charge. A few <u>ions</u> and the <u>ionic compounds</u> they form are shown below. You need to know how to draw them:

Sodium Chloride

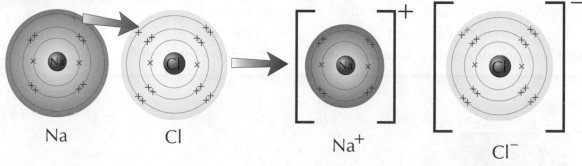

Na   Cl   Na$^+$ Cl$^-$

NaCl (Sodium Chloride)

Magnesium Oxide

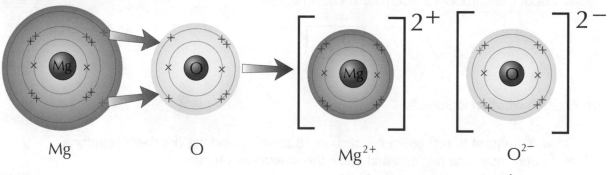

Mg   O   Mg^{2+} O^{2-}

MgO (Magnesium Oxide)

Calcium Chloride

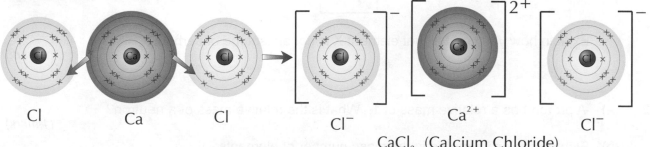

Cl   Ca   Cl   Cl$^-$ Ca^{2+} Cl$^-$

CaCl$_2$ (Calcium Chloride)

Show the electronic structure of ions with square brackets

Whether or not you're able to reproduce the drawings on this page all comes down to how well you've understood <u>ionic bonding</u>. (So if you're struggling, try reading the last few pages again.)

Warm-Up and Exam Questions

These questions will help you find out if you've learnt all the basics about atoms, compounds, isotopes and ionic bonding. Have a look back through the last few pages if you're unsure about any of these questions. It's really important to get these basics right.

Warm-Up Questions

1) Explain the difference between mass number and atomic number.
2) What is the name given to atoms of the same element with different mass numbers?
3) Sodium chloride has a giant ionic structure. Does it have a high or a low boiling point?
4) Why do ionic compounds conduct electricity when dissolved?
5) Do elements from Group 1 form positive ions or negative ions?
6) Do elements from Group 7 form positive ions or negative ions?
7) What is the formula of the compound containing Al^{3+} and OH^- ions only?

Exam Questions

1   Carbon has several isotopes, for example carbon-12 and carbon-13.
    Details about the carbon-13 isotope are shown below.

$$^{13}_{6}C$$

(a) Explain what an isotope is.

(3 marks)

(b) Draw a diagram to represent the carbon-13 atom. Label the number of protons
     and neutrons in the nucleus and show the electron arrangement.

(3 marks)

(c) Details of element **X** are shown below.

$$^{13}_{7}X$$

Explain how you can tell that element X is not an isotope of carbon.

(1 mark)

2   (a) A proton has a relative mass of 1. What is the relative mass of a neutron?

(1 mark)

(b) Electrons aren't counted in the mass number of elements.
     Give a reason for this.

(1 mark)

Exam Questions

3 When lithium reacts with oxygen it forms an ionic compound, Li_2O.
   (a) Name the compound formed.
   (1 mark)

   (b) (i) Complete the diagram below using arrows to show how the electrons are transferred when Li_2O is formed.
   (1 mark)

   (ii) Show the electron arrangements and the charges on the ions formed.
   (2 marks)

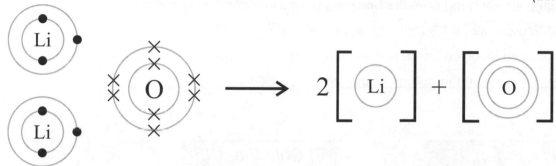

4 Magnesium (atomic number 12) and fluorine (atomic number 9) combine vigorously to form magnesium fluoride, an ionic compound.
   (a) Draw dot and cross diagrams to show the electron arrangement of each atom.
   (2 marks)

   (b) Give the symbol (including the charge) for each of the ions formed.
   (2 marks)

   (c) Using your answer to (b), work out the formula of magnesium fluoride.
   (1 mark)

   (d) Once formed, explain why the ions remain together in a compound.
   (1 mark)

   (e) Magnesium fluoride has a giant ionic structure. Explain why:
   (i) it doesn't melt easily.
   (2 marks)

   (ii) it conducts electricity when molten.
   (1 mark)

5 Potassium and chlorine react to form potassium chloride.
   (a) Complete the following table.
   (3 marks)

	Potassium atom, K	Potassium ion, K$^+$	Chlorine atom, Cl	Chloride ion, Cl$^-$
Number of electrons	19			
Electron arrangement	2, 8, 8, 1			

   (b) Draw a dot and cross diagram to show the formation of potassium chloride.
   (2 marks)

Covalent Bonding

Some elements bond ionically (see page 73) but others form strong <u>covalent bonds</u>.
This is where atoms <u>share electrons</u> with each other so that they've got <u>full outer shells</u>.

Covalent bonds — *sharing* electrons

1) Sometimes atoms prefer to make <u>covalent bonds</u> by <u>sharing</u> electrons with other atoms.

2) They only share electrons in their <u>outer shells</u> (highest energy levels).

3) This way <u>both</u> atoms feel that they have a <u>full outer shell</u>, and that makes them happy. Having a full outer shell gives them the electronic structure of a <u>noble gas</u>.

4) Each <u>covalent bond</u> provides one <u>extra</u> shared electron for each atom.

5) So, a covalent bond is a <u>shared pair</u> of electrons.

6) Each atom involved has to make <u>enough</u> covalent bonds to <u>fill up</u> its outer shell.

7) <u>Learn</u> these <u>seven important examples</u>:

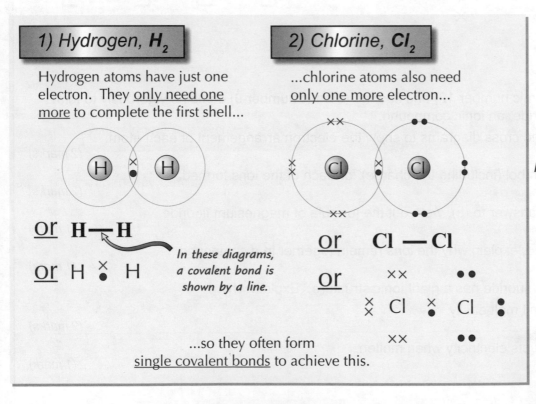

1) Hydrogen, H_2

Hydrogen atoms have just one electron. They <u>only need one more</u> to complete the first shell...

<u>or</u> H—H

In these diagrams, a covalent bond is shown by a line.

<u>or</u> H ×• H

...so they often form <u>single covalent bonds</u> to achieve this.

2) Chlorine, Cl_2

...chlorine atoms also need <u>only one more</u> electron...

In a dot and cross diagram, you only have to draw the outer shell of electrons.

<u>or</u> Cl — Cl

<u>or</u> Cl Cl

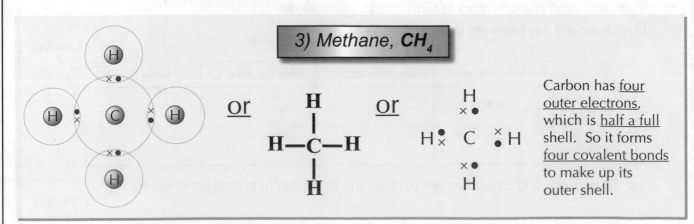

3) Methane, CH_4

<u>or</u> H—C—H

<u>or</u> H C H

Carbon has <u>four outer electrons</u>, which is <u>half a full shell</u>. So it forms <u>four covalent bonds</u> to make up its outer shell.

More Covalent Bonding

There are four more examples of covalent bonding on this page — just a few diagrams and a smattering of words. What a pleasant page.

4) Hydrogen Chloride, **HCl**

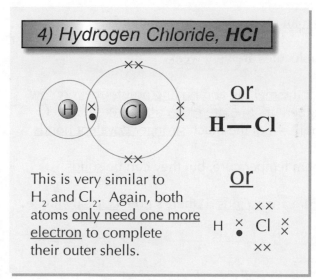

or

H—Cl

or

H ×• Cl ××

This is very similar to H_2 and Cl_2. Again, both atoms <u>only need one more electron</u> to complete their outer shells.

5) Ammonia, **NH₃**

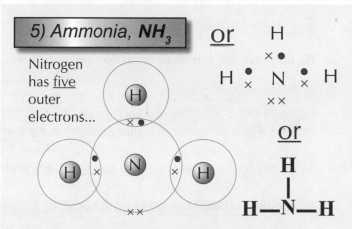

Nitrogen has <u>five</u> outer electrons...

or

H—N—H with H above

...so it needs to form <u>three covalent bonds</u> to make up the extra <u>three</u> electrons needed.

6) Water, **H₂O**

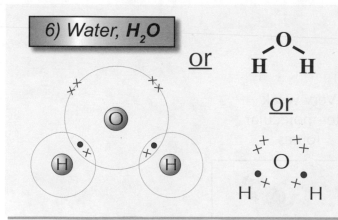

or

O with H H

or

O with H H

<u>Oxygen</u> atoms have <u>six</u> outer electrons. They sometimes form <u>ionic</u> bonds by <u>taking</u> two electrons to complete their outer shell. However they'll also cheerfully form <u>covalent bonds</u> and <u>share</u> two electrons instead. In <u>water molecules</u>, the oxygen <u>shares</u> electrons with the two H atoms.

7) Oxygen, **O₂**

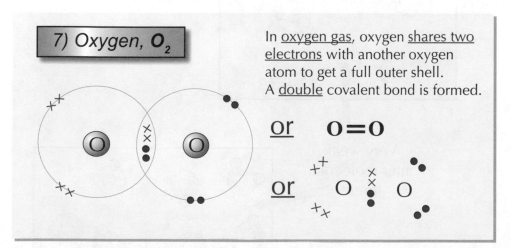

In <u>oxygen gas</u>, oxygen <u>shares two electrons</u> with another oxygen atom to get a full outer shell. A <u>double</u> covalent bond is formed.

or **O=O**

or O O

Remember — it's only the outer shells that share electrons with each other.

Covalent bonding involves sharing rather than giving electrons

Make sure you learn these seven really basic examples and <u>why they work</u>. Every atom wants a full outer shell, and they can get that either by becoming an <u>ion</u> (see page 73) or by <u>sharing electrons</u>. Once you understand that, you should be able to apply it to any example they give you in the exam.

Covalent Substances: Simple Molecular

Substances with <u>covalent bonds</u> (electron sharing) can form <u>simple molecules</u>.

Simple *molecular* substances

1) The atoms form <u>very strong</u> covalent bonds to form <u>small</u> molecules of several atoms.

2) By contrast, the forces of attraction <u>between</u> these molecules are <u>very weak</u>.

3) The result of these feeble <u>intermolecular forces</u> is that the <u>melting</u> and <u>boiling points</u> are <u>very low</u>, because the molecules are <u>easily parted</u> from each other. It's the <u>intermolecular forces</u> that get <u>broken</u> when simple molecular substances melt or boil — <u>not</u> the much <u>stronger covalent bonds</u>.

4) Most molecular substances are <u>gases or liquids</u> at room temperature, but they can be <u>solids</u>.

5) Molecular substances <u>don't conduct electricity</u> — there are <u>no ions</u> so there's <u>no electrical charge</u>.

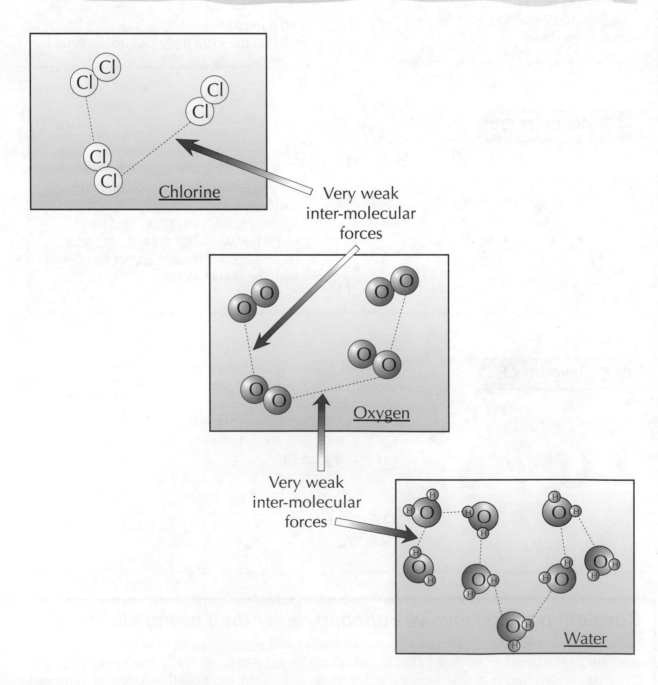

Very weak inter-molecular forces

<u>Chlorine</u>

Very weak inter-molecular forces

<u>Oxygen</u>

Very weak inter-molecular forces

<u>Water</u>

Covalent Substances: Giant Covalent

Substances formed from <u>covalent bonds</u> aren't always <u>simple molecules</u> (see p.82). They can also be <u>giant covalent structures</u>. There are three examples to learn.

Giant covalent structures are *macromolecules*

1) These are similar to giant ionic structures (lattices) <u>except</u> that there are <u>no charged ions</u>.

2) <u>All</u> the atoms are <u>bonded</u> to <u>each other</u> by <u>strong</u> covalent bonds.

3) This means that they have <u>very high</u> melting and boiling points.

4) They <u>don't conduct electricity</u> — not even when <u>molten</u> (except for graphite).

5) The <u>main examples</u> are <u>diamond</u> and <u>graphite</u>, which are both made only from <u>carbon atoms</u>, and <u>silicon dioxide</u> (silica).

Make sure you know these three examples

Diamond

1) Each carbon atom forms <u>four covalent bonds</u> in a <u>very rigid</u> giant covalent structure.

2) This structure makes diamond the <u>hardest</u> natural substance, so it's used for drill tips.

3) And it's <u>pretty</u> and <u>sparkly</u> too.

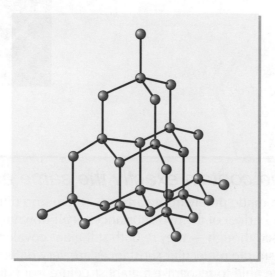

Covalent Substances: Giant Covalent

Here are the other two examples of <u>giant covalent structures</u> that you need to learn.

Graphite

1) Each carbon atom only forms <u>three covalent bonds</u>. This creates <u>layers</u> which are free to <u>slide over each other</u>, like a pack of cards — so graphite is <u>soft</u> and <u>slippery</u>.

2) The layers are held together so loosely that they can be <u>rubbed off</u> onto paper — that's how a <u>pencil</u> works. This is because there are <u>weak intermolecular forces</u> between the layers.

3) Graphite is the only <u>non-metal</u> which is a <u>good conductor of heat and electricity</u>. Each carbon atom has one <u>delocalised</u> (free) electron and it's these free electrons that <u>conduct</u> heat and electricity.

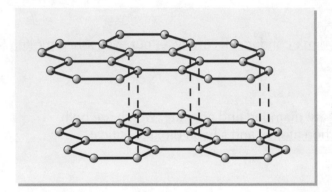

Silicon Dioxide (Silica)

1) Sometimes called <u>silica</u>, this is what <u>sand</u> is made of.

2) Each grain of sand is <u>one giant structure</u> of silicon and oxygen.

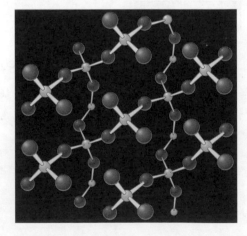

Graphite and diamond contain exactly the same atoms

Graphite and diamond are both made purely from <u>carbon</u> — there's no difference at all in their <u>atoms</u>. The difference in properties (and price) of the two substances is all down to the way the atoms are <u>held together</u>. Don't get confused though — they're both still giant covalent substances. Giant covalent substances and simple molecular substances are very different — make sure you know about them both. You should be able to recognise a <u>giant structure</u> from diagrams of its <u>bonding</u>.

Metallic Structures

Ever wondered what makes <u>metals</u> tick? Well, either way, this is the page for you.

Metal properties are all due to the sea of free electrons

1) <u>Metals</u> also consist of a <u>giant structure</u>.

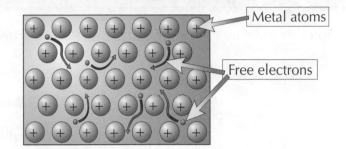

2) <u>Metallic bonds</u> involve the all-important 'free electrons' which produce <u>all</u> the properties of metals. These delocalised (free) electrons come from the <u>outer shell</u> of <u>every</u> metal atom in the structure.

3) These electrons are <u>free to move</u> through the whole structure and so metals are good conductors of <u>heat and electricity</u>.

4) These electrons also <u>hold</u> the <u>atoms</u> together in a <u>regular</u> structure. There are strong forces of <u>electrostatic attraction</u> between the <u>positive metal ions</u> and the <u>negative electrons</u>.

5) They also allow the layers of atoms to <u>slide</u> over each other, allowing metals to be <u>bent</u> and <u>shaped</u>.

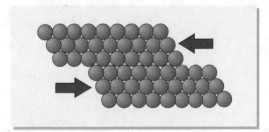

Alloys are harder than pure metals

1) <u>Pure metals</u> often aren't quite right for certain jobs. So scientists <u>mix two or more metals together</u> — creating an <u>alloy</u> with the properties they want.

2) Different elements have <u>different sized atoms</u>. So when another metal is mixed with a pure metal, the new metal atoms will <u>distort</u> the layers of metal atoms, making it more difficult for them to slide over each other. So alloys are <u>harder</u>.

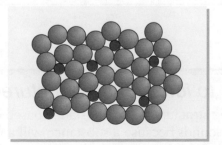

Identifying Structures

If you've learnt the <u>properties</u> of the four types of substance then this page shouldn't be a problem.
If you haven't then you should go and learn them first.

Identifying the structure of a substance by its properties

You should be able to easily <u>identify</u> most substances just by the way they <u>behave</u> as either:

- <u>giant ionic</u>,
- <u>simple molecular</u>,
- <u>giant covalent</u>,
- or <u>giant metallic</u>.

The way they might test you in the Exam is by describing the <u>physical properties</u>
of a substance and asking you to decide <u>which type of structure</u> it has.

Try this one:

> ## Example:
>
> Four substances were tested for various properties with the following results.
>
> Identify the structure of each substance. (Answers on page 244.)

Substance	Melting point (°C)	Boiling point (°C)	Good electrical conductor?
A	−219.62	−188.12	No
B	1535	2750	Yes
C	1410	2355	No
D	770	1420	When molten

Look at the properties to identify the structure

You have to be able to identify the structure of <u>any</u> substance based on its properties and justify your
answer too. It's not as hard as it sounds because a substance will always be one of four things —
giant ionic, simple molecular, giant covalent or giant metallic. So, if you know how to identify those
four substances, then you know how to identify anything. Phew.

Warm-Up and Exam Questions

Don't charge past this page, it's a lot more important than it looks.

Warm-Up Questions

1) How is covalent bonding different from ionic bonding?
2) Describe the differences in the physical properties of diamond and graphite.
3) Give another example of a substance that has a giant covalent structure.
4) Why does chlorine have a very low boiling point?

Exam Questions

1   Methane is a covalently bonded molecule with the formula CH_4.
Draw a dot and cross diagram for the methane molecule,
showing only the outer electrons.

(2 marks)

2   The table compares some physical properties of silicon dioxide, bromine and graphite.

Property	silicon dioxide	bromine	graphite
Melting point (°C)	1610	−7	3657
Electrical conductivity	poor	poor	good
Solubility in water	insoluble	slightly soluble	insoluble

(a) What is the structure in:
   (i)   silicon dioxide?

(1 mark)

   (ii) graphite?

(1 mark)

   (iii) bromine?

(1 mark)

(b) Explain why bromine has poor electrical conductivity.

(1 mark)

(c) Explain why graphite has good electrical conductivity.

(1 mark)

(d) Bromine is a liquid at room temperature (20 °C).
   Explain why bromine has such a low melting point compared with
   silicon dioxide and graphite.

(2 marks)

Exam Questions

3   The diagram below shows the arrangement of atoms in pure iron.

Steel is an alloy of iron and carbon.
(a)   Draw a similar diagram to show the arrangement of atoms in steel.

(2 marks)

(b)   Steel is harder than iron. Explain why.

(3 marks)

4   The table gives data for some physical properties of a selection of substances.

Substance	Melting point	Boiling point	Electrical conductivity
A	-219	-183	poor
B	3550	4827	poor
C	1495	2870	good
D	801	1413	good when molten

(a)   What state would you expect substance D to be at room temperature?

(1 mark)

(b)   What is the structure of:
(i)   substance B?

(1 mark)

(ii)   substance D?

(1 mark)

(c)   Substance A is oxygen.
(i)   Draw a dot and cross diagram to show the outer electrons in
an oxygen molecule.

(2 marks)

(ii)   Explain why oxygen has such a low melting point.

(2 marks)

(d)   Substance C is a metal. According to the table, it is a good conductor of electricity.
(i)   Explain why this is.

(2 marks)

(ii)   Would substance C be a good conductor of heat?

(1 mark)

New Materials

New materials are continually being developed, with new properties. The two groups of materials you really need to know about are <u>smart materials</u> and <u>nanoparticles</u>.

Smart materials have some really weird properties

1) <u>Smart</u> materials <u>behave differently</u> depending on the <u>conditions</u>, e.g. temperature.

2) A good example is <u>nitinol</u> — a "<u>shape memory alloy</u>".
It's a metal <u>alloy</u> (about half nickel, half titanium) but when it's cool you can <u>bend it</u> and <u>twist it</u> like rubber. Bend it too far, though, and it stays bent. But here's the really clever bit — if you heat it above a certain temperature, it goes back to a "<u>remembered</u>" shape.

3) It's really handy for <u>glasses frames</u>. If you accidentally bend them, you can just pop them into a bowl of hot water and they'll <u>jump</u> back <u>into shape</u>.

4) Nitinol is also used for <u>dental braces</u>. In the mouth it <u>warms</u> and tries to return to a 'remembered' shape, and so it gently <u>pulls the teeth</u> with it.

Nanoparticles are really really really really tiny ...smaller than that.

1) Really tiny particles, <u>1–100 nanometres</u> across, are called 'nanoparticles' (1 nm = 0.000 000 001 m).

2) Nanoparticles contain roughly <u>a few hundred atoms</u>.

3) Nanoparticles include <u>fullerenes</u>. These are molecules of <u>carbon</u>, shaped like <u>hollow balls</u> or <u>closed tubes</u>. The carbon atoms are arranged in <u>hexagonal rings</u>. Different fullerenes contain <u>different numbers</u> of carbon atoms.

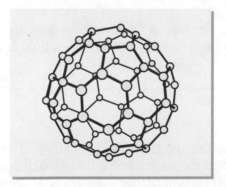

4) A nanoparticle has very <u>different properties</u> from the 'bulk' chemical that it's made from — e.g. <u>fullerenes</u> have different properties from big <u>lumps of carbon</u>.

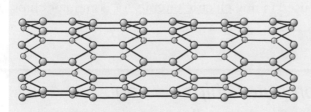

1) Fullerenes can be joined together to form <u>nanotubes</u> — teeny tiny hollow carbon tubes, a few nanometres across.

2) All those covalent bonds make carbon nanotubes <u>very strong</u>. They can be used to reinforce graphite in <u>tennis rackets</u>.

New Materials

Nanomaterials are becoming more and more widely used

Using nanoparticles is known as <u>nanoscience</u>. Many <u>new uses</u> of nanoparticles are being developed.

1) They have a <u>huge surface area to volume ratio</u>, so they could help make new industrial <u>catalysts</u> (see page 115).

2) You can use nanoparticles to make <u>sensors</u> to detect one type of molecule and nothing else. These <u>highly specific</u> sensors are already being used to test water purity.

3) Nanotubes can be used to make <u>stronger</u>, <u>lighter</u> building materials.

4) New cosmetics, e.g. <u>sun tan cream</u> and <u>deodorant</u>, have been made using nanoparticles. The small particles do their job but don't leave <u>white marks</u> on the skin.

5) <u>Nanomedicine</u> is a hot topic. The idea is that tiny fullerenes are <u>absorbed</u> more easily by the body than most particles. This means they could <u>deliver drugs</u> right into the cells where they're needed.

6) New <u>lubricant coatings</u> are being developed using fullerenes. These coatings reduce friction a bit like <u>ball bearings</u> and could be used in all sorts of places from <u>artificial joints</u> to <u>gears</u>.

7) Nanotubes <u>conduct</u> electricity, so they can be used in tiny <u>electric circuits</u> for computer chips.

Bendy specs, tennis rackets and computer chips — cool...

Some nanoparticles have really <u>unexpected properties</u>. Silver's normally very unreactive, but silver nanoparticles can kill bacteria. Gold nanoparticles aren't gold-coloured — they're either red or purple. On the flipside, we also need to watch out for any unexpected harmful properties.

Polymers

Plastics are made up of lots of molecules joined together in long chains.

Forces between molecules determine the properties of plastics

Strong covalent bonds hold the atoms together in long chains. But it's the bonds between the different molecule chains that determine the properties of the plastic.

Weak Forces:

Individual tangled chains of polymers, held together by weak intermolecular forces, are free to slide over each other.

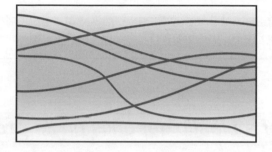

1) THERMOSOFTENING POLYMERS don't have cross-linking between chains.

2) The forces between the chains are really easy to overcome, so it's easy to melt the plastic.

3) When it cools, the polymer hardens into a new shape.

4) You can melt these plastics and remould them as many times as you like.

Strong Forces:

Some plastics have stronger intermolecular forces between the polymer chains, called crosslinks, that hold the chains firmly together.

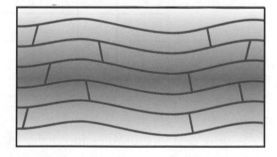

1) THERMOSETTING POLYMERS have crosslinks.

2) These hold the chains together in a solid structure.

3) The polymer doesn't soften when it's heated.

4) Thermosetting polymers are strong, hard and rigid.

Polymers

There's plastic and there's... well, plastic. You wouldn't want to make a chair with the same plastic that gets used for flimsy old carrier bags. But whatever the plastic, it's always a polymer.

How you **make** a **polymer** affects its **properties**

1) The starting materials and reaction conditions will both affect the properties of a polymer.

2) Two types of polythene can be made using different conditions:

> • Low density (LD) polythene is made by heating ethene to about 200 °C under high pressure. It's flexible and is used for bags and bottles.
>
> • High density (HD) polythene is made at a lower temperature and pressure (with a catalyst). It's more rigid and is used for water tanks and drainpipes.

The **use** of a plastic depends on its **properties**

You might need to answer a question like this one in the exam.

Choose from the table the plastic that would be best suited for making:

a) a disposable cup for hot drinks,

b) clothing,

c) a measuring cylinder.

Give reasons for each choice.

Plastic	Cost	Resistance to chemicals	Melting point	Transparency	Rigidity	Can be made into fibres
W	High	High	High	Low	High	No
X	Low	Low	Low	Low	Low	Yes
Y	High	High	High	High	High	No
Z	Low	Low	High	High	High	No

Answers

a) Z — low cost (disposable) and high melting point (for hot drinks),

b) X — flexible (essential for clothing) and able to be made into fibres (clothing is usually woven),

c) Y — transparent and resistant to chemicals (you need to be able to see the liquid inside and the liquid and measuring cylinder mustn't react with each other).

Polymers have different uses

You need to understand that different reaction conditions result in polymers with different properties (like low density and high density polythene). You also might be given information about the properties of a certain polymer and have to explain why it's suited to its use.

Warm-Up and Exam Questions

Warm-Up Questions

1) What is nitinol?
2) What does a plastic's melting point tell you about the forces between its polymer chains?
3) What are intermolecular forces between polymer chains called?
4) Give two things that can affect the properties of a polymer.

Exam Questions

1   Scientists have developed new materials using nanoparticles, which show different properties from the same materials in bulk.

   (a) Use words from the box to help you complete the sentences below.

   volume   mm   catalysts   surface area   nm   circuits

   (i)   Nanoparticles are up to 100 .... in size.

   (1 mark)

   (ii) Nanoparticles have a large .... to

   .... ratio.

   (2 marks)

   (b) Floyd Landis used a bike in the Tour de France with a frame weighing about 1 kg. Carbon nanotubes (CNT) were used in the manufacture of the frame of the bike.

   (i)   Suggest two properties of a material made using CNTs that make it suitable for use in a bike frame.

   (2 marks)

   (ii) Give the name of a type of molecule that can be joined together to make carbon nanotubes.

   (1 mark)

   (c) Give one other application of nanoparticles.

   (1 mark)

2   The table below shows the properties of three polymers, **A**, **B** and **C**.

Give the polymer that would be best suited for each of the following uses:

Polymer	Properties
A	heat resistant and strong
B	very flexible and biodegradable
C	very rigid

   (a) sandwich bag

   (1 mark)

   (b) drainpipe

   (1 mark)

   (c) disposable cup

   (1 mark)

Relative Formula Mass

The biggest trouble with <u>relative atomic mass</u> and <u>relative formula mass</u> is that they <u>sound</u> so blood-curdling. Take a few deep breaths, and just enjoy, as the mists slowly clear...

Relative atomic mass, A_r, is easy

1) This is just a way of saying how <u>heavy</u> different atoms are <u>compared</u> with the mass of an atom of carbon-12. So carbon-12 has A_r of <u>exactly 12</u>.

2) It turns out that the <u>relative atomic mass</u> A_r is usually just the same as the <u>mass number</u> of the element.

3) In the periodic table, the elements all have <u>two</u> numbers. The smaller one is the atomic number (how many protons it has). But the <u>bigger one</u> is the <u>mass number</u> or <u>relative atomic mass</u>.

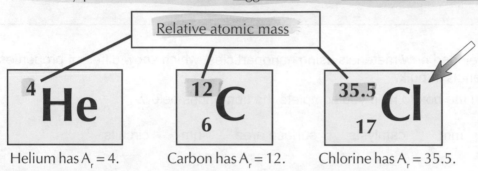

Relative atomic mass

^{4}He

Helium has A_r = 4.

$^{12}_{6}$C

Carbon has A_r = 12.

$^{35.5}_{17}$Cl

Chlorine has A_r = 35.5.

When an element has more than one stable isotope, the relative atomic mass is an average value of all the different isotopes (taking into account how much there is of each isotope).

Relative formula mass, M_r, is also easy

If you have a compound like $MgCl_2$ then it has a <u>relative formula mass</u>, M_r, which is just all the relative atomic masses <u>added together</u>.

For $MgCl_2$ it would be:

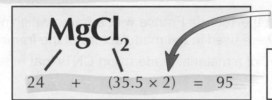

$MgCl_2$

24 + (35.5 × 2) = 95

The relative atomic mass of chlorine is multiplied by 2 because there are two chlorine atoms.

So M_r for $MgCl_2$ is simply <u>95</u>.

You can easily get A_r for any element from the periodic table, but in a lot of questions they give you them anyway. And that's all it is. A big fancy name like <u>relative formula mass</u> and all it means is "<u>add up all the relative atomic masses</u>".

*"ONE MOLE" of a substance is **equal** to its M_r in grams*

The <u>relative formula mass</u> (A_r or M_r) of a substance <u>in grams</u> is known as <u>one mole</u> of that substance.

<u>Examples:</u>

Iron has an A_r of 56. So one mole of iron weighs exactly 56 g

Nitrogen gas, N_2, has an M_r of 28 (2 × 14). So one mole of N_2 weighs exactly 28 g

You can convert between moles and grams using this formula:

<u>NUMBER OF MOLES</u> = $\dfrac{\text{Mass in g (of element or compound)}}{M_r \text{ (of element or compound)}}$

<u>Example:</u> How many moles are there in 42 g of carbon?

<u>Answer:</u> No. of moles = Mass (g) / M_r = 42/12 = <u>3.5 moles</u> Easy Peasy

Formula Mass Calculations

Although relative atomic mass and relative formula mass are <u>easy enough</u>, it can get just a tad <u>trickier</u> when you start getting into other calculations which use them. It depends on how good your maths is basically, because it's all to do with ratios and percentages.

Calculating % mass of an element in a compound

This is actually dead easy — so long as you've learnt this formula:

$$\text{Percentage mass of an element in a compound} = \frac{A_r \times \text{no. of atoms (of that element)}}{M_r \text{ (of whole compound)}} \times 100$$

If you don't learn the formula then you'd better be pretty smart — or you'll struggle.

Example:

> Find the percentage mass of sodium in sodium carbonate, Na_2CO_3.

<u>ANSWER:</u>

- A_r of sodium = 23
- A_r of carbon = 12
- A_r of oxygen = 16

M_r of $Na_2CO_3 = (2 \times 23) + 12 + (3 \times 16) = 106$

Now use the formula:

$$\text{Percentage Mass} = \frac{A_r \times \text{No. of atoms}}{M_r} \times 100 = \frac{23 \times 2}{106} \times 100 = 43.4\%$$

And there you have it.
Sodium makes up <u>43.4%</u> of the mass of sodium carbonate.

You can't just read these pages — work through the examples too

As usual with these calculations, <u>practice makes perfect</u>. Try these:

Find the percentage mass of oxygen in each of these:

Don't skip this bit, you'll be glad you're perfect when it comes to exam day.

a) Fe_2O_3
b) H_2O
c) $CaCO_3$
d) H_2SO_4

Answers on page 245.

Formula Mass Calculations

Finding the **empirical formula** *(from masses or percentages)*

This also sounds a lot worse than it really is. Try this for a nice simple <u>stepwise method</u>:

1) <u>List all the elements</u> in the compound (there's usually only two or three).

2) <u>Underneath them</u>, write their <u>experimental masses or percentages</u>.

3) <u>Divide</u> each mass or percentage <u>by the A_r</u> for that particular element.

4) Turn the numbers you get into <u>a nice simple ratio</u>
by multiplying and/or dividing them by well-chosen numbers.

5) Get the ratio in its <u>simplest form</u>, and that tells you the <u>empirical formula</u> of the compound.

Example:

Find the empirical formula of the iron oxide produced when 44.8 g of iron react with 19.2 g of oxygen.
(A_r for iron = 56, A_r for oxygen = 16)

<u>METHOD:</u>

	Fe	O
1) <u>List the two elements:</u>	**Fe**	**O**
2) Write in the <u>experimental masses</u>:	44.8	19.2
3) <u>Divide by the A_r</u> for each element:	$44.8/56 = 0.8$	$19.2/16 = 1.2$
4) Multiply by 10...	8	12
...then divide by 4:	2	3

5) So the <u>simplest formula</u> is 2 atoms of Fe to 3 atoms of O, i.e. Fe_2O_3.

You need to realise (for the exam) that this <u>empirical method</u> (i.e. based on <u>experiment</u>) is the <u>only way</u> of finding out the formula of a compound. Rust is iron oxide, sure, but is it FeO, or Fe_2O_3? Only an experiment to determine the empirical formula will tell you for certain.

Don't learn that list of instructions — practise using it (it's much quicker)

These sort of questions are the backbone of chemistry. They're really common exam questions as well. If you find them a bit scary, just keep practising using the stepwise method until you've mastered it.

Try this:
Find the empirical formula of the compound formed from 2.4 g of carbon and 0.8 g of hydrogen.

Calculating Masses in Reactions

You can also work out masses of reactants (starting materials) and products in reactions.

The three important steps — *not to be missed...*

1) <u>Write out</u> the balanced <u>equation</u>.

2) <u>Work out</u> M_r — just for the <u>two bits you want</u>.

3) Apply the rule: <u>Divide to get one, then multiply to get all</u>.
   (But you have to apply this first to the substance they
   give you information about, and then the other one!)

Don't worry — these steps should all make sense when you look at the example below.

Example:

What mass of magnesium oxide is produced when 60 g of magnesium is burned in air?

<u>Answer</u>:

1) Write out the <u>balanced equation</u>: $2Mg + O_2 \rightarrow 2MgO$

2) Work out the <u>relative formula masses</u>: $2 \times 24 \rightarrow 2 \times (24 + 16)$
   (don't do the oxygen — you don't need it) $48 \rightarrow 80$

3) Apply the rule: <u>Divide to get one, then multiply to get all</u>:

   **The two numbers, 48 and 80, tell us that 48 g of Mg react to give 80 g of MgO.
   Here's the tricky bit. You've now got to be able to write this down:**

   > 48 g of Mg ...... reacts to give ...... 80g of MgO
   > 1 g of Mg ...... reacts to give ......
   > 60 g of Mg ...... reacts to give ......

<u>The big clue</u> is that in the question they've said we want to burn "<u>60 g of magnesium</u>",
i.e. they've told us how much <u>magnesium</u> to have, and that's how you know to write down
the <u>left-hand side</u> of it first, because:

**We'll first need to ÷ by 48 to get 1 g of Mg
and then need to × by 60 to get 60 g of Mg.**

<u>Then</u> you can work out the numbers on the other side (shown in blue below) by realising
that you must <u>divide both sides by 48</u> and then <u>multiply both sides by 60</u>.

÷ 48   48 g of Mg .... 80 g of MgO   ÷ 48
       1 g of Mg .... 1.67 g of MgO
× 60   60 g of Mg .... 100 g of MgO   × 60

The mass of product is called the yield of a reaction. You should realise that in practice you never get 100% of the yield, so the amount of product will be slightly less than calculated (see page 100).

This finally tells us that <u>60 g of magnesium will produce 100 g of magnesium oxide</u>.

If the question had said "Find how much magnesium gives 500 g of magnesium oxide",
you'd fill in the MgO side first, <u>because that's the one you'd have the information about</u>.

Warm-Up and Exam Questions

Lots to remember on those four pages. Try these and see how good your understanding really is.

Warm-Up Questions

1) What name is given to the average mass of isotopes of an element?
2) What name is given to the sum of the relative atomic masses of the atoms in a molecule?
3) Write down the definition of a mole.
4) What is the mass of one mole of oxygen gas?

Exam Questions

1 (a) Boron has two main isotopes, $^{11}_{5}B$ and $^{10}_{5}B$. Its A_r value is 10.8.

    (i) What does A_r stand for?

(1 mark)

    (ii) What is the difference in structure between the two boron isotopes?

(1 mark)

    (iii) Which isotope is the most abundant? Explain your reasoning.

(2 marks)

  (b) Use the A_r values B = 11, O = 16, F = 19 and H = 1 to calculate the relative formula masses of these boron compounds:

    (i) BF_3

(1 mark)

    (ii) $B(OH)_3$.

(1 mark)

2 Analysis of an oxide of sulfur shows that it contains 60% oxygen by mass.
(A_r values: S = 32, O = 16.)

  (a) What is the percentage mass of sulfur in the oxide?

(1 mark)

  (b) Work out the formula of the oxide.

(2 marks)

3 Heating a test tube containing 2 g of calcium carbonate produced 1.08 g of calcium oxide when it was reweighed. The equation for the reaction is:

    $CaCO_3(s) \rightarrow CaO(s) + CO_2(g)$

    (M_r values: $CaCO_3$ = 100, CaO = 56.)

  (a) Calculate the amount of calcium oxide you would expect to be formed from 2 g of calcium carbonate.

(1 mark)

  (b) Compare the value to the mass obtained in the experiment.
Suggest a possible reason for the difference.

(1 mark)

Percentage Yield

Percentage yield tells you about the <u>overall success</u> of an experiment. It compares what you calculate you should get (<u>predicted yield</u>) with what you get in practice (<u>actual yield</u>).

Percentage yield compares *actual* and *predicted* yield

The amount of product you get is known as the <u>yield</u>. The more reactants you start with, the higher the <u>actual yield</u> will be — that's pretty obvious. But the <u>percentage yield doesn't</u> depend on the amount of reactants you started with — it's a <u>percentage</u>.

1) The <u>predicted yield</u> of a reaction can be calculated from the <u>balanced reaction equation</u>.

2) Percentage yield is given by the formula:

$$\text{percentage yield} = \frac{\text{actual yield (grams)}}{\text{predicted yield (grams)}} \times 100$$

The predicted yield is sometimes called the theoretical yield.

3) Percentage yield is <u>always</u> somewhere between 0 and 100%.

4) A 100% percentage yield means that you got <u>all</u> the product you expected to get.

5) A 0% yield means that <u>no</u> reactants were converted into product, i.e. no product at all was <u>made</u>.

Yields are always *less than 100%*

Even though <u>no atoms are gained or lost</u> in reactions, in real life, you <u>never</u> get a 100% percentage yield. Some product or reactant <u>always</u> gets lost along the way — and that goes for big <u>industrial processes</u> as well as school lab experiments.

Lots of things can go wrong, but you can find the three you need to know about conveniently located on the next page.

Even with the best equipment, you can't get the maximum product

A high percentage yield means there's <u>not much waste</u> — which is good for <u>preserving resources</u> and keeping production <u>costs down</u>. If a reaction's going to be worth doing commercially, it generally has to have a high percentage yield or recyclable reactants. Learn the <u>formula</u> for working out the all important percentage yield — if it comes up in the exam, it's easy calculation marks.

Percentage Yield and Sustainable Development

Learn these *three reasons* why yields *can't* be 100%

1) The reaction is *reversible*

> A <u>reversible reaction</u> is one where the <u>products</u> of the
> reaction can <u>themselves react</u> to produce the <u>original reactants</u>
>
> A + B ⇌ C + D
>
> <u>For example:</u>
> ammonium chloride ⇌ ammonia + hydrogen chloride

1) This means that the reactants will never be completely converted to products because the reaction goes both ways.

2) Some of the <u>products</u> are always <u>reacting together</u> to change back to the original reactants.

3) This will mean a <u>lower yield</u>.

2) Filtration

1) When you <u>filter a liquid</u> to remove <u>solid particles</u>, you nearly always <u>lose</u> a bit of liquid or a bit of solid.

2) So, some of the product may be lost when it's <u>separated</u> from the reaction mixture.

3) Unexpected reactions

1) Things don't always go exactly to plan. Sometimes there can be other <u>unexpected reactions</u> happening which <u>use up the reactants</u>.

2) This means there's not as much reactant to make the <u>product</u> you want.

Product yield is important for sustainable development

1) Thinking about product yield is important for <u>sustainable development</u>.

2) Sustainable development is about making sure that we don't use <u>resources</u> faster than they can be <u>replaced</u> — there needs to be enough for <u>future generations</u> too.

3) So, for example, using as <u>little energy</u> as possible to create the <u>highest product yield possible</u> means that resources are <u>saved</u>. A low yield means wasted chemicals — not very sustainable.

Chemical Analysis

Now time for some proper chemistry. You can sometimes tell what substances are present in a mixture using chromatography.

Artificial colours can be separated using paper *chromatography*

A food colouring might contain one dye or it might be a mixture of dyes.

Here's how you can tell:

1) Extract the colour from a food sample by placing it in a small cup with a few drops of solvent (can be water, ethanol, salt water, etc).

2) Put spots of the coloured solution on a pencil baseline on filter paper. (Don't use pen because it might dissolve in the solvent and confuse everything.)

3) Roll up the sheet and put it in a beaker with some solvent — but keep the baseline above the level of the solvent.

4) The solvent seeps up the paper, taking the dyes with it. Different dyes form spots in different places.

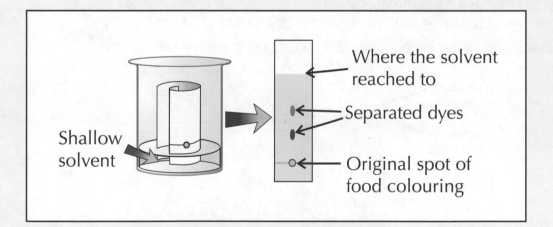

Shallow solvent

Where the solvent reached to

Separated dyes

Original spot of food colouring

5) Watch out though — a chromatogram with four spots means at least four dyes, not exactly four dyes. There could be five dyes, with two of them making a spot in the same place. It can't be three dyes though, because one dye can't split into two spots.

Make sure your solvent level is lower than the spots...

Chromatography is used all the time in industry — it can separate accurately even dead complex mixtures if you choose the right solvent, "filter paper" and conditions.

Chemical Analysis and Instrumental Methods

Nowadays there are some pretty clever ways of <u>identifying</u> substances. We don't have to stick to filter paper — we can use <u>machines</u> as well.

Machines can also analyse unknown substances

You can identify elements and compounds using <u>instrumental methods</u> — this just means using machines.

<u>Advantages of Using Machines</u>
1) <u>Very sensitive</u> — can detect even the <u>tiniest amounts</u> of substances.
2) <u>Very fast</u> and tests can be automated.
3) <u>Very accurate</u>

Gas chromatography can be used to identify substances

Gas chromatography can <u>separate out</u> a mixture of compounds and help you <u>identify</u> the substances present.

1) A <u>gas</u> is used to <u>carry</u> substances through a <u>column</u> packed with a <u>solid material</u>.

2) The substances travel through the tube at <u>different speeds</u>, so they're <u>separated</u>.

3) The time they take to reach the <u>detector</u> is called the <u>retention time</u>. It can be used to help <u>identify</u> the substances.

4) The recorder draws a <u>gas chromatograph</u>. The number of <u>peaks</u> shows the number of <u>different compounds</u> in the sample.

5) The <u>position of the peaks</u> shows the <u>retention time</u> of each substance.

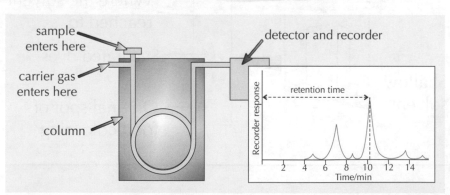

6) The gas chromatography column can also be linked to a <u>mass spectrometer</u>. This process is known as <u>GC-MS</u> and can identify the substances leaving the column very <u>accurately</u>.

7) You can work out the <u>relative molecular mass</u> of each of the substances from the graph it draws. You just <u>read off</u> from the <u>molecular ion peak</u>.

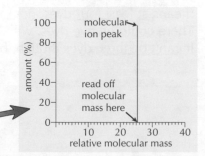

Unfortunately, machines can't do the exam for you...

Make sure you don't get the two types of chromatography muddled up... there's <u>paper</u> and then there's <u>gas</u>. Gas chromatography can tell you a lot more information about substances.

Warm-Up and Exam Questions

Try these questions to help make sure you won't get stuck in the exam. First a (fairly) gentle warm-up, and then some more exam-like questions to give you an idea of what you can expect.

Warm-Up Questions

1) Why might a reaction with a low percentage yield be bad for sustainable development?
2) Give three advantages of using instrumental methods to identify elements and compounds.
3) How can gas chromatography be used to work out the relative molecular mass of a substance?

Exam Questions

1 A sample of copper was made by reducing 4 g of copper oxide with methane gas. When the black copper oxide turned orange-red, the sample was scraped out into a beaker. Sulfuric acid was added to dissolve any copper oxide that remained. The sample was then washed, filtered and dried. 2.8 g of copper was obtained.
   (A_r values: Cu = 63.5, O = 16.)

   The equation for this reaction is: $CH_4 + 4CuO \rightarrow 4Cu + 2H_2O + CO_2$

   (a) Use the equation to calculate the maximum mass of copper which could be obtained from the reaction (the predicted yield).

   (3 marks)

   (b) Calculate the percentage yield of the reaction.

   (2 marks)

   (c) Suggest three different reasons why the yield of the reaction was less than 100%.

   (3 marks)

2 Scientists analysed the composition of six food colourings using chromatography. Four of the colourings were unknown (**1 – 4**), and the other two were known, sunrise yellow and sunset red. The results are shown below.

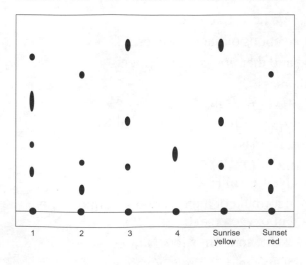

   (a) Which food colouring is most likely to be a pure compound?

   (1 mark)

   (b) Which food colouring contains at least four different compounds?

   (1 mark)

   (c) Which food colouring contains the same compounds as sunrise yellow?

   (1 mark)

   (d) Which food colouring contains the same compounds as sunset red?

   (1 mark)

Revision Summary for Chemistry 2a

Some people skip these pages. But what's the point in reading that great big section if you're not going to check if you really know it or not? Look, just read the first ten questions, and I guarantee there'll be an answer you'll have to look up. And when it comes up in the exam, you'll be so glad you did.

1) What do the mass number and atomic number represent?

2) Draw a table showing the relative masses of the three types of particle in an atom.

3) What is a compound?

4) Define the term isotope.

5) Describe the process of ionic bonding.

6) Describe the structure of a crystal of sodium chloride.

7) List the main properties of ionic compounds.

8) What type of ion do elements from the following groups form?
    a) Group 1   b) Group 7

9)* Use information from the periodic table to help you work out the formulas of these ionic compounds:
    a) potassium chloride   b) calcium chloride

10)* Draw a diagram to show the electronic structure of an Mg^{2+} ion (magnesium's atomic number is 12).

11) What is covalent bonding?

12) Sketch dot and cross diagrams showing the bonding in molecules of:
    a) hydrogen,   b) hydrogen chloride,   c) water,   d) ammonia

13) What are the two types of covalent substance? Give three examples of each.

14) List three properties of metals and explain how metallic bonding causes these properties.

15) Explain why alloys are harder than pure metals.

16)* Identify the structure of each of the substances in the table:

Substance	Melting point (°C)	Electrical conductivity	Hardness [scale of 0 – 10 (10 being diamond)]
A	3410	Very high	7.5
B	2072	Zero	9
C	605	Zero in solid form High when molten	Low

17) Give an example of a "smart" material and describe how it behaves.

18) What are nanoparticles? Give two different applications of nanoparticles.

19) Explain the difference between thermosoftening and thermosetting polymers.

20) Define relative atomic mass and relative formula mass.

21)* Find A_r or M_r for these (use the periodic table at the front of the book):
    a) Ca   b) Ag   c) CO_2 d) $MgCO_3$ e) Na_2CO_3 f) ZnO   g) KOH   h) NH_3

22) What is the link between moles and relative formula mass?

23)* a) Calculate the percentage mass of carbon in: i) $CaCO_3$ ii) CO_2 iii) CH_4
    b) Calculate the percentage mass of metal in: i) Na_2O ii) Fe_2O_3 iii) Al_2O_3

24)* What is an empirical formula? Find the empirical formula of the compound formed when 21.9 g of magnesium, 29.2 g of sulfur and 58.4 g of oxygen react.

25)* What mass of sodium is needed to produce 108.2 g of sodium oxide (Na_2O)?

26) Describe three factors that can reduce the percentage yield of a reaction.

27) Explain how paper chromatography can be used to analyse the dyes used in a brown sweet.

28) Briefly describe how gas chromatography works.

* Answers on page 245.

Rate of Reaction

Reactions can be <u>fast</u> or <u>slow</u> — you've probably already realised that. But you need to know what affects the <u>rate of a reaction</u>, as well as what you can do to <u>measure it</u>.

Reactions can go at all sorts of *different rates*

1) One of the <u>slowest</u> is the <u>rusting</u> of iron.

2) A <u>moderate speed</u> reaction is a <u>metal</u> (like magnesium) reacting with <u>acid</u> to produce a gentle stream of <u>bubbles</u>.

3) A <u>really fast</u> reaction is an <u>explosion</u>, where it's all over in a <u>fraction</u> of a second.

The *rate of a reaction* depends on *four things*:

1) Temperature

2) Concentration   — (or <u>pressure</u> for gases)

3) Catalyst

4) Surface area of solids   — (or <u>size</u> of solid pieces)

Typical graphs for rate of reaction

The plot below shows how the rate of a particular reaction varies under <u>different conditions</u>. The <u>quickest reaction</u> is shown by the line with the <u>steepest slope</u>. Also, the faster a reaction goes, the sooner it finishes, which means that the line becomes <u>flat</u> earlier.

1) <u>Graph 1</u> represents the original <u>fairly slow</u> reaction. The graph is not too steep.

2) <u>Graphs 2 and 3</u> represent the reaction taking place <u>quicker</u> but with the <u>same initial amounts</u>. The slope of the graphs gets steeper.

3) The <u>increased rate</u> could be due to <u>any</u> of these:

> a) increase in <u>temperature</u>
> b) increase in <u>concentration</u> (or pressure)
> c) <u>catalyst</u> added
> d) solid reactant crushed up into <u>smaller bits</u>.

You could also show the amount of reactant used up over time instead — the graphs would have the same shape.

Amount of product evolved

④ faster, and more reactants

end of reaction

③ much faster reaction

② faster reaction

① original reaction

Time

4) <u>Graph 4</u> produces <u>more product</u> as well as going <u>faster</u>. This can <u>only</u> happen if <u>more reactant(s)</u> are added at the start. <u>Graphs 1, 2 and 3</u> all converge at the same level, showing that they all produce the same amount of product, although they take <u>different</u> times to get there.

It's really important that you understand the graph above

<u>Industrial</u> reactions generally use a <u>catalyst</u> and are done at <u>high temperature and pressure</u>. Time is money, so the faster an industrial reaction goes the better... but only <u>up to a point</u>. Chemical plants are quite expensive to rebuild if they get blown into lots and lots of teeny tiny pieces.

Measuring Rates of Reaction

If you want to know the rate of reaction then it's fairly easy to <u>measure</u> it.
There are <u>three</u> ways of measuring rate of reaction that you should know about.

Ways to **measure the rate** of a reaction

The <u>rate of a reaction</u> can be observed <u>either</u> by measuring how quickly the reactants are used up or how quickly the products are formed. It's usually a lot easier to measure <u>products forming</u>.

The rate of reaction can be calculated using the following formula:

$$\text{Rate of reaction} = \frac{\text{amount of reactant used or amount of product formed}}{\text{time}}$$

There are different ways that the rate of a reaction can be <u>measured</u>. Learn these three:

1) Precipitation

1) This is when the product of the reaction is a <u>precipitate</u> which <u>clouds</u> the solution.

2) Observe a <u>mark</u> through the solution and measure how long it takes for it to <u>disappear</u>.

3) The <u>quicker</u> the mark disappears, the <u>quicker</u> the reaction.

4) This only works for reactions where the initial solution is rather <u>see-through</u>.

5) The result is very <u>subjective</u> — <u>different people</u> might not agree over the <u>exact</u> point when the mark 'disappears'.

Measuring Rates of Reaction

2) Change in mass (usually gas given off)

1) Measuring the speed of a reaction that produces a gas can be carried out on a mass balance.

2) As the gas is released the mass disappearing is easily measured on the balance.

3) The quicker the reading on the balance drops, the faster the reaction.

4) Rate of reaction graphs are particularly easy to plot using the results from this method.

5) This is the most accurate of the three methods described because the mass balance is very accurate. But it has the disadvantage of releasing the gas straight into the room.

3) The volume of gas given off

1) This involves the use of a gas syringe to measure the volume of gas given off.

2) The more gas given off during a given time interval, the faster the reaction.

3) A graph of gas volume against time elapsed could be plotted to give a rate of reaction graph.

4) Gas syringes usually give volumes accurate to the nearest millilitre, so they're quite accurate. You have to be quite careful though — if the reaction is too vigorous, you can easily blow the plunger out of the end of the syringe.

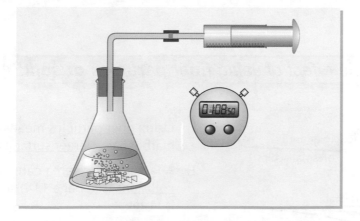

Each of these methods has pros and cons

The mass balance method is only accurate as long as the flask isn't too hot, otherwise you lose mass by evaporation as well as in the reaction. The first method isn't very accurate, but if you're not producing a gas you can't use either of the other two. Ah well.

Rate of Reaction Experiments

Remember: Any reaction can be used to investigate any of the four factors that affect the rate.
The next four pages illustrate four important reactions, but only one factor is considered for each.
But you can just as easily use, say, the marble chips/acid reaction to test the effect of temperature instead.

1) Reaction of **hydrochloric acid** and **marble chips**

This experiment is often used to demonstrate the effect of breaking the solid up into small bits.

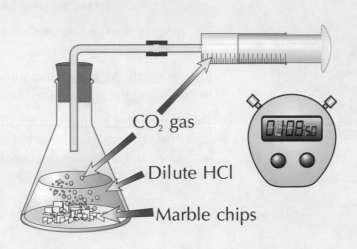

CO$_2$ gas

Dilute HCl

Marble chips

1) Measure the volume of gas evolved with a gas syringe and take readings at regular intervals.

2) Make a table of readings and plot them as a graph. You choose regular time intervals, and time goes on the x-axis and volume goes on the y-axis.

3) Repeat the experiment with exactly the same volume of acid, and exactly the same mass of marble chips, but with the marble more crunched up.

4) Then repeat with the same mass of powdered chalk instead of marble chips.

This graph shows the effect of using **finer particles of solid**

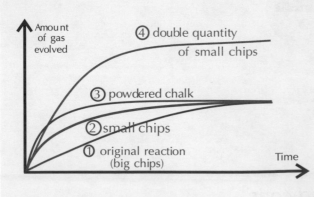

Amount of gas evolved

④ double quantity of small chips

③ powdered chalk

② small chips

① original reaction (big chips)

Time

1) Using finer particles means that the marble has a larger surface area.

2) A larger surface area causes more frequent collisions (see page 114) so the rate of reaction is faster.

3) Line 4 shows the reaction if a greater mass of small marble chips is added.
The extra surface area gives a quicker reaction and there is also more gas evolved overall.

Rate of Reaction Experiments

The reaction of <u>magnesium metal</u> with <u>dilute HCl</u> is often used to determine the effect of <u>concentration</u>.

2) Reaction of *magnesium metal* with *dilute HCl*

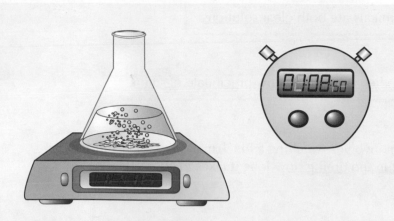

1) <u>This reaction</u> is good for measuring the effects of <u>increased concentration</u> (as is the marble/acid reaction).

2) This reaction gives off <u>hydrogen gas</u>, which we can measure with a <u>mass balance</u>, as shown.

3) In this experiment, <u>time</u> also goes on the <u>x-axis</u> and <u>volume</u> goes on the <u>y-axis</u>.
(The other method is to use a gas syringe, see page 107.)

This graph shows the effect of using *more concentrated acid solutions*

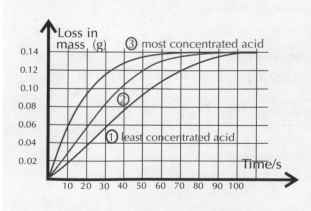

1) Take <u>readings</u> of mass at <u>regular</u> time intervals.

2) Put the results in a <u>table</u> and work out the <u>loss in mass</u> for each reading. <u>Plot a graph.</u>

3) <u>Repeat</u> with <u>more concentrated</u> acid solutions, but always with the <u>same</u> amount of magnesium.

4) The <u>volume</u> of acid must always be kept <u>the same</u> too — only the <u>concentration</u> is increased.

5) The three graphs show the <u>same</u> old pattern — a <u>higher</u> concentration giving a <u>steeper graph</u>, with the reaction <u>finishing</u> much quicker.

Rate of Reaction Experiments

The effect of <u>temperature</u> on the rate of a reaction can be measured using a <u>precipitation</u> reaction.

3) *Sodium thiosulfate* and *HCl* produce a *cloudy precipitate*

1) These two chemicals are both <u>clear solutions</u>.

2) They react together to form a <u>yellow precipitate</u> of <u>sulfur</u>.

3) The experiment involves watching a black mark <u>disappear</u> through the <u>cloudy sulfur</u> and <u>timing</u> how long it takes to go.

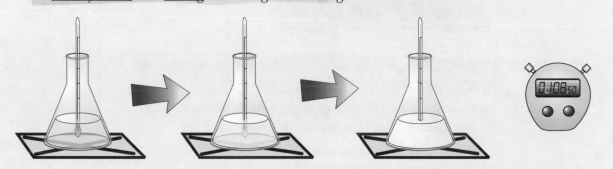

4) The reaction can be <u>repeated</u> for solutions at different <u>temperatures</u>. In practice, that's quite hard to do accurately and safely (it's not a good idea to heat an acid directly). The best way to do it is to use a <u>water bath</u> to heat both solutions to the right temperature <u>before you mix them</u>.

5) The <u>depth</u> of liquid must be kept the <u>same</u> each time, of course.

6) The results will of course show that the <u>higher</u> the temperature the <u>quicker</u> the reaction and therefore the <u>less time</u> it takes for the mark to <u>disappear</u>. These are typical results:

Temperature (°C)	20	25	30	35	40
Time taken for mark to disappear (s)	193	151	112	87	52

This reaction can <u>also</u> be used to test the effects of <u>concentration</u>.

This reaction <u>doesn't</u> give a set of graphs. All you get is a set of <u>readings</u> of how long it took till the mark disappeared for each temperature.

Rate of Reaction Experiments

Good news — this is the last rate experiment. This one looks at how a <u>catalyst</u> affects rate of reaction.

4) The **decomposition** of **hydrogen peroxide**

This is a <u>good</u> reaction for showing the effect of different <u>catalysts</u>.
The decomposition of hydrogen peroxide is:

$$2H_2O_{2\,(aq)} \quad \rightarrow \quad 2H_2O_{(l)} + O_{2\,(g)}$$

1) This is normally quite <u>slow</u> but a sprinkle of <u>manganese(IV) oxide catalyst</u> speeds it up no end. Other catalysts which work are found in:
   a) <u>potato peel</u> and b) <u>blood</u>.

2) <u>Oxygen gas</u> is given off, which provides an <u>ideal way</u> to measure the rate of reaction using the <u>gas syringe</u> method.

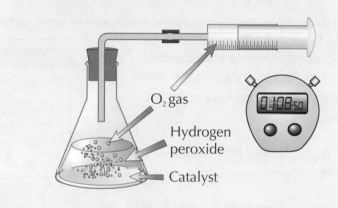

O₂ gas

Hydrogen peroxide

Catalyst

This graph shows the effect of using **different catalysts**

1) Same old graphs of course.
2) <u>Better</u> catalysts give a <u>quicker reaction</u>, which is shown by a <u>steeper graph</u> which levels off quickly.
3) This reaction can also be used to measure the effects of <u>temperature</u>, or of <u>concentration</u> of the H_2O_2 solution. The graphs will look just the same.

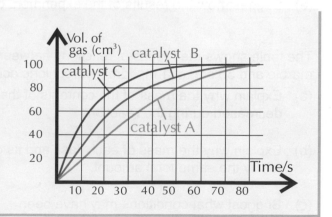

Blood is a catalyst? — eeurgh...

You don't need to know all the details of these specific reactions — but you do need to be able to look at <u>graphs</u> showing the amount of product formed (or reactant used up) over time and comment on the <u>reaction rate</u>. If you understand how all this works, you should be able to apply it to <u>any</u> reaction.

Warm-Up and Exam Questions

Time to test your knowledge again. This time on the rates of chemical reactions. If you struggle with these questions and you don't feel up to speed, it's time to have another look at the last few pages.

Warm-Up Questions

1) Give an example of a reaction that happens very slowly, and one that is very fast.
2) Give three ways of increasing the rate of a reaction between magnesium and sulfuric acid.
3) Describe one way of monitoring a reaction in which a gas is given off.
4) How would reducing the concentration of an acid affect the time taken for a piece of zinc to react with it?
5) Oxidation of lactose in milk makes it go 'sour'. How could this reaction be slowed down?

Exam Questions

1   Set volumes of sodium thiosulfate and hydrochloric acid were reacted at different temperatures. The time taken for a black cross to be obscured by the sulfur precipitated was measured at each temperature. The results are shown in the table.

Temperature (°C)	Time (s)
55	6
36	11
24	17
16	27
9	40
5	51

   (a) Give two variables that should be kept constant in this experiment.
(2 marks)

   (b) Plot the results on a graph (with time on the x-axis) and draw a best-fit curve.
(2 marks)

   (c) Describe the relationship illustrated by your graph.
(1 mark)

   (d) Describe how the results would change if the sodium thiosulfate concentration was reduced.
(2 marks)

   (e) Suggest how the results of the experiment could be made more reliable.
(1 mark)

2   The table shows the results of reactions between excess marble and 50 cm³ of 1 mol/dm³ hydrochloric acid.

Time (min)	Mass of flask A (g)	Mass of flask B (g)
0	121.6	121.6
1	120.3	119.8
2	119.7	119.2
3	119.4	119.1
4	119.2	119
5	119.1	119
6	119	119
7	119	

   (a) Explain why the mass of the contents of the flasks decreased during the reaction.
(1 mark)

   (b) Explain why the mass of each flask and its contents fell by the same total amount.
(1 mark)

   (c) Suggest what conditions may have been different inside flask B.
(1 mark)

   (d) In both reactions, the rate is fastest at the beginning. Suggest why.
(1 mark)

Collision Theory

Reaction rates are explained by <u>collision theory</u>. It's really simple.

1) Collision theory just says that <u>the rate of a reaction</u> simply depends on <u>how often</u> and <u>how hard</u> the reacting particles <u>collide</u> with each other.

2) The basic idea is that particles have to <u>collide</u> in order to <u>react</u>, and they have to collide <u>hard enough</u> (with enough energy).

More collisions increases the rate of reaction

The effects of temperature, concentration and surface area on the <u>rate of reaction</u> can be <u>explained</u> in terms of <u>how often</u> the reacting particles collide <u>successfully</u>.

1) HIGHER TEMPERATURE increases collisions

When the <u>temperature is increased</u> the particles all <u>move quicker</u>. If they're moving quicker, they're going to <u>collide more often</u>.

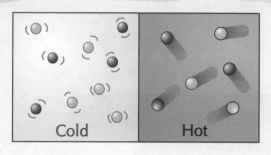

Cold   Hot

2) HIGHER CONCENTRATION (or PRESSURE) increases collisions

If a solution is made more <u>concentrated</u> it means there are more particles of <u>reactant</u> knocking about <u>between the water molecules</u> which makes collisions between the <u>important</u> particles <u>more likely</u>.

In a <u>gas</u>, increasing the <u>pressure</u> means the particles are <u>more squashed up</u> together so there will be <u>more frequent collisions</u>.

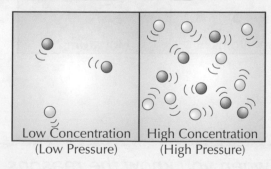

Low Concentration   High Concentration
(Low Pressure)   (High Pressure)

Collision Theory

3) LARGER SURFACE AREA increases collisions

If one of the reactants is a solid then breaking it up into smaller pieces will increase the total surface area. This means the particles around it in the solution will have more area to work on, so there'll be more frequent collisions.

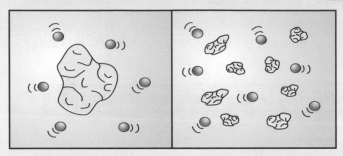

Small surface area   Big surface area

Faster collisions increase the rate of reaction

Higher temperature also increases the energy of the collisions, because it makes all the particles move faster.

Increasing the temperature causes faster collisions.

Reactions only happen if the particles collide with enough energy.

The minimum amount of energy needed by the particles to react is known as the activation energy.

At a higher temperature there will be more particles colliding with enough energy to make the reaction happen.

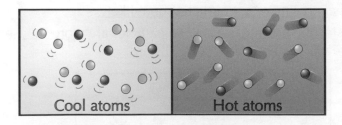

Cool atoms   Hot atoms

It's easier to learn stuff when you know the reasons for it

Once you've learnt everything off this page, the rates of reaction stuff should start making a lot more sense to you. The concept's fairly simple — the more often particles bump into each other, and the harder they hit when they do, the faster the reaction happens.

Catalysts

In industrial reactions, the main thing they're interested in is making a <u>nice profit</u>.
Catalysts are helpful for this — they can reduce costs and increase the amount of product.

Catalysts *speed up* reactions

Many reactions can be <u>speeded up</u> by adding a <u>catalyst</u>.

> A <u>catalyst</u> is a substance which <u>speeds up</u> a reaction,
> without being <u>changed</u> or <u>used up</u> in the reaction.

A <u>solid catalyst</u> works by giving the <u>reacting particles</u> a <u>surface</u> to <u>stick to</u>.
This increases the number of <u>successful collisions</u> (and so speeds the reaction up).

Catalysts help *reduce costs* in industrial reactions

1) Catalysts are <u>very important</u> for <u>commercial reasons</u> — most industrial reactions use them.

2) <u>Catalysts</u> increase the rate of the reaction, which saves a lot of <u>money</u> simply because the plant doesn't need to operate for <u>as long</u> to produce the <u>same amount</u> of stuff.

3) Alternatively, a catalyst will allow the reaction to work at a <u>much lower temperature</u>. That reduces the <u>energy</u> used up in the reaction (the <u>energy cost</u>), which is good for <u>sustainable development</u> (see page 100) and can save a lot of money too.

4) There are <u>disadvantages</u> to using catalysts, though.

5) They can be very expensive to buy, and often need to be removed from the product and cleaned. They never get <u>used up</u> in the reaction though, so once you've got them you can use them <u>over and over</u> again.

6) Different <u>reactions</u> use different <u>catalysts</u>, so if you make <u>more than one product</u> at your plant, you'll probably need to buy different catalysts for them.

7) Catalysts can be '<u>poisoned</u>' by impurities, so they <u>stop working</u>, e.g. sulfur impurities can poison the iron catalyst used in the Haber process (used to make ammonia for fertilisers). That means you have to keep your reaction mixture very <u>clean</u>.

A big advantage of catalysts is that they can be used over and over

And they're not only used in <u>industry</u>... every useful chemical reaction in the human body is catalysed by a <u>biological catalyst</u> (an enzyme). If the reactions in the body were just left to their own devices, they'd take so long to happen, we couldn't exist. Quite handy then, these catalysts.

Energy Transfer in Reactions

Whenever chemical reactions occur <u>energy</u> is <u>transferred to</u> or <u>from</u> the <u>surroundings</u>.

In an **exothermic** reaction, heat is **given out**

An <u>EXOTHERMIC reaction</u> is one which <u>gives out energy</u> to the surroundings, usually in the form of <u>heat</u> and usually shown by a <u>rise in temperature</u>.

1) *Burning* fuels

The best example of an <u>exothermic</u> reaction is <u>burning fuels</u> — also called <u>COMBUSTION</u>. This gives out a lot of heat — it's very exothermic.

2) *Neutralisation* reactions

<u>Neutralisation reactions</u> (acid + alkali) are also exothermic — see page 119.

ACID

<u>Don't</u> do it like this!

ALKALI

3) *Oxidation* reactions

Many <u>oxidation reactions</u> are exothermic. For example:

Adding sodium to water <u>produces heat</u>, so it must be <u>exothermic</u>. The sodium emits <u>heat</u> and moves about on the surface of the water as it is oxidised.

Exothermic reactions have lots of <u>everyday uses</u>. For example, some <u>hand warmers</u> use the exothermic <u>oxidation of iron</u> in air (with a salt solution catalyst) to generate <u>heat</u>. <u>Self heating cans</u> of hot chocolate and coffee also rely on exothermic reactions between <u>chemicals</u> in their bases.

Energy Transfer in Reactions

In an **endothermic** reaction, heat is **taken in**

An __ENDOTHERMIC reaction__ is one which __takes in energy__ from the surroundings, usually in the form of __heat__ and is usually shown by a __fall in temperature__.

Endothermic reactions are much __less common__. __Thermal decompositions__ are a good example:

Heat must be supplied to make calcium carbonate __decompose__ to make quicklime.

$$CaCO_3 \rightarrow CaO + CO_2$$

Endothermic reactions also have everyday uses. For example, some __sports injury packs__ use endothermic reactions — they __take in heat__ and the pack becomes very __cold__. More __convenient__ than carrying ice around.

Reversible reactions can be **endothermic** and **exothermic**

In reversible reactions (see page 100), if the reaction is __endothermic__ in __one direction__, it will be __exothermic__ in the __other direction__. The __energy absorbed__ by the endothermic reaction is __equal__ to the __energy released__ during the exothermic reaction.

A good example is the __thermal decomposition of hydrated copper sulfate__.

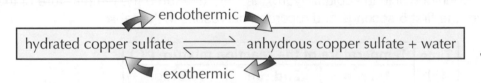

endothermic

hydrated copper sulfate ⇌ anhydrous copper sulfate + water

exothermic

"Anhydrous" just means "without water", and "hydrated" means "with water".

1) If you __heat blue hydrated__ copper(II) sulfate crystals it drives the water off and leaves __white anhydrous__ copper(II) sulfate powder. This is endothermic.

Water vapour

2) If you then __add__ a couple of drops of __water__ to the __white powder__ you get the __blue crystals__ back again. This is exothermic.

Right, so burning gives out heat — really...

This whole energy transfer thing is a fairly simple idea — don't be put off by the long words. Remember, "exo-" = exit, "-thermic" = heat, so an exothermic reaction is one that gives out heat. And "endo-" = erm... the other one. Okay, so there's no easy way to remember that one. Tough.

Warm-Up and Exam Questions

Here are some more questions to have a go at. If you can't do these ones then you won't be able to do the ones in the exam either. And you don't want that. If you're struggling, read the pages over again.

Warm-Up Questions

1) According to collision theory, what must happen in order for two particles to react?
2) Why does an increase in concentration of solutions increase the rate of a reaction?
3) Give a definition of a catalyst.
4) An endothermic reaction happens when ammonium nitrate is dissolved in water. Predict how the temperature of the solution will change during the reaction.

Exam Questions

1   *In this question you will be assessed on the quality of your English, the organisation of your ideas and your use of appropriate specialist vocabulary.*

Hydrogen and ethene react to form ethane. Nickel can be used as a catalyst for this reaction.

Using your knowledge of collision theory, suggest how the rate of this reaction can be increased.

(6 marks)

2   A student added hydrochloric acid to sodium hydroxide. He measured the temperature of the reaction mixture over the first 5 seconds and recorded his results in the table.

Time (s)	Temperature of the reaction mixture (°C)		
	1st run	2nd run	Average
0	22.0	22.0	
1	25.6	24.4	
2	28.3	28.1	
3	29.0	28.6	
4	28.8	28.8	
5	28.3	28.7	

(a) State the name given to this type of reaction.

(1 mark)

(b) Complete the table by calculating the average temperature of the reaction mixture during the two runs.

(2 marks)

(c) Calculate the maximum average increase in temperature during the reaction.

(1 mark)

(d) Is this reaction exothermic or endothermic? Explain your answer.

(2 marks)

Acids and Alkalis

Testing the pH of a solution means using an <u>indicator</u> — and that means pretty <u>colours</u>...

The *pH scale* goes from *0 to 14*

1) The <u>pH scale</u> is a measure of how <u>acidic</u> or <u>alkaline</u> a solution is.
2) The <u>strongest acid</u> has <u>pH 0</u>. The <u>strongest alkali</u> has <u>pH 14</u>.
3) A <u>neutral</u> substance has <u>pH 7</u> (e.g. pure water).

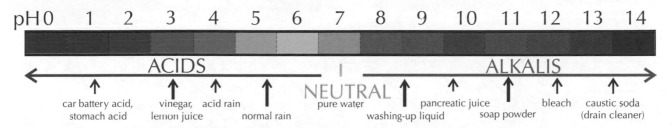

pH 0 1 2 3 4 5 6 7 8 9 10 11 12 13 14

ACIDS | ALKALIS

NEUTRAL

car battery acid, stomach acid   vinegar, lemon juice   acid rain   normal rain   pure water   washing-up liquid   pancreatic juice   soap powder   bleach   caustic soda (drain cleaner)

4) You can test the pH of a solution using an <u>indicator</u>.
5) The dye in an indicator <u>changes colour</u> depending on whether it's <u>above or below a certain pH</u>.
6) <u>Universal indicator</u> is a <u>combination of dyes</u> which gives the colours shown above.

Acids and *bases* neutralise each other

An <u>ACID</u> is a substance with a pH of less than 7. Acids form <u>H^+ ions</u> in <u>water</u>.
A <u>BASE</u> is a substance with a pH of greater than 7.
An <u>ALKALI</u> is a base that <u>dissolves in water</u>. Alkalis form <u>OH^- ions</u> in <u>water</u>.
So, <u>H^+</u> ions make solutions <u>acidic</u> and <u>OH^-</u> ions make them <u>alkaline</u>.

The reaction between acids and bases is called <u>neutralisation</u>. Make sure you learn it:

$$acid + base \rightarrow salt + water$$

Neutralisation can also be seen in terms of <u>H^+</u> and <u>OH^- ions</u> like this, so learn it too:

$$H^+_{(aq)} + OH^-_{(aq)} \rightarrow H_2O_{(l)}$$

Hydrogen (H^+) ions react with hydroxide (OH^-) ions to produce water.

When an acid neutralises a base (or vice versa), the <u>products</u> are <u>neutral</u>, i.e. they have a <u>pH of 7</u>. An indicator can be used to show that a neutralisation reaction is over (Universal indicator will go green).

State symbols tell you what *physical state* it's in

These are easy enough, <u>so make sure you know them</u> — especially aq (aqueous).

(s) — Solid	(l) — Liquid	(g) — Gas	(aq) — Dissolved in water

E.g. $2Mg_{(s)} + O_{2(g)} \rightarrow 2MgO_{(s)}$

Interesting(ish) fact — your skin is slightly acidic (pH 5.5)...

That neutralisation reaction is important. Make sure you understand it in terms of the ions.

Acids Reacting With Metals

There are loads of different salts out there. Some of them are made when an <u>acid</u> reacts with a <u>metal</u>.

Metals *react with* acids *to give* salts

$$\text{acid} + \text{metal} \rightarrow \text{salt} + \text{hydrogen}$$

That's written big because it's really worth remembering. Here's the <u>typical experiment</u>:

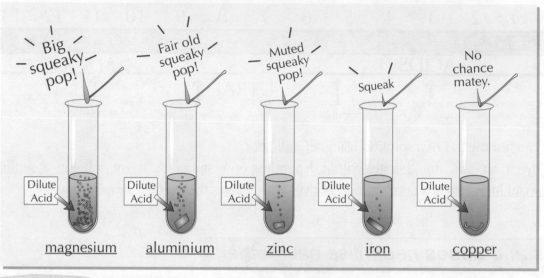

1) The more <u>reactive</u> the metal, the <u>faster</u> the reaction will go — very reactive metals (e.g. sodium) react <u>explosively</u>.

2) <u>Copper</u> does <u>not</u> react with dilute acids <u>at all</u> — because it's <u>less</u> reactive than <u>hydrogen</u>.

3) The <u>speed</u> of reaction is indicated by the <u>rate</u> at which the <u>bubbles</u> of hydrogen are given off.

4) The <u>hydrogen</u> is confirmed by the <u>burning splint test</u> giving the notorious 'squeaky pop'.

5) The <u>name</u> of the <u>salt</u> produced depends on which <u>metal</u> is used, and which <u>acid</u> is used:

Hydrochloric acid *will always produce* chloride *salts:*

$$2HCl + Mg \rightarrow MgCl_2 + H_2 \qquad \text{(Magnesium chloride)}$$
$$6HCl + 2Al \rightarrow 2AlCl_3 + 3H_2 \qquad \text{(Aluminium chloride)}$$
$$2HCl + Zn \rightarrow ZnCl_2 + H_2 \qquad \text{(Zinc chloride)}$$

Sulfuric acid *will always produce* sulfate *salts:*

$$H_2SO_4 + Mg \rightarrow MgSO_4 + H_2 \qquad \text{(Magnesium sulfate)}$$
$$3H_2SO_4 + 2Al \rightarrow Al_2(SO_4)_3 + 3H_2 \qquad \text{(Aluminium sulfate)}$$
$$H_2SO_4 + Zn \rightarrow ZnSO_4 + H_2 \qquad \text{(Zinc sulfate)}$$

Nitric acid *produces* nitrate *salts when NEUTRALISED, but...*

Nitric acid reacts fine with alkalis, to produce nitrates, but it can play silly devils with metals and produce nitrogen oxides instead, so we'll ignore it here.

Oxides, Hydroxides and Ammonia

I'm afraid there's more stuff on <u>neutralisation</u> reactions coming up...

Metal **oxides** and metal **hydroxides** are **bases**

1) Some <u>metal oxides</u> and <u>metal hydroxides</u> dissolve in <u>water</u>. These soluble compounds are <u>alkalis</u>.
2) Even bases that won't dissolve in water will still react with <u>acids</u>.
3) So, all <u>metal oxides</u> and <u>metal hydroxides</u> react with <u>acids</u> to form a <u>salt</u> and <u>water</u>.

acid + metal oxide → salt + water

acid + metal hydroxide → salt + water

These are neutralisation reactions.

The **combination** of metal and acid decides the **salt**

This isn't exactly exciting but it's pretty easy, so try and get the hang of it:

hydrochloric acid + copper oxide → copper chloride + water
hydrochloric acid + sodium hydroxide → sodium chloride + water

sulfuric acid + zinc oxide → zinc sulfate + water
sulfuric acid + calcium hydroxide → calcium sulfate + water

nitric acid + magnesium oxide → magnesium nitrate + water
nitric acid + potassium hydroxide → potassium nitrate + water

The symbol equations are all pretty much the same. Here are two of them:

$$H_2SO_{4\ (aq)} + ZnO_{\ (s)} \rightarrow ZnSO_{4\ (aq)} + H_2O_{\ (l)}$$
$$HNO_{3\ (aq)} + KOH_{\ (aq)} \rightarrow KNO_{3\ (aq)} + H_2O_{\ (l)}$$

Ammonia can be **neutralised** with HNO_3 to make **fertiliser**

<u>Ammonia</u> dissolves in water to make an <u>alkaline solution</u>.
When it reacts with <u>nitric acid</u>, you get a <u>neutral salt</u> — <u>ammonium nitrate</u>:

$$NH_{3\ (aq)} + HNO_{3\ (aq)} \rightarrow NH_4NO_{3\ (aq)}$$
ammonia + nitric acid → ammonium nitrate

This is a bit different from most neutralisation reactions because there's <u>NO WATER</u> produced — just the ammonium salt.

<u>Ammonium nitrate</u> is an especially good fertiliser because it has <u>nitrogen</u> from <u>two sources</u>, the ammonia and the nitric acid. Kind of a <u>double dose</u>. Plants need nitrogen to make <u>proteins</u>.

Making Salts

Most chlorides, sulfates and nitrates are soluble in water (the main exceptions are lead chloride, lead sulfate and silver chloride). Most oxides and hydroxides are insoluble in water.
The method you use to make a soluble salt depends on whether the base you use is soluble or not.

Making **soluble salts** using a **metal** or an **insoluble base**

1) You need to pick the right acid, plus a metal or an insoluble base (a metal oxide or metal hydroxide). E.g. if you want to make copper chloride, mix hydrochloric acid and copper oxide.

Remember some metals are unreactive and others are too reactive to use for this reaction (see page 120).

$$CuO_{(s)} + 2HCl_{(aq)} \rightarrow CuCl_{2\,(aq)} + H_2O_{(l)}$$

2) You add the metal, metal oxide or hydroxide to the acid — the solid will dissolve in the acid as it reacts. You will know when all the acid has been neutralised because the excess solid will just sink to the bottom of the flask.

filter paper

filter funnel

3) Then filter out the excess metal, metal oxide or metal hydroxide to get the salt solution. To get pure, solid crystals of the salt, evaporate some of the water (to make the solution more concentrated) and then leave the rest to evaporate very slowly. This is called crystallisation.

Making **soluble salts** using an **alkali**

1) You can't use the method above with alkalis (soluble bases) like sodium, potassium or ammonium hydroxides, because you can't tell whether the reaction has finished — you can't just add an excess to the acid and filter out what's left.

2) You have to add exactly the right amount of alkali to just neutralise the acid — you need to use an indicator (see page 119) to show when the reaction's finished. Then repeat using exactly the same volumes of alkali and acid so the salt isn't contaminated with indicator.

3) Then just evaporate off the water to crystallise the salt as normal.

Make sure you pick the right method...

Think very carefully in the exam if you are asked for the method to make a salt. You'll be throwing marks away if you write about filtering the mixture when you used a soluble base in the first place.

Making Salts

That last page was all about making <u>soluble salts</u>. This one's about making <u>insoluble salts</u>.

Making **insoluble** salts — **precipitation** reactions

1) If the salt you want to make is <u>insoluble</u>, you can use a <u>precipitation reaction</u>.

2) You just need to pick <u>two solutions</u> that contain the <u>ions</u> you need. E.g. to make <u>lead chloride</u> you need a solution which contains <u>lead ions</u> and one which contains <u>chloride ions</u>. So you can mix <u>lead nitrate solution</u> (most nitrates are soluble) with <u>sodium chloride solution</u> (all group 1 compounds are soluble).

$$\text{E.g.} \quad Pb(NO_3)_{2\,(aq)} + 2NaCl_{(aq)} \longrightarrow PbCl_{2\,(s)} + 2NaNO_{3\,(aq)}$$

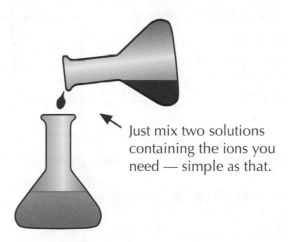

Just mix two solutions containing the ions you need — simple as that.

3) Once the salt has precipitated out (and is lying at the bottom of your flask), all you have to do is <u>filter</u> it from the solution, <u>wash</u> it and then <u>dry</u> it on filter paper.

4) <u>Precipitation reactions</u> can be used to remove <u>poisonous ions</u> (e.g. lead) from <u>drinking water</u>. <u>Calcium</u> and <u>magnesium</u> ions can also be removed from water this way — they make water "<u>hard</u>", which stops soap lathering properly. Another use of precipitation is in <u>treating effluent</u> (sewage) — again, <u>unwanted ions</u> can be removed.

Precipitation reaction — put up an umbrella...

In the exam you may get a question asking you to select <u>two solutions</u> to mix together to make a certain salt. All you need is two solutions that contain the <u>ions you need</u> and Bob's your uncle.

Warm-Up and Exam Questions

Now try these questions — you're less likely to get a nasty surprise in the exam if you do.

Warm-Up Questions

1) What name is given to the type of reaction in which an acid reacts with a base?
2) Which two substances are formed when an acid reacts with a metal such as zinc?
3) Which two substances are formed when nitric acid reacts with copper oxide?
4) Explain what you would do to make a dry sample of a soluble salt from an insoluble base.
5) Write down the word equation for the precipitation reaction between barium chloride and sodium sulfate.

Exam Questions

1   An experiment was carried out in which sodium hydroxide solution was added, 2 cm³ at a time, to 10 cm³ of sulfuric acid. The pH was estimated after each addition using universal indicator paper.

The results are shown in the table.

Volume of sodium hydroxide added (cm³)	pH
0	1
2	1
4	2
6	4
8	12
10	13
12	13

(a) Plot the results on a graph, with pH on the vertical axis and volume of sodium hydroxide added on the horizontal axis.
Draw a best fit curve.

(2 marks)

(b) Estimate the volume of sodium hydroxide needed to neutralise the acid.

(1 mark)

(c) How do the results show that sulfuric acid is a strong acid?

(1 mark)

(d) Name the salt formed in the reaction.

(1 mark)

2   Jenny wanted to make a dry sample of silver chloride, AgCl, by precipitation.

(a) What property must a salt have to be made by precipitation?

(1 mark)

(b) Jenny looked up the solubilities of some compounds she might use.
Write down a word equation using substances from the table that she could use to make silver chloride by precipitation.

Compound	Formula	Solubility
silver oxide	Ag_2O	insoluble
silver nitrate	$AgNO_3$	soluble
silver carbonate	$AgCO_3$	insoluble
sulfuric acid	H_2SO_4	soluble
nitric acid	HNO_3	soluble
hydrochloric acid	HCl	soluble

(1 mark)

(c) Outline the steps needed to give a pure dry sample of silver chloride after mixing the solutions.

(3 marks)

Electrolysis

Examiners love <u>electrolysis</u>. It's just a shame that no one else does.

Electrolysis means "splitting up with electricity"

1) If you pass an <u>electric current</u> through an <u>ionic substance</u> that's <u>molten</u> or in <u>solution</u>, it breaks down into the <u>elements</u> it's made of. This is called <u>electrolysis</u>.

2) It requires a <u>liquid</u> to <u>conduct</u> the <u>electricity</u>, called the <u>electrolyte</u>.

3) Electrolytes contain <u>free ions</u> — they're usually the <u>molten</u> or <u>dissolved ionic substance</u>.

NaCl dissolved

Molten NaCl

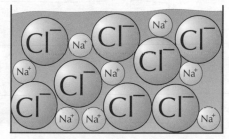

4) In either case it's the <u>free ions</u> which <u>conduct</u> the electricity and allow the whole thing to work.

5) For an electrical circuit to be complete, there's got to be a <u>flow of electrons</u>. Electrons are taken <u>away from</u> ions at the <u>positive electrode</u> and <u>given to</u> other ions at the <u>negative electrode</u>. As ions gain or lose electrons they become atoms or molecules and are released.

*Electrolysis reactions involve **oxidation** and **reduction***

1) Back in Core Science you learnt about <u>reduction</u> involving the <u>loss of oxygen</u>. However...

2) <u>Reduction</u> is also a <u>gain of electrons</u>.

3) On the other hand, <u>oxidation</u> is a gain of oxygen or a <u>loss of electrons</u>.

4) So "reduction" and "oxidation" don't have to involve <u>oxygen</u>.

5) Electrolysis <u>ALWAYS</u> involves an oxidation and a reduction.

<u>O</u>xidation
<u>I</u>s
<u>L</u>oss

<u>R</u>eduction
<u>I</u>s
<u>G</u>ain

Remember it as OIL RIG.

Electrolysis needs a liquid to conduct the electricity

Before you electrolyse a substance it has to be <u>liquid</u>. This allows the ions to <u>move</u> towards the <u>positive</u> or <u>negative</u> electrode. The next few pages are about the electrolysis of different substances.

Electrolysis of Lead Bromide

Molten lead bromide can be broken down by electrolysis. You end up with lead and bromine.

The *electrolysis* of molten *lead bromide*

When a salt (e.g. lead bromide) is molten it will conduct electricity.

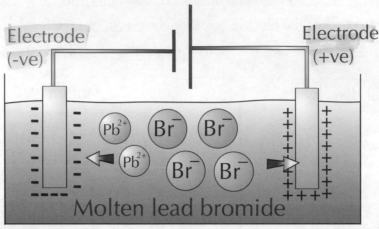

Electrode (-ve)   Electrode (+ve)

Molten lead bromide

HEAT

+ve ions are attracted to the –ve electrode. Here they gain electrons (reduction).

–ve ions are attracted to the +ve electrode. Here they lose electrons (oxidation).

Lead is produced at the –ve electrode.

Bromine is produced at the +ve electrode.

1) At the –ve electrode, one lead ion accepts two electrons to become one lead atom.

2) At the +ve electrode, two bromide ions lose one electron each and become one bromine molecule.

Reactivity affects the *products* formed by *electrolysis*

1) Sometimes there are more than two free ions in the electrolyte. For example, if a salt is dissolved in water there will also be some H^+ and OH^- ions.

2) At the negative electrode, if metal ions and H^+ ions are present, the metal ions will stay in solution if the metal is more reactive than hydrogen. This is because the more reactive an element, the keener it is to stay as ions. So, hydrogen will be produced unless the metal is less reactive than it.

3) At the positive electrode, if OH^- and halide ions (Cl^-, Br^-, I^-) are present then molecules of chlorine, bromine or iodine will be formed. If no halide is present, then oxygen will be formed.

So, lead bromide splits into lead and bromine — I know, it's tricky

The electrolysis of lead bromide is pretty simple — bromine ions are oxidised so bromine is produced at the positive electrode and lead ions are reduced so lead is produced at the negative electrode. But when your substance is dissolved in water things get trickier — as you'll see on the next page.

Electrolysis of Sodium Chloride

You need to know about the electrolysis of salt (sodium chloride) solution. Get learning...

The *electrolysis* of *sodium chloride solution*

When common salt (sodium chloride) is dissolved in water and electrolysed, it produces three useful products — hydrogen, chlorine and sodium hydroxide.

H+ ions are released from the water.

+ve ions are attracted to the –ve electrode. Here they gain electrons (reduction).

Hydrogen is produced at the –ve electrode.

–ve ions are attracted to the +ve electrode. Here they lose electrons (oxidation).

Chlorine is produced at the +ve electrode.

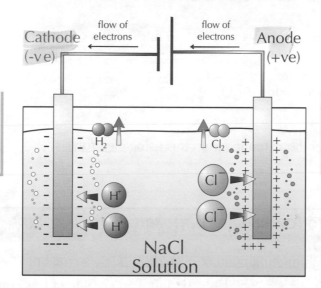

1) At the negative electrode, two hydrogen ions accept two electrons to become one hydrogen molecule.

2) At the positive electrode, two chloride (Cl⁻) ions lose their electrons and become one chlorine molecule.

3) The sodium ions stay in solution because they're more reactive than hydrogen. Hydroxide ions from water are also left behind. This means that sodium hydroxide (NaOH) is left in the solution.

The **half-equations** — *make sure* **the electrons balance**

1) Half equations show the reactions at the electrodes. The main thing is to make sure the number of electrons is the same for both half-equations.

2) For the electrolysis of sodium chloride the half-equations are:

You need to make sure the atoms are balanced too.

Negative Electrode: $2H^+ + 2e^- \rightarrow H_2$
Positive Electrode: $2Cl^- \rightarrow Cl_2 + 2e^-$
or $2Cl^- - 2e^- \rightarrow Cl_2$

For the electrolysis of molten lead bromide (previous page) the half equations would be:
$$Pb^{2+} + 2e^- \rightarrow Pb$$
$$and\ 2Br^- \rightarrow Br_2 + 2e^-$$

Useful products from the *electrolysis of sodium chloride solution*

The products of the electrolysis of sodium chloride solution are pretty useful in industry.

1) Chlorine has many uses, e.g. in the production of bleach and plastics.

2) Sodium hydroxide is a very strong alkali and is used widely in the chemical industry, e.g. to make soap.

Electrolysis of Aluminium

OK — one more example to learn about. This is the electrolysis of <u>aluminium oxide</u>.

*Electrolysis is used to remove **aluminium** from its **ore***

1) Aluminium's a very <u>abundant</u> metal, but it is always found naturally in <u>compounds</u>.

2) Its main ore is <u>bauxite</u>, and after mining and purifying, a <u>white powder</u> is left.

3) This is <u>pure</u> aluminium oxide, Al_2O_3.

4) The <u>aluminium</u> has to be extracted from this using <u>electrolysis</u>.

***Cryolite** is used to **lower** the **temperature** (and costs)*

1) Al_2O_3 has a very <u>high melting point</u> of over <u>2000 °C</u> — so melting it would be very <u>expensive</u>.

2) <u>Instead</u> the aluminium oxide is <u>dissolved</u> in <u>molten cryolite</u> (a less common ore of aluminium).

3) This brings the <u>temperature down</u> to about <u>900 °C</u>, which makes it much <u>cheaper</u> and <u>easier</u>.

4) The <u>electrodes</u> are made of <u>carbon</u> (graphite), a good conductor of electricity (see page 84).

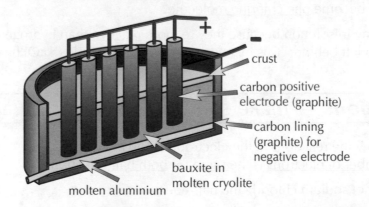

crust

carbon positive electrode (graphite)

carbon lining (graphite) for negative electrode

bauxite in molten cryolite

molten aluminium

Negative Electrode: $Al^{3+} + 3e^- \rightarrow Al$	Positive Electrode: $2O^{2-} \rightarrow O_2 + 4e^-$

5) <u>Aluminium</u> forms at the <u>negative electrode</u> and <u>oxygen</u> forms at the <u>positive electrode</u>.

6) The <u>oxygen</u> then reacts with the <u>carbon</u> in the electrode to produce <u>carbon dioxide</u>. This means that the <u>positive electrodes</u> gradually get 'eaten away' and have to be <u>replaced</u> every now and again.

It's all about lowering the cost...

The electrolysis of aluminium oxide may look <u>a bit different</u> to the examples on the other pages but don't be fooled. It's the same story — the positive aluminium ions go to the <u>negative</u> electrode and the negative oxygen ions are attracted to the <u>positive</u> electrode. Learn the whole lot before you turn over.

Electroplating

Electroplating coats one metal onto the surface of another. It's really useful...

Electroplating uses electrolysis

1) Electroplating uses electrolysis to <u>coat</u> the <u>surface of one metal</u> with <u>another metal</u>, e.g. you might want to electroplate silver onto a brass cup to make it look nice.

2) The <u>negative electrode</u> is the <u>metal object</u> you want to plate and the <u>positive electrode</u> is the <u>pure metal</u> you want it to be plated with. You also need the <u>electrolyte</u> to contain <u>ions</u> of the <u>plating metal</u>. (The ions that plate the metal object come from the solution, while the positive electrode keeps the solution 'topped up'.)

> <u>Example</u>: To electroplate <u>silver</u> onto a <u>brass cup</u>, you'd make the <u>brass cup</u> the negative electrode (to attract the positive silver ions), a lump of <u>pure silver</u> the positive electrode and dip them in a solution of <u>silver ions</u>, e.g. silver nitrate.

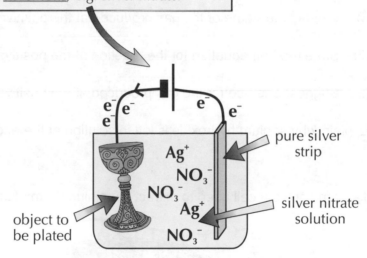

object to be plated — pure silver strip — silver nitrate solution

Ag^+ NO_3^- NO_3^- Ag^+ NO_3^-

3) There are lots of different <u>uses</u> for electroplating:

- <u>Decoration</u>: Silver is <u>attractive</u>, but very <u>expensive</u>. It's much <u>cheaper</u> to plate a brass cup with silver, than it is to make the cup out of solid silver — but it looks just as <u>pretty</u>.
- <u>Conduction</u>: Metals like <u>copper</u> conduct <u>electricity</u> well — because of this they're often used to plate metals for <u>electronic circuits</u> and <u>computers</u>.

Silver electroplated text is worth a fortune...

There are loads of metals you can use for electroplating, but you just need to know about silver and copper plating. The tricky bit is remembering that the metal <u>object you want to plate</u> is the <u>negative electrode</u> and the <u>metal</u> you're plating it with is the <u>positive electrode</u>.

Warm-Up and Exam Questions

It's question time again. You know the drill. Off you go...

Warm-Up Questions

1) What state must an ionic compound be in if it's to be used as an electrolyte?
2) In electrolysis, what is meant by the terms oxidation and reduction?
3) At which electrode are metals deposited during electrolysis?
4) During the electrolysis of molten lead bromide, which gas is produced at the positive electrode?
5) An object requires electroplating. Which electrode should it be used as?

Exam Questions

1   When sodium chloride solution is electrolysed a gas is produced at each electrode.

    (a) (i)   What is the name of the gas produced at the negative electrode?

(1 mark)

         (ii) State the half equation for the reaction at the negative electrode.

(1 mark)

    (b) (i)   What is the name of the gas produced at the positive electrode?

(1 mark)

         (ii) State the half equation for the reaction at the positive electrode.

(1 mark)

         (iii) Suggest one use for the gas produced at the positive electrode.

(1 mark)

    (c) Explain why sodium hydroxide is left in solution at the end of the reaction.

(3 marks)

2   The diagram shows a cell used to extract aluminium from aluminium oxide.

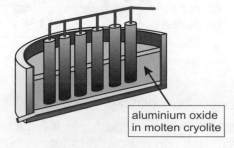

aluminium oxide
in molten cryolite

    (a) Explain why the aluminium oxide is dissolved in molten cryolite.

(2 marks)

    (b) Complete the half-equation below for the reaction at the negative electrode.

$$\underline{\hspace{2cm}} + 3e^- \rightarrow \underline{\hspace{2cm}}$$

(1 mark)

    (c) The positive electrode is made out of carbon. Explain why it will need to be replaced over time.

(3 marks)

Revision Summary for Chemistry 2b

Well, I don't think that was too bad, was it... Four things affect the rate of reactions, there are loads of ways to measure reaction rates and it's all explained by collision theory. Reactions can be endothermic or exothermic, and quite a few of them are reversible. And so on... Easy. Ahem. Well here are some more of those nice questions that you enjoy so much. If there are any you can't answer, go back to the appropriate page, do a bit more learning, then try again.

1) What are the four factors that affect the rate of a reaction?
2) Describe three different ways of measuring the rate of a reaction.
3) A student carries out an experiment to measure the effect of surface area on the reaction between marble and hydrochloric acid. He measures the amount of gas given off at regular intervals.
   a) What factors must he keep constant for it to be a fair test?
   b)*He uses four samples for his experiment:
      Sample A – 10 g of powdered marble
      Sample B – 10 g of small marble chips
      Sample C – 10 g of large marble chips
      Sample D – 5 g of powdered marble
   Sketch a typical set of graphs for this experiment.
4) Explain how higher temperature and larger surface area increase the frequency of successful collisions between particles.
5) What is activation energy?
6) Discuss the advantages and disadvantages of using catalysts in industrial processes.
7) What is an exothermic reaction? Give three examples.
8) The reaction to split ammonium chloride into ammonia and hydrogen chloride is endothermic. What can you say for certain about the reverse reaction?
9) What does the pH scale show?
10) What type of ions are always present in a) acids and   b) alkalis?
11) What is neutralisation? Write down the general equation for neutralisation in terms of ions.
12) Write down the state symbol that means 'dissolved in water'.
13) What is the general equation for reacting an acid with a metal?
14) Name a metal that doesn't react at all with dilute acids.
15) What type of salts do hydrochloric acid and sulfuric acid produce?
16) What type of reaction is "acid + metal oxide", or "acid + metal hydroxide"?
17) Write a balanced symbol equation for the reaction between ammonia and nitric acid. What is the product of this reaction useful for?
18) Suggest a suitable acid and a suitable metal oxide/hydroxide to mix to form the following salts.
   a) copper chloride   b) calcium nitrate   c) zinc sulfate
   d) magnesium nitrate   e) sodium sulfate   f) potassium chloride
19) Iron chloride can made by mixing iron hydroxide (an insoluble base) with hydrochloric acid. Describe the method you would use to produce pure, solid iron chloride in the lab.
20) How can you tell when a neutralisation reaction is complete if both the base and the salt are soluble in water?
21) Give a practical use of precipitation reactions.
22) What is electrolysis? Explain why only liquids can be electrolysed.
23) Draw a detailed diagram with half equations showing the electrolysis of sodium chloride.
24) Give one industrial use of sodium hydroxide and two uses of chlorine.
25) Why is cryolite used during the electrolysis of aluminium oxide?
26) Give two different uses of electroplating.

* Answers on page 247.

Velocity and Distance-Time Graphs

Speed and velocity aren't the same thing, you know. There's more to velocity than meets the eye.

Speed and velocity are both how fast you're going

Speed and velocity are both measured in m/s (or km/h or mph). They both simply say how fast you're going, but there's a subtle difference between them which you need to know:

> Speed is just how fast you're going (e.g. 30 mph or 20 m/s) with no regard to the direction.
> Velocity however must also have the direction specified, e.g. 30 mph north or 20 m/s, 060°.

Seems kinda fussy I know, but they expect you to remember that distinction, so there you go.

Distance-time graphs

These are a very nifty way of describing something travelling through time and space:

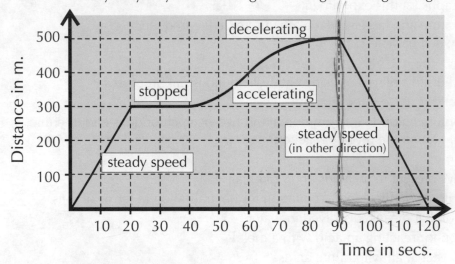

As you probably know, speed = distance ÷ time. So the gradient of a distance-time graph tells you how fast your object is travelling. This is because the gradient is the change in the distance (vertical axis) divided by the change in time (horizontal axis). See — it's easy when you know how.

Very important notes:

1) Gradient = speed.
2) Flat sections are where it's stationary — it's stopped.
3) Straight uphill or downhill sections mean it is travelling at a steady speed.
4) The steeper the graph, the faster it's going.
5) Downhill sections mean it's going back toward its starting point.
6) Curves represent acceleration or deceleration.
7) A steepening curve means it's speeding up (increasing gradient).
8) A levelling off curve means it's slowing down (decreasing gradient).

Calculating speed from a distance-time graph — it's just the gradient

For example the speed of the return section of the graph is:

$$\text{Speed} = \text{gradient} = \frac{\text{vertical}}{\text{horizontal}} = \frac{500}{30} = 16.7 \text{ m/s}$$

Don't forget that you have to use the scales of the axes to work out the gradient. Don't measure in cm!

Acceleration and Velocity-Time Graphs

If something is speeding up, we say that it is accelerating.

Acceleration is how quickly velocity is changing

Acceleration is definitely not the same as velocity or speed.

> 1) Acceleration is how quickly the velocity is changing.
> 2) This change in velocity can be a CHANGE IN SPEED or a CHANGE IN DIRECTION or both.

(You only have to worry about the change in speed bit for calculations.)

Acceleration — the formula:

$$\text{acceleration} = \frac{\text{change in velocity}}{\text{time taken}}$$

Acceleration is the change in velocity (m/s) per second (s), = m/s².

$$\frac{v - u}{a \times t}$$

Here 'v' is the final velocity and 'u' is the initial velocity.

Well, it's just another formula. And it's got a formula triangle.

Mind you, there are two tricky things with this one:

First there's the 'v – u', which means working out the 'change in velocity', as shown in the example below, rather than just putting a simple value for velocity or speed in.

Secondly there's the unit of acceleration, which is m/s².

Not m/s, which is velocity, but m/s². Got it? No? Let's try once more: Not m/s, but m/s².

Example

A skulking cat accelerates from 2 m/s to 6 m/s in 5.6 s. Find its acceleration.

ANSWER: Using the formula triangle:
$a = (v - u) / t = (6 - 2) / 5.6 = 4 \div 5.6 = \underline{0.71 \text{ m/s}^2}$

Acceleration and Velocity-Time Graphs

Here's the distance-time graph's big brother — the <u>velocity-time</u> graph.

Velocity-time graphs

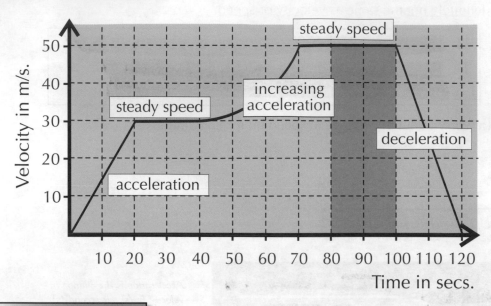

Very important notes:

1) <u>GRADIENT = ACCELERATION</u>.
2) <u>Flat sections</u> represent <u>steady speed</u>.
3) The <u>steeper</u> the graph, the <u>greater</u> the <u>acceleration</u> or <u>deceleration</u>.
4) <u>Uphill</u> sections (/) are <u>acceleration</u>.
5) <u>Downhill</u> sections (\) are <u>deceleration</u>.
6) The <u>area</u> under any section of the graph (or all of it) is equal to the <u>distance travelled in that time interval</u>.
7) A <u>curve</u> means <u>changing acceleration</u>.

Calculating **acceleration**, **velocity** and **distance** from a **V-T** graph

1) The <u>acceleration</u> represented by the <u>first section</u> of the graph is:

$$\underline{\text{Acceleration}} = \underline{\text{gradient}} = \frac{\text{vertical change}}{\text{horizontal change}} = \frac{30}{20} = \underline{1.5 \text{ m/s}^2}$$

2) The <u>velocity</u> at any point is simply found by <u>reading the value</u> off the <u>velocity axis</u>.
3) The <u>distance travelled</u> in any time interval is equal to the <u>area</u> under the graph. For example, the distance travelled between $t = 80$ s and $t = 100$ s is equal to the <u>shaded area</u>, which is equal to $20 \times 50 = \underline{1000 \text{ m}}$.

Don't get distance-time graphs and velocity-time graphs confused

Make sure you know all there is to know about velocity-time graphs — i.e. learn those numbered points. You work out acceleration from the graph simply by applying the acceleration formula — change in velocity is the change on the vertical axis and time taken is the change on the horizontal axis.

Weight, Mass and Gravity

Now for something a bit more attractive — the force of gravity.

Gravitational force is the force of attraction between all masses

Gravity attracts all masses, but you only notice it when one of the masses is really really big, e.g. a planet. Anything near a planet or star is attracted to it very strongly.

This has two important effects:

1) On the surface of a planet, it makes all things accelerate (see page 133) towards the ground (all with the same acceleration, g, which is about 10 m/s² on Earth).

2) It gives everything a weight.

Weight and mass are not the same

1) Mass is just the amount of 'stuff' in an object. For any given object this will have the same value anywhere in the universe.

2) Weight is caused by the pull of the gravitational force. In most questions the weight of an object is just the force of gravity pulling it towards the centre of the Earth.

3) An object has the same mass whether it's on Earth or on the Moon — but its weight will be different. A 1 kg mass will weigh less on the Moon (about 1.6 N) than it does on Earth (about 10 N), simply because the gravitational force pulling on it is less.

4) Weight is a force measured in newtons. It's measured using a spring balance or newton meter. Mass is not a force. It's measured in kilograms with a mass balance (an old-fashioned pair of balancing scales).

The very important formula relating mass, weight and gravity

weight = mass × gravitational field strength

$$W = m \times g$$

The acceleration due to gravity and the gravitational field strength are always the same value, no matter what planet or moon you're on.

1) Remember, weight and mass are not the same. Mass is in kg, weight is in newtons.

2) The letter "g" represents the strength of the gravity and its value is different for different planets. On Earth g ≈ 10 N/kg. On the Moon, where the gravity is weaker, g is only about 1.6 N/kg.

3) This formula is hideously easy to use:

EXAMPLE: What is the weight, in newtons, of a 5 kg mass, both on Earth and on the Moon?

ANSWER: "W = m × g". On Earth: W = 5 × 10 = 50 N   (The weight of the 5 kg mass is 50 N.)
On the Moon: W = 5 × 1.6 = 8 N   (The weight of the 5 kg mass is 8 N.)

See what I mean. Hideously easy — as long as you've learnt what all the letters mean.

Warm-Up and Exam Questions

Here's another set of questions to test your knowledge.
Make sure you can answer them all before you go steaming on.

Warm-Up Questions

1) What does the gradient of a distance-time graph show?
2) What are the units of acceleration? and of mass? and of weight?
3) A car goes from 0 to 30 m/s in 6 seconds. Calculate its acceleration.
4) Name the force that keeps the Earth orbiting around the Sun.

Exam Questions

1   A racing car is driven round a circular track of length 2400 m at a constant speed of 45 m/s.

   (a)   Explain why the car's velocity is not constant.

(1 mark)

   (b)   On one lap, the speed of the car increases from 45 m/s to 59 m/s over a period of
       5 seconds. Calculate its acceleration.

(2 marks)

2   The graph below shows the distance of a shuttle-bus from its start point plotted against time.

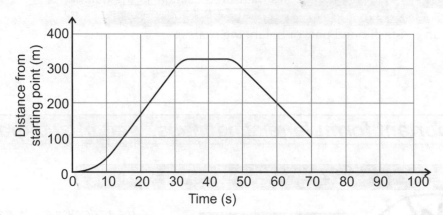

Use the graph to answer the following questions:

   (a)   Between 15 and 30 seconds:

      (i)   how far does the bus travel?

(1 mark)

      (ii)   how fast is the bus going?

(2 marks)

   (b)   For how long does the bus stop?

(1 mark)

   (c)   Describe the bus's speed and direction between 50 and 70 seconds.

(1 mark)

   (d)   Between 70 and 100 seconds, the bus slows, coming to a standstill at 100 s to finish
       up where it started. Show this on the graph.

(1 mark)

Exam Questions

3   The diagram below shows the velocity of a cyclist plotted against time.

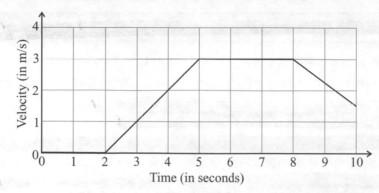

(a)   Describe the motion of the cyclist between 5 and 8 seconds.

(1 mark)

(b)   Describe what is happening to the cyclist's speed between 8 and 10 seconds.

(1 mark)

(c)   Calculate how far the cyclist travelled between 2 and 5 seconds.

(1 mark)

4   A spring increases in length when masses are suspended
from it, as shown. When a metal ball with a mass of 0.1 kg
is suspended from the spring, the spring stretches by 3 cm.

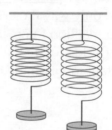

If the experiment was repeated on Mars, the spring would
only be stretched by 1.1 cm.

(a)   Explain why the spring would stretch less on Mars, given
       that the Earth's mass is 5.97×10^{24} kg and the mass of Mars is 6.42×10^{23} kg.

(3 marks)

(b)   Calculate an estimate for g on Mars, assuming that g on Earth is 10 m/s^2.

(3 marks)

5   A stone falls from the edge of a cliff. After falling for 1 second the stone has a downwards
     velocity of 10 m/s.

(a)   Calculate the stone's acceleration during the first second it falls.

(1 mark)

(b)   Assuming no air resistance, calculate the stone's velocity after three seconds
       of falling.

(2 marks)

(c)   The stone has a mass of 0.12 kg. Calculate its weight.

(2 marks)

(d)   Describe the effect of doubling the stone's mass on its acceleration due to gravity.

(1 mark)

6   Which of the following masses exert a gravitational attraction on other masses
     — the Sun, the Earth, a human being, a feather, an atom? Explain your answer.

(1 mark)

Resultant Forces

Gravity isn't the only force in town — there are other forces such as <u>driving forces</u> or
What you need to be able to work out is how all these forces <u>add up together</u>.

Resultant force is the overall force on a point or object

The notion of <u>resultant force</u> is a really important one for you to get your head round

1) In most <u>real</u> situations there are at least <u>two forces</u> acting on an object along any
2) The <u>overall effect</u> of these forces will decide the <u>motion</u> of the object
   — whether it will <u>accelerate</u>, <u>decelerate</u> or stay at a <u>steady speed</u>.
3) If you have a <u>number of forces</u> acting at a single point, you can replace them with
   (so long as the single force has the <u>same effect on the motion</u> as the original forces a
4) If the forces all act along the same line (they're all parallel and act in the same or th
   direction), the <u>overall effect</u> is found by just <u>adding or subtracting</u> them.
5) The overall force you get is called the <u>resultant force</u>.

Example: stationary teapot — all forces balance

1) The force of <u>GRAVITY</u> (or weight) is acting <u>downwards</u>.
2) This causes a <u>REACTION FORCE</u> (see page 140) from the surface <u>pushing up</u> on the object.
3) This is the <u>only way</u> it can be in <u>BALANCE</u>.
4) <u>Without</u> a reaction force, it would <u>accelerate downwards</u> due to the pull of gravity.
5) The <u>resultant</u> force on the teapot is zero: 10 N – 10 N = 0 N.

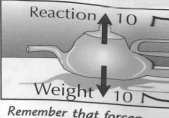

Remember that forces measured in newto

A resultant force means a change in velocity

1) If there is a resultant force acting on an object, then the object will <u>change its state of rest or motion</u>.
2) In other words it causes a <u>change in the object's velocity</u>.

You should be able to find the resultant force acting in a straight li

<u>EXAMPLE:</u> Benny is driving in his car. He applies a driving force of <u>1000 N</u>, but has to overcome air resistance of <u>600 N</u>.
What is the <u>resultant force</u>? Will the car's velocity <u>change</u>?

Driving Force: 1000 N   Air Resistance: 600 N   Resultant Force: 400 N

<u>ANSWER:</u> Say that the forces pointing to the <u>left</u> are pointing in the <u>positive direction</u>.
The resultant force = 1000 N – 600 N = <u>400 N to the left</u>.
If there is a resultant force then there is always an acceleration, so Benny's velocity <u>will</u> change.

Exam Questions

3   The diagram below shows the velocity of a cyclist plotted against time.

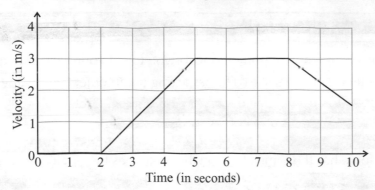

(a)   Describe the motion of the cyclist between 5 and 8 seconds.

(1 mark)

(b)   Describe what is happening to the cyclist's speed between 8 and 10 seconds.

(1 mark)

(c)   Calculate how far the cyclist travelled between 2 and 5 seconds.

(1 mark)

4   A spring increases in length when masses are suspended
from it, as shown. When a metal ball with a mass of 0.1 kg
is suspended from the spring, the spring stretches by 3 cm.

If the experiment was repeated on Mars, the spring would
only be stretched by 1.1 cm.

(a)   Explain why the spring would stretch less on Mars, given
that the Earth's mass is 5.97×10^{24} kg and the mass of Mars is 6.42×10^{23} kg.

(3 marks)

(b)   Calculate an estimate for g on Mars, assuming that g on Earth is 10 m/s².

(3 marks)

5   A stone falls from the edge of a cliff. After falling for 1 second the stone has a downwards
velocity of 10 m/s.

(a)   Calculate the stone's acceleration during the first second it falls.

(1 mark)

(b)   Assuming no air resistance, calculate the stone's velocity after three seconds
of falling.

(2 marks)

(c)   The stone has a mass of 0.12 kg. Calculate its weight.

(2 marks)

(d)   Describe the effect of doubling the stone's mass on its acceleration due to gravity.

(1 mark)

6   Which of the following masses exert a gravitational attraction on other masses
— the Sun, the Earth, a human being, a feather, an atom? Explain your answer.

(1 mark)

Resultant Forces

Gravity isn't the only force in town — there are other forces such as <u>driving forces</u> or <u>air resistance</u>. What you need to be able to work out is how all these forces <u>add up together</u>.

Resultant force *is the* overall force *on a point or object*

The notion of <u>resultant force</u> is a really important one for you to get your head round:

1) In most <u>real</u> situations there are at least <u>two forces</u> acting on an object along any direction.

2) The <u>overall effect</u> of these forces will decide the <u>motion</u> of the object
   — whether it will <u>accelerate</u>, <u>decelerate</u> or stay at a <u>steady speed</u>.

3) If you have a <u>number of forces</u> acting at a single point, you can replace them with a <u>single force</u>
   (so long as the single force has the <u>same effect on the motion</u> as the original forces acting all together).

4) If the forces all act along the same line (they're all parallel and act in the same or the opposite direction), the <u>overall effect</u> is found by just <u>adding or subtracting</u> them.

5) The overall force you get is called the <u>resultant force</u>.

Example: stationary teapot — all forces balance

1) The force of <u>GRAVITY</u> (or weight) is acting <u>downwards</u>.

2) This causes a <u>REACTION FORCE</u> (see page 140)
   from the surface <u>pushing up</u> on the object.

3) This is the <u>only way</u> it can be in <u>BALANCE</u>.

4) <u>Without</u> a reaction force, it would <u>accelerate</u>
   <u>downwards</u> due to the pull of gravity.

5) The <u>resultant</u> force on the teapot is zero: 10 N – 10 N = 0 N.

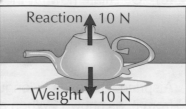

Remember that forces are always measured in newtons (N).

A resultant force *means a* change in velocity

1) If there is a resultant force acting on an object, then the object will <u>change its state of rest or motion</u>.

2) In other words it causes a <u>change in the object's velocity</u>.

You should be able to find the resultant force *acting in a* straight line

<u>EXAMPLE:</u> Benny is driving in his car. He applies a driving force of <u>1000 N</u>,
             but has to overcome air resistance of <u>600 N</u>.
             What is the <u>resultant force</u>? Will the car's velocity <u>change</u>?

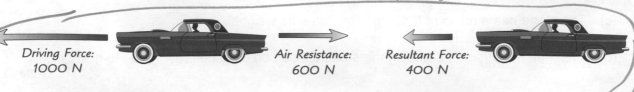

Driving Force: Air Resistance: Resultant Force:
1000 N   600 N   400 N

<u>ANSWER:</u> Say that the forces pointing to the <u>left</u> are pointing in the <u>positive direction</u>.
             The resultant force = 1000 N – 600 N = <u>400 N to the left</u>.
             If there is a resultant force then there is always an acceleration,
             so Benny's velocity <u>will</u> change.

Forces and Acceleration

Around about the time of the Great Plague in the 1660s, a chap called <u>Isaac Newton</u> worked out his <u>Laws of Motion</u>. At first they might seem kind of obscure or irrelevant, but if you can't understand this page then you'll never understand <u>forces and motion</u>.

An object needs a **force** to start **moving**

> If the resultant force on a <u>stationary</u> object is <u>zero</u>, the object will <u>remain stationary</u>.

Things <u>don't just start moving</u> on their own, there has to be a <u>resultant force</u> (see page 138) to get them started.

No resultant force means no change in velocity

> If there is <u>no resultant force</u> on a <u>moving object</u> it'll just carry on moving at the <u>same velocity</u>.

1) When a train or car or bus or anything else is <u>moving</u> at a <u>constant velocity</u> then the <u>forces</u> on it must all be <u>balanced</u>.

2) Never let yourself entertain the <u>ridiculous idea</u> that things need a constant overall force to <u>keep</u> them moving — NO NO NO NO NO NO!

3) To keep going at a <u>steady speed</u>, there must be <u>zero resultant force</u> — and don't you forget it.

A resultant force means acceleration

> If there is a <u>non-zero resultant force</u>, then the object will <u>accelerate</u> in the direction of the force.

1) A non-zero <u>resultant</u> force will always produce <u>acceleration</u> (or deceleration).

2) This "<u>acceleration</u>" can take <u>five</u> different forms: <u>Starting</u>, <u>stopping</u>, <u>speeding up</u>, <u>slowing down</u> and <u>changing direction</u>.

3) On a force diagram, the <u>arrows</u> will be <u>unequal</u>:

<u>Don't ever say</u>: "If something's moving there must be an overall resultant force acting on it". Not so. If there's an <u>overall</u> force it will always <u>accelerate</u>.

You get <u>steady</u> speed when there is <u>zero</u> resultant force.
I wonder how many times I need to say that same thing before you remember it?

Forces and Acceleration

More on forces and acceleration here. The big equation to learn is <u>F = ma</u> — it's a really important one and you <u>will</u> be tested on it. Remember that the F is always the <u>resultant force</u> — that's important too.

A *non-zero* resultant force produces an *acceleration*

Any <u>resultant force</u> will produce <u>acceleration</u>, and this is the <u>formula</u> for it:

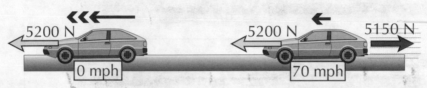

$$F = ma \qquad or \qquad a = F/m$$

m = mass in kilograms (kg)   a = acceleration in metres per second squared (m/s²)
F is the <u>resultant force</u> in newtons (N)

Important! → $\frac{F}{M \times a}$

> **EXAMPLE:** A car of mass of 1750 kg has an engine which provides a driving force of 5200 N. At 70 mph the drag force acting on the car is 5150 N.
>
> Find its acceleration: a) when first setting off from rest   b) at 70 mph.

<u>ANSWER:</u> 1) First draw a force diagram for both cases (no need to show the vertical forces):

5200 N   0 mph   5200 N   5150 N   70 mph

2) Work out the resultant force and acceleration of the car in each case.

Resultant force = 5200 N   Resultant force = 5200 – 5150 = 50 N
a = F/m = 5200 ÷ 1750 = <u>3.0 m/s²</u>   a = F/m = 50 ÷ 1750 = <u>0.03 m/s²</u>

Reaction forces are equal and opposite

> When <u>two objects interact</u>, the forces they exert on each other are <u>equal and opposite</u>.

1) That means if you <u>push</u> something, say a shopping trolley, the trolley will <u>push back</u> against you, <u>just as hard</u>.

2) And as soon as you <u>stop</u> pushing, <u>so does the trolley</u>. Kinda clever really.

3) So far so good. The slightly tricky thing to get your head round is this — if the forces are always equal, <u>how does anything ever go anywhere?</u> The important thing to remember is that the two forces are acting on <u>different objects</u>.

Example — a pair of ice skaters

When skater A pushes on skater B (the '<u>action</u>' force), she feels an equal and opposite force from skater B's hand (the '<u>reaction</u>' force).

Both skaters feel the <u>same sized force</u>, in <u>opposite directions</u>, and so accelerate away from each other.

Skater A will be <u>accelerated</u> more than skater B, though, because she has a smaller mass — remember <u>a = F/m</u>.

Skater A   Skater B   mass = 55 kg   mass = 65 kg

It's the same sort of thing when you go <u>swimming</u>. You <u>push</u> back against the <u>water</u> with your arms and legs, and the water pushes you forwards with an <u>equal-sized force</u> in the <u>opposite direction</u>.

Frictional Force and Terminal Velocity

Friction is found nearly everywhere and it acts to <u>slow down</u> and <u>stop</u> moving objects.
Sometimes friction is a pain, but at other times it's very helpful.

Friction is always there to slow things down

1) If an object has <u>no force</u> propelling it along it will always <u>slow down and stop</u> because of <u>friction</u> (unless you're in space where there's nothing to rub against).
2) Friction always acts in the <u>opposite</u> direction to movement.
3) To travel at a <u>steady</u> speed, the driving force needs to <u>balance</u> the frictional forces.
4) You get friction between <u>two surfaces</u> in contact, or when an object passes <u>through a fluid</u> (<u>drag</u>).

Resistance *or "drag" from* fluids *(air or liquid)*

Most of the resistive forces are caused by <u>air resistance</u> or "<u>drag</u>".
The most important factor <u>by far</u> in <u>reducing drag</u> in fluids is keeping the shape of the object <u>streamlined</u>.

The <u>opposite</u> extreme is a <u>parachute</u> which is about as <u>high drag</u> as you can get — which is, of course, <u>the whole idea</u>.

Drag *increases as the* speed increases

<u>Frictional forces</u> from fluids always <u>increase with speed</u>.
A car has <u>much more</u> friction to <u>work against</u> when travelling at <u>70 mph</u> compared to <u>30 mph</u>.
So at 70 mph the engine has to work <u>much harder</u> just to maintain a <u>steady speed</u>.

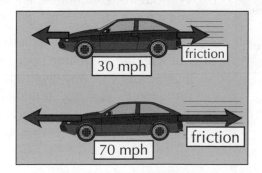

Friction's annoying when it's slowing down your boat, car or lorry...

... but it can be useful too. As well as stopping parachutists ending up as nasty messes on the floor, friction's good for <u>other stuff</u> — e.g. without it, you wouldn't be able to walk or run or skip or write.

Frictional Force and Terminal Velocity

Frictional forces <u>increase</u> with speed — but only up to a certain point. Read on...

Objects falling through fluids reach a terminal velocity

1) When falling objects first <u>set off</u>, the force of gravity is <u>much more</u> than the <u>frictional force</u> slowing them down, so they accelerate.

2) As the <u>speed increases</u> the friction <u>builds up</u>.

3) This gradually <u>reduces</u> the <u>acceleration</u> until eventually the <u>frictional force</u> is <u>equal</u> to the <u>accelerating force</u> and then it won't accelerate any more.

4) It will have reached its maximum speed or <u>terminal velocity</u> and will fall at a steady speed.

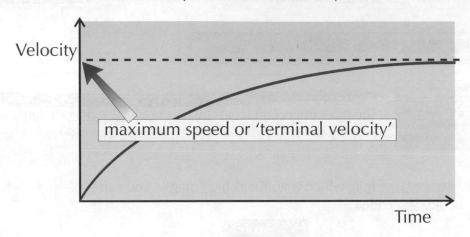

Terminal velocity of falling objects depends on shape and area

1) The <u>accelerating force</u> acting on <u>all</u> falling objects is <u>gravity</u> and it would make them all fall at the <u>same</u> rate, if it wasn't for <u>air resistance</u>.

2) This means that on the Moon, where there's <u>no air</u>, hammers and feathers dropped simultaneously will hit the ground <u>together</u>.

3) However, on Earth, <u>air resistance</u> causes things to fall at <u>different</u> speeds, and the <u>terminal velocity</u> of any object is determined by its <u>drag</u> in <u>comparison</u> to its <u>weight</u>.

4) The frictional force depends on its <u>shape and area</u>.

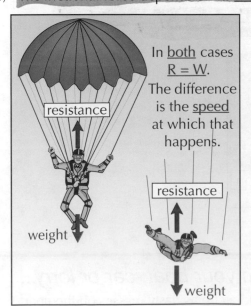

In <u>both</u> cases <u>R = W</u>. The difference is the <u>speed</u> at which that happens.

5) The most important example is the human <u>skydiver</u>.

6) Without his parachute open he has quite a <u>small</u> area and a force of "<u>W = mg</u>" pulling him down.

7) He reaches a <u>terminal velocity</u> of about <u>120 mph</u>.

8) But with the parachute <u>open</u>, there's much more <u>air resistance</u> (at any given speed) and still only the same force "<u>W = mg</u>" pulling him down.

9) This means his <u>terminal velocity</u> comes right down to about <u>15 mph</u>, which is a <u>safe speed</u> to hit the ground at.

Warm-Up and Exam Questions

You're just over a quarter of the way through this section and it's time for some more questions.

Warm-Up Questions

1) A rowing boat is being pulled to shore by two people with a force of 30 N each. A force of 10 N is resisting the movement in the opposite direction. What is the resultant force on the boat?
2) What is the resultant force on a body moving at constant velocity?
3) What happens to the acceleration of a body if the resultant force on it is doubled?
4) In which direction does friction act on a body — with or against the body's motion?

Exam Questions

1 Two parachutists, A and B, are members of the same club.
   (a) The diagram shows the forces acting on parachutist A.

   ↑ 900 N
   ↓ 900 N

   (i) What is the resultant force acting on parachutist A?
       (1 mark)

   (ii) Describe the velocity of parachutist A.
       (1 mark)

   (b) Parachutist B is in free fall.
       The total mass of parachutist B and her equipment is 70 kg.
       (i) What will the force of air resistance on parachutist B be when she reaches terminal velocity? Explain your answer.
       (3 marks)

       (ii) Which parachutist, A or B, would have a higher terminal velocity?
           Explain your answer.
       (3 marks)

   (c) Explain why a parachutist slows down when they open their parachute.
       (1 mark)

2 Stefan weighs 600 newtons. He is accelerating upwards in a lift at 2.5 m/s².
   (a) The forces acting on Stefan are his weight and the upwards force exerted on him by the floor of the lift. Which force is greater? Explain your answer.
       (2 marks)

   (b) Calculate the size of the resultant force acting on Stefan.
       (3 marks)

3 Damien's cricket bat has a mass of 1.2 kg. He uses it to hit a ball with a mass of 160 g forwards with a force of 500 N.
   (a) State the force that the ball exerts on the bat.
       Explain your answer.
       (2 marks)

   (b) Which is greater — the acceleration of the bat or the ball? Explain your answer.
       (2 marks)

Stopping Distances

If you need to stop in a given distance, then the faster you're going, the bigger the braking force you'll need. But there are lots of other factors that also affect how far you travel before you stop...

Many factors affect your total stopping distance

1) If you need to stop in a given distance, then the faster a vehicle's going, the bigger braking force it'll need.

2) Likewise, for any given braking force, the faster you're going, the greater your stopping distance. But in real life it's not quite that simple — if your maximum braking force isn't enough, you'll go further before you stop.

3) The total stopping distance of a vehicle is the distance covered in the time between the driver first spotting a hazard and the vehicle coming to a complete stop.

4) The stopping distance is the sum of the thinking distance and the braking distance.

1) Thinking distance

"The distance the vehicle travels during the driver's reaction time". *The reaction time is the time between the driver spotting a hazard and taking action.*

It's affected by two main factors:

a) How fast you're going — Whatever your reaction time, the faster you're going, the further you'll go.

b) How dopey you are — This is affected by tiredness, drugs, alcohol and a careless blasé attitude.

Bad visibility and distractions can also be a major factor in accidents — lashing rain, messing about with the radio, bright oncoming lights, etc. might mean that a driver doesn't notice a hazard until they're quite close to it. It doesn't affect your thinking distance, but you start thinking about stopping nearer to the hazard, and so you're more likely to crash.

2) Braking distance

"The distance the car travels under the breaking force".

It's affected by four main factors:

a) How fast you're going — The faster you're going, the further it takes to stop.

b) How good your brakes are — All brakes must be checked and maintained regularly. Worn or faulty brakes will let you down catastrophically just when you need them the most, i.e. in an emergency.

c) How good the tyres are — Tyres should have a minimum tread depth of 1.6 mm in order to be able to get rid of the water in wet conditions. Leaves, diesel spills and muck on the road can greatly increase the braking distance, and cause the car to skid too.

d) How good the grip is — This depends on three things:
1) road surface, 2) weather conditions, 3) tyres.

The figures below for typical stopping distances are from the Highway Code. It's frightening to see just how far it takes to stop when you're going at 70 mph.

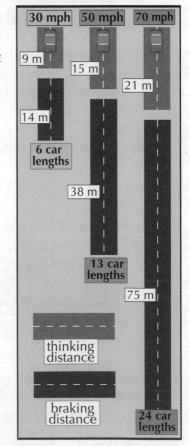

Wet or icy roads are always much more slippy than dry roads, but often you only discover this when you try to brake hard. You don't have as much grip, so you travel further before stopping.

Work Done

Work (like a lot of things) means something slightly different in Physics than it does in everyday life.

Doing *work* involves *transferring energy*

When a force moves an object through a distance,
ENERGY IS TRANSFERRED and WORK IS DONE.

That statement sounds far more complicated than it needs to. Try this:

1) Whenever something moves, something else is providing some sort of 'effort' to move it.

2) The thing putting the effort in needs a supply of energy (like fuel or food or electricity etc.).

3) It then does 'work' by moving the object — and one way or another it transfers the energy it receives (as fuel) into other forms.

4) Whether this energy is transferred 'usefully' (e.g. by lifting a load) or is 'wasted' (e.g. lost as heat through friction), you can still say that 'work is done'. Just like Batman and Bruce Wayne, 'work done' and 'energy transferred' are indeed 'one and the same'. (And they're both given in joules.)

Important!

It's just *another trivial formula*:

work done = force × distance

$$\frac{W}{F \times d}$$

Whether the force is friction or weight or tension in a rope, it's always the same. To find how much energy has been transferred (in joules), you just multiply the force in N by the distance moved in m.

Example

Some kids drag an old tractor tyre 5 m over rough ground.
They pull with a total force of 340 N. Find the energy transferred.

ANSWER: W = F×d = 340 × 5 = 1700 J.

Remember "energy transferred" and "work done" are the same thing

By lifting something up you do work by transferring chemical energy to gravitational potential energy (p.146).

Potential and Kinetic Energy

<u>Gravitational potential energy</u> is the energy an object has because of its height. <u>Kinetic energy</u> is the energy something has when it is moving. But it isn't just the definitions of them you need to know...

Gravitational potential energy is energy *due to height*

gravitational potential energy = mass × g × height

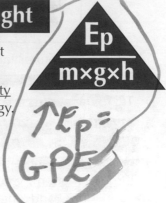

1) <u>Gravitational potential energy</u> (measured in joules) is the energy that an object has by virtue of (because of) its <u>vertical position</u> in a <u>gravitational field</u>.

2) When an object is raised vertically, <u>work is done</u> against the <u>force of gravity</u> (it takes effort to lift it up) and the object gains gravitational potential energy.

3) On <u>Earth</u> the gravitational field strength (g) is approximately <u>10 N/kg</u>.

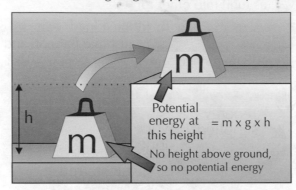

Potential energy at this height = m × g × h

No height above ground, so no potential energy

<u>EXAMPLE</u>: An object of mass 47 kg is slowly raised through 6.3 m. Find the gain in potential energy.

<u>ANSWER</u>: Just plug the numbers into the formula:

E_p = mgh = 47 × 10 × 6.3 = <u>2961 J</u>   (<u>Joules</u> because it's <u>energy</u>.)

Kinetic energy is energy of *movement*

Anything that's <u>moving</u> has <u>kinetic energy</u>.
There's a slightly <u>tricky formula</u> for it, so you have to concentrate a little bit <u>harder</u> for this one.

kinetic energy = ½ × mass × speed^2

$$\frac{E_k}{\frac{1}{2} \times m \times v^2}$$

<u>EXAMPLE</u>: A car of mass 2450 kg is travelling at 38 m/s.
            Calculate its kinetic energy.

<u>ANSWER</u>: It's pretty easy. You just plug the numbers into the formula — but watch the 'v²'!
            Ek = ½mv² = ½ × 2450 × 38² = <u>1 768 900 J</u> (<u>Joules</u> because it's <u>energy</u>.)

Remember, the <u>kinetic energy</u> of something depends both on <u>mass</u> and <u>speed</u>.
The <u>more it weighs</u> and the <u>faster it's going</u>, the <u>bigger</u> its kinetic energy will be.

small mass, not fast
low kinetic energy

big fast
lorries Ltd

big mass, very fast
high kinetic energy

Kinetic Energy

Moving objects have kinetic energy — to <u>stop</u> them, that energy needs to be <u>transferred</u> into other types.

Kinetic energy transferred is **work done**

When a car is **moving** *it has* **kinetic energy**

Conservation of energy states that energy can never be created or destroyed — only converted into different forms.

1) A <u>moving car</u> can have a lot of <u>kinetic energy</u>. To slow a car down this kinetic energy needs to be <u>converted into other types of energy</u> (using the law of conservation of energy).

2) To stop a car, the <u>kinetic energy</u> ($\frac{1}{2}mv^2$) has to be <u>converted to heat energy</u> as <u>friction</u> between the <u>wheels</u> and the <u>brake pads</u>, causing the <u>temperature</u> of the brakes to <u>increase</u>:

> **Kinetic Energy Transferred = Work Done by Brakes**
> $$\frac{1}{2} \times m \times v^2 = F \times d$$

m = <u>mass</u> of car and passengers (in kg)
v = <u>speed</u> of car (in m/s)
F = maximum <u>braking force</u> (in N)
d = <u>braking distance</u> (in m)

Falling objects convert E_P *into* E_K...

When something falls, its <u>potential energy</u> (see page 146) is <u>converted into</u> <u>kinetic energy</u>. So the <u>further</u> it falls, the <u>faster</u> it goes.

> **Kinetic energy <u>gained</u> = Potential Energy <u>lost</u>**

...*and some of this* E_K *is* **transferred** *into* **heat** *and* **sound**

1) When <u>meteors</u> and <u>space shuttles</u> enter the atmosphere, they have a <u>very high kinetic energy</u>.

2) <u>Friction</u> due to collisions with particles in the atmosphere transfers some of their kinetic energy to <u>heat energy</u> and <u>work is done</u>.

3) The temperatures can become so <u>extreme</u> that <u>most</u> meteors <u>burn up</u> completely and never hit the Earth.

4) <u>Only the biggest meteors make it through</u> to the Earth's surface — these are called <u>meteorites</u>.

5) Space shuttles have heat shields made from <u>special</u> <u>materials</u> which lose heat <u>quickly</u>, allowing the shuttle to re-enter the atmosphere <u>without burning up</u>.

Ek and Ep are closely linked for falling objects

The braking distance of a vehicle increases as speed increases. <u>Doubling</u> the speed <u>increases</u> the braking distance by a factor of <u>four</u>, and <u>tripling</u> the speed increases it by <u>nine times</u>. It's all do with v^2.

Forces and Elasticity

Forces aren't just important for cars and falling objects — you can <u>stretch things</u> with them as well.

Elastic objects store energy as elastic potential energy

1) When you apply a force to an object you may cause it to <u>stretch</u> and <u>change in shape</u>.

2) Any object that can <u>go back</u> to its <u>original shape</u> after the force has been removed is an <u>elastic object</u>.

3) <u>Work is done</u> to an elastic object to <u>change</u> its shape.
   This energy is not lost but is <u>stored</u> by the object as <u>elastic potential energy</u>.

4) The elastic potential energy is then <u>converted to kinetic energy</u> when the <u>force is removed</u> and the object returns to its original shape, e.g. when a spring or an elastic band bounces back.

Extension of an elastic object is directly proportional to force...

If a spring is supported at the top and then a weight attached to the bottom, it <u>stretches</u>.

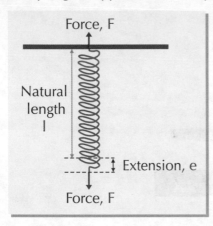

1) The <u>extension</u>, <u>e</u>, of a stretched spring (or other elastic object) is <u>directly proportional</u> to the load or <u>force</u> applied, <u>F</u>. The extension is measured in metres, and the force is measured in newtons.

2) This is the equation you need to learn:

$$F = k \times e$$

3) k is the <u>spring constant</u>. Its value depends on the <u>material</u> that you are stretching and it's measured in newtons per metre (N/m).

...but this stops working when the force is great enough

There's a <u>limit</u> to the amount of force you can apply to an object for the extension to keep on increasing <u>proportionally</u>.

1) The graph shows <u>force against extension</u> for an elastic object.

2) For small forces, force and extension are <u>proportional</u>. So the first part of the graph shows a straight-line relationship between force and extension.

3) There is a <u>maximum</u> force that the elastic object can take and still extend proportionally. This is known as the <u>limit of proportionality</u> and is shown on the graph at the point marked P.

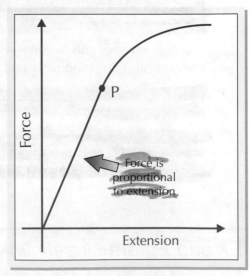

Force is proportional to extension

Warm-Up and Exam Questions

There were lots of definitions and equations to get to grips with on the last five pages.
Try these questions to see what you can remember.

Warm-Up Questions

1) What is meant by 'thinking distance' as part of the total stopping distance of a car?
2) What must be added to thinking distance to find the total stopping distance of a car?
3) Why can 'work done' be measured in the same units as energy?
4) What is gravitational potential energy?
5) Why don't many meteors hit the Earth?
6) What type of energy does an elastic object store when work is done to it?
7) What is the limit of proportionality?

Exam Questions

1   The graph below shows how thinking distance and stopping distance vary with speed.

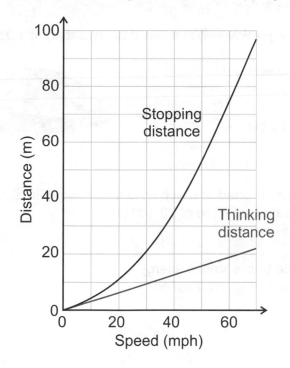

(a)   Use the graph to determine the following distances for a car travelling at 40 mph.
  (i)   Thinking distance
  (ii) Total stopping distance
  (iii) Braking distance

(3 marks)

(b)   Which is greater at 50 miles per hour, thinking distance or braking distance?

(1 mark)

(c)   Is stopping distance proportional to speed?
    Explain how this can be seen from the graph.

(2 marks)

If you need help with part c) — see page 13.

Exam Questions

2 A teacher is setting up an experiment.

(a) He lifts a 2.5 kg mass from the floor onto a table that is 1.3 m tall.
Calculate the gain in gravitational potential energy of the mass.
(Use g = 10 N/kg.)

(2 marks)

(b) The mass is accidentally knocked off the table and falls to the floor.
Calculate the speed of the mass as it hits the floor.

(3 marks)

(c) The teacher shows his students an experiment to show how
a spring extends when masses are hung from it. When a force
of 4 N is applied to the spring, the spring extends by 3.5 cm.

Calculate the spring constant of the spring.
Clearly show how you work out your answer.

(3 marks)

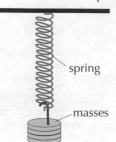

3 A train with a mass of 40 000 kg is driven 700 m while accelerating at 1.05 m/s^2.

(a) Calculate the driving force acting on
the train. Ignore any friction.

(2 marks)

(b) Calculate the work done by the
driving force.

(2 marks)

(c) The train reaches a constant speed at which its kinetic energy is 29 400 000 J.
It then decelerates with a braking force of 29 400 N.
Calculate its braking distance.

(2 marks)

(d) What form of energy is the train's kinetic energy
transformed into when the brakes are applied?

(1 mark)

4 A car with a mass of 2750 kg is travelling at 12 m/s.

(a) Calculate its kinetic energy.

(2 marks)

(b) A van with a mass of 3120 kg is travelling at the same speed.
Which has more kinetic energy?

(1 mark)

(c) The car accelerates and reaches a constant speed at which its kinetic energy
is 550 000 J. The car then brakes and comes to rest in 25 m.
Calculate its braking force.

(2 marks)

Power

Power is a concept that pops up in both <u>forces</u> and <u>electricity</u>. This is because, at its most fundamental level, power is just about the rate of <u>energy transferred</u> — and energy is transferred wherever you look.

Power is the "rate of doing work" — i.e. how much per second

<u>Power</u> is <u>not</u> the same thing as <u>force</u>, nor <u>energy</u>. A <u>powerful</u> machine is not necessarily one which can exert a strong <u>force</u> (though it usually ends up that way).

A <u>powerful</u> machine is one which transfers <u>a lot of energy in a short space of time</u>.

This is the <u>very easy formula</u> for power:

$$\text{Power} = \frac{\text{Work done (or energy transferred)}}{\text{Time taken}} \qquad P = \frac{E}{t}$$

Power is measured in watts (or J/s)

The proper unit of power is the <u>watt</u>. <u>One watt = 1 joule of energy transferred per second</u>. <u>Power</u> means "how much energy <u>per second</u>", so <u>watts</u> are the same as "<u>joules per second</u>" (J/s). Don't ever say "watts per second" — it's <u>nonsense</u>.

> <u>EXAMPLE</u>: A motor transfers 4.8 kJ of useful energy in 2 minutes. Find its power output.
>
> <u>ANSWER</u>: P = E / t = 4800/120 = 40 W (or 40 J/s)
>
> (Note that the kJ had to be turned into J, and the minutes into seconds.)

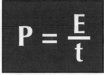

4.8 kJ of useful energy in 2 minutes

Calculating your power output

There are a few different ways to measure the power output of a <u>person</u>:

a) The timed run upstairs:

In this case the "<u>energy transferred</u>" is the <u>potential energy you gain</u> (= mgh). Hence <u>Power = mgh/t</u>

62 kg   12 m   Time taken =14 s

Power output
= En. transferred/time
= mgh/t
= (62×10×12)÷14
= <u>531 W</u>

b) The timed acceleration:

This time the <u>energy transferred</u> is the <u>kinetic energy you gain</u> (= ½mv²). Hence <u>Power = ½mv²/t</u>

62 kg   0 → 8 m/s   time taken = 4 s

Power output
= En. transferred/time
= ½mv²/t
= (½×62×8²)÷4
= <u>496 W</u>

To get <u>accurate results</u> from these experiments, you have to do them several times and find an <u>average</u>.

Watt is the unit of power?

Power is the amount of energy transferred per second, and it's measured in <u>watts</u>. The watt is named after James Watt, a Scottish inventor and engineer who did a lot of work on steam engines in the 1700s. Nice. Make sure you <u>learn the formula</u> and power questions should be easy.

Momentum and Collisions

A <u>large</u> rugby player running very <u>fast</u> is going to be a lot harder to stop than a scrawny one out for a Sunday afternoon stroll — that's <u>momentum</u> for you.

Momentum = mass × velocity

1) Momentum (p) is a <u>property</u> of <u>moving objects</u>.

2) The <u>greater</u> the <u>mass</u> of an object and the <u>greater</u> its <u>velocity</u> (see page 132) the <u>more momentum</u> the object has.

3) Momentum is a <u>vector</u> quantity — it has size <u>and</u> direction (like <u>velocity</u>, but not speed).

Momentum (kg m/s) = Mass (kg) × Velocity (m/s)

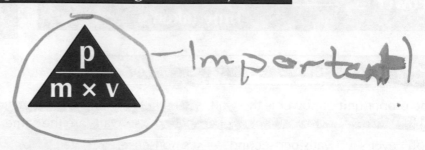

$$\frac{p}{m \times v}$$

— Important!

*Momentum **before** = momentum **after***

In a <u>closed system</u>, the total momentum <u>before</u> an event (e.g. a collision) is the same as <u>after</u> the event. This is called <u>Conservation of Momentum</u>.

A <u>closed system</u> is just a fancy way of saying that no external forces act.

Example 1: Collisions

Two skaters approach each other, collide and move off together as shown. At what velocity do they move after the collision?

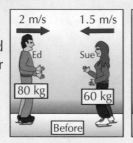

2 m/s 1.5 m/s | velocity (v) = ?
Ed | Sue
80 kg | 60 kg | (80+60) kg
Before | After

1) Choose which direction is <u>positive</u>.
   I'll say "<u>positive</u>" means "<u>to the right</u>".

2) <u>Total momentum before</u> collision
   = momentum of Ed + momentum of Sue
   = {80 × 2} + {60 × (−1.5)}
   = <u>70 kg m/s</u>

3) <u>Total momentum after</u> collision
   = momentum of Ed and Sue together
   = <u>140 × v</u>

4) So 140v = 70, i.e. <u>v = 0.5 m/s to the right</u>

Example 2: Explosions

A gun fires a bullet as shown. At what speed does the gun move backwards?

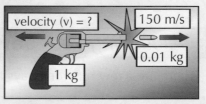

velocity (v) = ? | 150 m/s
1 kg | 0.01 kg

1) Choose which direction is <u>positive</u>.
   Again, I reckon "<u>positive</u>" means "<u>to the right</u>".

2) <u>Total momentum before</u> firing = <u>0 kg m/s</u>

3) <u>Total momentum after</u> firing
   = momentum of bullet + momentum of gun
   = (0.01 × 150) + (1 × v)
   = <u>1.5 + v</u>

   This is the gun's recoil.

   The momentum of a system <u>before</u> an explosion is <u>zero</u>, so, due to <u>conservation of momentum</u>, the total momentum after an explosion is <u>zero too</u>.

4) So 1.5 + v = 0, i.e. v = −1.5 m/s
   So the gun moves <u>backwards</u> at <u>1.5 m/s</u>.

Momentum's a pretty fundamental bit of Physics — learn it well

Momentum is always <u>conserved</u> in collisions and explosions when there are no external forces acting.

Car Design and Safety

Nowadays, cars usually come with lots of different safety features all designed to slow you down over a longer time in a crash. This page is all about how they work.

Forces cause changes in momentum

1) When a force acts on an object, it causes a change in momentum.

2) A larger force means a faster change of momentum (and so a greater acceleration).

3) Likewise, if someone's momentum changes very quickly (like in a car crash), the forces on the body will be very large, and more likely to cause injury.

4) This is why cars are designed with safety features that slow people down over a longer time when they have a crash — the longer it takes for a change in momentum, the smaller the force.

Cars are designed to convert kinetic energy safely in a crash

1) If a car crashes it will slow down very quickly — this means that a lot of kinetic energy is converted into other forms of energy in a short amount of time, which can be dangerous for the people inside.

2) In a crash, there'll be a big change in momentum over a very short time, so the people inside the car experience huge forces that could be fatal.

3) Cars are designed to convert the kinetic energy of the car and its passengers in a way that is safest for the car's occupants. They often do this by increasing the time over which momentum changes happen, which lessens the forces on the passengers.

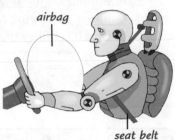

airbag

seat belt

Examples

> CRUMPLE ZONES at the front and back of the car crumple up on impact.
> - The car's kinetic energy is converted into other forms of energy by the car body as it changes shape.
> - Crumple zones increase the impact time, decreasing the force produced by the change in momentum.

> SEAT BELTS stretch slightly, increasing the time taken for the wearer to stop. This reduces the forces acting in the chest. Some of the kinetic energy of the wearer is absorbed by the seat belt stretching.

> SIDE IMPACT BARS are strong metal tubes fitted into car door panels. They help direct the kinetic energy of the crash away from the passengers to other areas of the car, such as the crumple zones.

> AIR BAGS also slow you down more gradually and prevent you from hitting hard surfaces inside the car.

Car Design and Safety

Here's a bit more about the design of cars.
First up, a new type of braking system that stores energy rather than wasting it. How handy.

Brakes do work against the kinetic energy of the car

1) When you apply the brakes to slow down a car, work is done (see page 145).

2) The brakes reduce the kinetic energy of the car by transferring it into heat (and sound) energy (see page 147).

3) In traditional braking systems that would be the end of the story, but new regenerative braking systems used in some electric or hybrid cars make use of the energy, instead of converting it all into heat during braking.

Regenerative braking systems:

1) Regenerative brakes use the system that drives the vehicle to do the majority of the braking.

2) Rather than converting the kinetic energy of the vehicle into heat energy, the brakes put the vehicle's motor into reverse. With the motor running backwards, the wheels are slowed.

3) At the same time, the motor acts as an electric generator, converting kinetic energy into electrical energy that is stored as chemical energy in the vehicle's battery. This is the advantage of regenerative brakes — they store the energy of braking rather than wasting it. It's a nifty chain of energy transfer.

Cars have different power ratings

1) The size and design of car engines determine how powerful they are.

2) The more powerful an engine is, the more energy it transfers from its fuel every second, and so the faster its top speed can be.

3) E.g. the power output of a typical small car will be around 50 kW and a sports car will be about 100 kW (some are much higher).

Sports car power = 100 kW

Small car power = 50 kW

4) Cars are also designed to be aerodynamic. This means that they are shaped in such a way that air flows very easily and smoothly past them, so minimising their air resistance.

5) Cars reach their top speed when the resistive force equals the driving force provided by the engine (see page 142).

6) So, with less air resistance to overcome, the car can reach a higher speed before this happens. Aerodynamic cars therefore have higher top speeds.

The more powerful an engine, the faster it transfers energy from fuel

The more powerful the engine of a car, generally the faster its top speed will be. Make sure you can say why cars are designed to be aerodynamic — it isn't just so they look better.

Warm-Up and Exam Questions

The end of this section is getting closer. But don't shed a tear — try these questions instead.

Warm-Up Questions

1) What is meant by power in terms of work done?
2) Give the equation for momentum.
3) What is meant by the conservation of momentum?
4) Name two safety features that increase the time taken for the car driver to stop in a collision.
5) Give two factors that will affect the top speed of a car.

Exam Questions

1   The images below show two different cars, car A and car B.

Car A

Car B

(a)   Car A has side impact bars.
      Describe how side impact bars work during a crash to help protect passengers.

(2 marks)

(b)   Both cars have seat belts.
      Explain why seat belts are made of a slightly stretchy material.

(3 marks)

(c)   Car A is more aerodynamic than car B.
      Explain why aerodynamic cars tend to have higher top speeds.

(3 marks)

2   Two ice hockey players are skating towards the puck. Player A has a mass of 100 kg and is travelling right at 6 m/s. Player B has a mass 80 kg and is travelling left at 9 m/s.

(a)   Calculate the momentum of:
      (i)   Player A

(2 marks)

      (ii)   Player B

(2 marks)

(b)   The two players collide and become joined together.
      (i)   Calculate the speed of the two joined players just after the collision.

(3 marks)

      (ii)   State the direction they move.

(1 mark)

Exam Questions

3   The picture shown below is a hybrid bus used for public transport in a city centre.

(a)   The engine of the bus has a power rating of 90 kW.
      Calculate the energy transferred by the engine in 5 seconds.

(2 marks)

(b)   The bus has a regenerative braking system which is used to store energy in the
      battery of the bus.

      (i)   Explain how a regenerative braking system works.

(3 marks)

      (ii)   Give **one** advantage of regenerative braking systems over
             traditional braking systems.

(1 mark)

4   A runner of mass 60 kg is taking part in some training exercises.
     It takes him 50 s to run from the bottom to the top of a hill which
     is 35 m high.

     Calculate his power during the run. (Assume g = 10 N/kg).
     Clearly show how you work out your answer.

(4 marks)

5   A fast-moving neutron collides with a uranium-235 atom and bounces off.
     The diagram shows the particles before and after the collision.

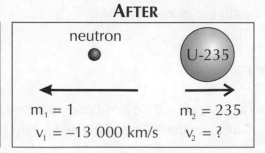

BEFORE		AFTER	
neutron	U-235	neutron	U-235
$m_1 = 1$	$m_2 = 235$	$m_1 = 1$	$m_2 = 235$
$v_1 = 14\ 000$ km/s	$v_2 = 0$ km/s	$v_1 = -13\ 000$ km/s	$v_2 = ?$

     Find the velocity of the U-235 atom after the collision.

(3 marks)

Static Electricity

Static electricity is all about charges which are <u>not</u> free to move, e.g. in insulating materials. This causes them to build up in one place and it often ends with a <u>spark</u> or a <u>shock</u> when they do finally move.

Build-up of **static** is caused by **friction**

1) When certain <u>insulating</u> materials are <u>rubbed</u> together, negatively charged electrons will be <u>scraped off one</u> and <u>dumped</u> on the other.

2) This'll leave a <u>positive</u> static charge on one and a <u>negative</u> static charge on the other.

3) <u>Which way</u> the electrons are transferred <u>depends</u> on the <u>two materials</u> involved.

4) Electrically charged objects <u>attract</u> small objects placed near them.
(Try this: rub a balloon on a woolly pully — then put it near tiddly bits of paper and watch them jump.)

5) The classic examples are <u>polythene</u> and <u>acetate</u> rods being rubbed with a <u>cloth duster</u>, as shown in the diagrams.

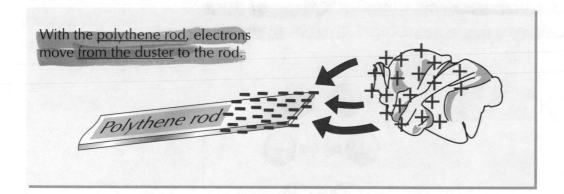

With the <u>polythene rod</u>, electrons move <u>from the duster</u> to the rod.

Polythene rod

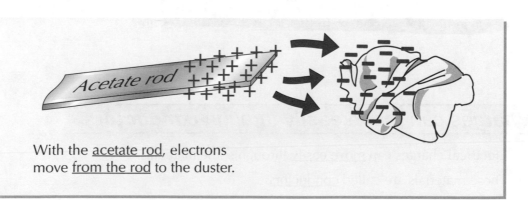

Acetate rod

With the <u>acetate rod</u>, electrons move <u>from the rod</u> to the duster.

Static electricity is caused by electrons being transferred

Static electricity's great fun. You must have tried it — rubbing a balloon against your jumper and trying to get it to stick to the ceiling. It really works... well, sometimes. Bad hair days are caused by static too — it builds up on your hair, so your strands of hair repel each other. Which is nice...

Static Electricity

Only electrons move — *never the positive charges*

1) <u>Watch out for this in exams</u>. Both +ve and –ve electrostatic charges are only ever produced by the movement of <u>electrons</u>.

2) The positive charges <u>definitely do not move</u>!

3) A positive static charge is always caused by electrons <u>moving</u> away elsewhere.

4) The material that <u>loses</u> the electrons loses some negative charge, and is <u>left with an equal positive charge</u> (see previous page). Don't forget!

Like charges repel, *opposite* charges attract

1) This is <u>easy</u> and, I'd have thought, <u>kind of obvious</u>. When two electrically charged objects are brought close together they <u>exert a force</u> on one another.

2) Two things with <u>opposite</u> electric charges are <u>attracted</u> to each other.

3) Two things with the <u>same</u> electric charge will <u>repel</u> each other.

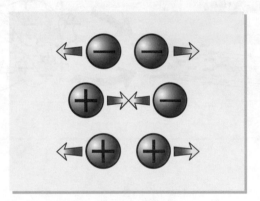

4) These forces get <u>weaker</u> the <u>further apart</u> the two things are.

Charges can *move easily* through *conductors*

1) Electrical charges can <u>move easily</u> through some materials.

2) These materials are called <u>conductors</u>.

3) <u>Metals</u> are known to be <u>good</u> conductors.

Don't forget that opposites attract

The bog standard electrical charge carrier is the electron. Those little devils get just about everywhere in metals, taking charge pretty much wherever you want it. But in insulators they're stuck and can't move easily — it's only when they're manually scraped off that they ever get to go anywhere.

Warm-Up and Exam Questions

By this point you'll probably have worked out that static electricity isn't the most exciting of topics. Don't worry — there are just these few questions before you get on to much more interesting stuff.

Warm-Up Questions

1) Is a polythene rod an insulator or a conductor?
2) What are the two types of electric charge?
3) Do similar charges attract or repel one another?
4) Are metals good or bad insulators?

Exam Questions

1   Jane hangs an uncharged balloon from a thread. She brings a negatively charged polythene rod towards the balloon. The diagram below shows how the positive and negative charges in the balloon rearrange themselves when she does this.

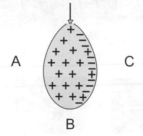

(a)   In which of the positions labelled A, B and C on the diagram did Jane hold the polythene rod? Explain your answer.

(2 marks)

(b)   Jane brings the rod closer to the balloon. Explain why the balloon swings towards it.

(2 marks)

2   A positive static charge builds up on a cloth when it is used to wipe a surface.

(a)   Describe the movement of charged particles that gives the cloth its charge.

(1 mark)

(b)   The cloth has a relative charge of +23. Circle the correct answer below to show the charge on the surface.

| +23 | +46 | -46 | -23 |

(1 mark)

(c)   The cloth is an insulator so charges can't easily flow through it. Give **one** example of a material that charges can flow easily through.

(1 mark)

Current and Potential Difference

Isn't <u>electricity</u> great. Mind you it's pretty bad news if the <u>words</u> don't mean anything to you...

1) <u>Current</u> is the <u>flow</u> of electric charge round the circuit. Current will <u>only flow</u> through a component if there is a <u>potential difference</u> across that component. Unit: ampere, A.

2) <u>Potential difference</u> is the <u>driving force</u> that pushes the current round. Unit: volt, V.

3) <u>Resistance</u> is anything in the circuit which <u>slows the flow down</u>. Unit: ohm, Ω.

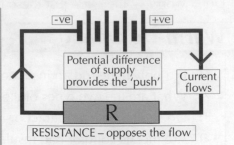

Potential difference of supply provides the 'push'

Current flows

RESISTANCE – opposes the flow

> The <u>greater the resistance</u> across a component, the <u>smaller the current</u> that flows (for a given potential difference across the component).

Total charge through a circuit depends on current and time

1) <u>Current</u> is the <u>rate of flow</u> of <u>charge</u>. When <u>current</u> (I) flows past a point in a circuit for a length of <u>time</u> (t) then the <u>charge</u> (Q) that has passed is given by this formula:

$$\text{Current} = \frac{\text{Charge}}{\text{Time}} \qquad I = \frac{Q}{t}$$

I – Current
Q – Charge

2) <u>Current</u> is measured in <u>amperes</u> (A), <u>charge</u> is measured in <u>coulombs</u> (C), <u>time</u> is measured in <u>seconds</u> (s).

3) <u>More charge</u> passes around the circuit when a <u>bigger current</u> flows.

> <u>EXAMPLE</u>: A battery charger passes a current of 2.5 A through a cell over a period of 4 hours. How much charge does the charger transfer to the cell altogether?
>
> <u>ANSWER</u>: Q = I × t = 2.5 × (4 × 60 × 60) = 36 000 C (36 kC).

Potential difference (P.D.) is the work done per unit charge

1) The potential difference (or <u>voltage</u>) is the <u>work done</u> (the energy transferred, measured in joules, J) <u>per coulomb of charge</u> that passes between <u>two points</u> in an electrical circuit.

2) It's given by this formula:

$$\text{P.D.} = \frac{\text{Work done}}{\text{Charge}}$$

3) So, the potential difference across an electrical component is the <u>amount of energy</u> that is transferred by that electrical component (e.g. to light and heat energy by a bulb) <u>per unit of charge</u>.

4) <u>Voltage</u> and <u>potential difference</u> mean the <u>same thing</u>. You can use <u>either</u> in your exam and scoop up the marks (so long as you use it <u>correctly</u>).

Circuits — The Basics

Formulas are mighty pretty and all, but you might have to design some <u>electrical circuits</u> as well one day. For that you're going to need <u>circuit symbols</u>...

Circuit symbols you should know — learn them well

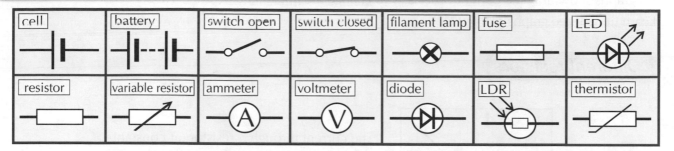

cell	battery	switch open	switch closed	filament lamp	fuse	LED
resistor	variable resistor	ammeter	voltmeter	diode	LDR	thermistor

The standard test circuit

This is the circuit you use if you want to know the <u>resistance of a component</u>. You find the resistance by measuring the <u>current through</u> and the <u>potential difference across</u> the component. It is absolutely the most <u>bog standard</u> circuit you could know. <u>So know it</u>.

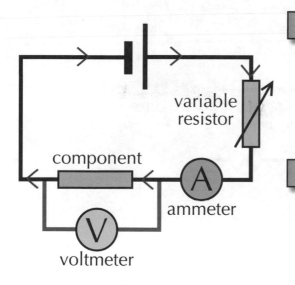

The ammeter

1) Measures the <u>current</u> (in <u>amps</u>) flowing through the component.
2) Must be placed <u>in series</u> (see page 166).
3) Can be put <u>anywhere</u> in series in the <u>main circuit</u>, but <u>never</u> in parallel like the voltmeter.

The voltmeter

1) Measures the <u>potential difference</u> (in <u>volts</u>) across the component.
2) Must be placed <u>in parallel</u> (see page 168) around the <u>component</u> under test — <u>NOT</u> around the variable resistor or the battery!

Five important points

1) This <u>very basic</u> circuit is used for testing <u>components</u>, and for getting <u>V-I graphs</u> from them (see next page).
2) The <u>component</u>, the <u>ammeter</u> and the <u>variable resistor</u> are all in <u>series</u>, which means they can be put in <u>any order</u> in the main circuit. The <u>voltmeter</u>, on the other hand, can only be placed <u>in parallel</u> around the component under test, as shown. Anywhere else is a definite <u>no-no</u>.
3) As you <u>vary</u> the <u>variable resistor</u> it alters the <u>current</u> flowing through the circuit.
4) This allows you to take several <u>pairs of readings</u> from the <u>ammeter</u> and <u>voltmeter</u>.
5) You can then <u>plot</u> these values for <u>current</u> and <u>voltage</u> on a <u>V-I graph</u> and find the <u>resistance</u>.

Resistance and V = I × R

With your current and your potential difference measured, you can now make some graphs...

Three *hideously important* **potential difference-current graphs**

V-I graphs show how the <u>current</u> varies as you <u>change</u> the <u>potential difference</u> (P.D.).
Learn these three graphs really well:

Different resistors

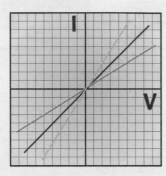

The current through a <u>resistor</u> (at constant temperature) is <u>directly proportional to P.D.</u>
<u>Different resistors</u> have different <u>resistances</u>, hence the different <u>slopes</u>.

Filament lamp

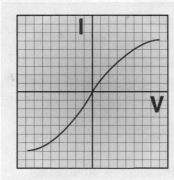

As the <u>temperature</u> of the filament <u>increases</u>, the <u>resistance increases</u>, hence the <u>curve</u> (see next page for more).

Diode

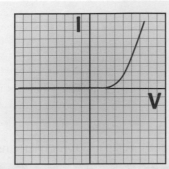

<u>Current will only flow through a diode in one direction</u>, as shown. The diode has very <u>high resistance</u> in the opposite direction.

You have to be able to interpret V-I graphs for your exam

Learn the shape of each of the three graphs above — and make sure you can explain why they're shaped that way too. There's more on the next page about the shape of the filament lamp graph.

Resistance and V = I × R

Prepare yourself to meet the <u>most important</u> equation in electrics, bar none.
But first up, a bit more about resistance...

Resistance *increases* with *temperature*

1) When an electrical charge flows through a resistor, some of the electrical energy is <u>transferred to heat energy</u> and the resistor gets <u>hot</u>.

2) This heat energy causes the <u>ions</u> in the conductor to <u>vibrate more</u>.

3) This makes it <u>more difficult</u> for the charge-carrying electrons to get through the resistor — the <u>current can't flow</u> as easily and the <u>resistance increases</u>.

4) For most resistors there is a <u>limit</u> to the amount of current that can flow.

5) More current means an <u>increase</u> in <u>temperature</u>, which means an <u>increase</u> in <u>resistance</u>, which means the <u>current decreases</u> again.

6) This is why the graph for the filament lamp <u>levels off</u> at high currents (see previous page).

Important ↑

Resistance, *potential difference* and *current*: V = I × R

Potential Difference = Current × Resistance

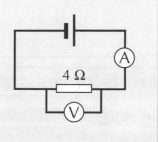

For the <u>straight-line graphs</u> on the previous page, the resistance of the component is <u>steady</u> and is equal to the <u>inverse</u> of the <u>gradient</u> of the line, or "<u>1/gradient</u>". In other words, the <u>steeper</u> the graph the <u>lower</u> the resistance.

If the graph <u>curves</u>, it means the resistance is <u>changing</u>. In that case R can be found for any point by taking the <u>pair of values</u> (V, I) from the graph and sticking them in the formula <u>R = V/I</u>. Easy.

Example

Voltmeter V reads 6 V and resistor R is 4 Ω.
What is the current through ammeter A?

<u>ANSWER</u>: Use the formula triangle for V = I × R.
We need to find I, so the version we need is I = V/R.
The answer is then: I = 6 ÷ 4 = <u>1.5 A</u>.

4 Ω

Learn the all important formula: V = I × R

Make sure you can explain why the <u>resistance</u> of a resistor <u>increases</u> as its <u>temperature increases</u>. And you need to know that formula inside out, back to front, upside down — it's really useful and important.

Circuit Devices

You might consider yourself a bit of an <u>expert</u> in circuit components — you're enlightened about bulbs, you're switched on to switches... Just make sure you know these ones as well — they're a <u>bit trickier</u>.

Current only flows in **one direction** through a **diode**

1) A diode is a special device made from <u>semiconductor</u> material such as <u>silicon</u>.

2) It is used to <u>regulate</u> the <u>potential difference</u> in circuits.

3) It lets current flow freely through it in <u>one direction</u>, but <u>not</u> in the other (i.e. there's a very high resistance in the <u>reverse</u> direction).

4) This turns out to be really useful in various <u>electronic circuits</u>.

Light-emitting diodes are **very useful**

1) A <u>light-emitting diode</u> (LED) emits light when a current flows through it in the <u>forward direction</u>.

2) LEDs are being used more and more as lighting, as they use a much <u>smaller current</u> than other forms of lighting.

3) LEDs indicate the presence of current in a circuit. They're often used in appliances (e.g. TVs) to show that they are <u>switched on</u>.

4) They're also used for the numbers on <u>digital clocks</u>, in <u>traffic lights</u> and in <u>remote controls</u>.

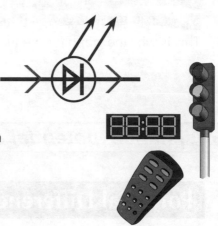

A **Light-Dependent Resistor** or "LDR"

1) An LDR is a resistor that is <u>dependent</u> on the <u>intensity</u> of <u>light</u>. Simple really.

2) In <u>bright light</u>, the resistance <u>falls</u>.

3) In <u>darkness</u>, the resistance is <u>highest</u>.

4) They have lots of applications including <u>automatic night lights</u>, outdoor lighting and <u>burglar detectors</u>.

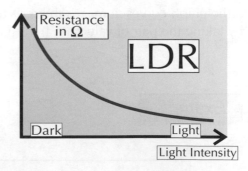

Thermistor resistance decreases as temperature increases

1) A <u>thermistor</u> is a <u>temperature dependent</u> resistor.

2) In <u>hot</u> conditions, the resistance <u>drops</u>.

3) In <u>cool</u> conditions, the resistance goes <u>up</u>.

4) Thermistors make useful <u>temperature detectors</u>, e.g. <u>car engine temperature sensors</u> and electronic <u>thermostats</u>.

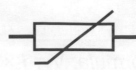

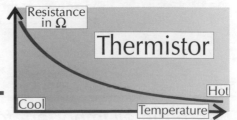

Warm-Up and Exam Questions

Phew — circuits aren't the easiest thing in the world, are they? Make sure you've understood the last few pages by trying these questions. If you get stuck, just go back and re-read the relevant page.

Warm-Up Questions

1) What are the units of resistance?
2) Write down the formula that links potential difference, work done and charge.
3) Draw the symbol for a light-emitting diode (LED).
4) Give one use of a light-dependant resistor (LDR).
5) What happens to the resistance of a thermistor as temperature increases?

Exam Questions

1   Shown below is a circuit diagram for a standard test circuit.

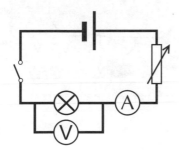

(a)   When the switch is closed, the ammeter reads 0.3 A and the voltmeter reads 1.5 V.

(i)   Calculate the resistance of the filament lamp.

(2 marks)

(ii)   The switch is closed for 35 seconds. Calculate the total charge that flows through the filament lamp.

(2 marks)

(b)   The variable resistor is used to increase the resistance in the circuit. Describe how this will affect the current flowing through the circuit.

(1 mark)

(c)   The resistance of a filament lamp changes with temperature.

(i)   On the graph to the right, sketch the potential difference-current graph for a filament lamp.

(1 mark)

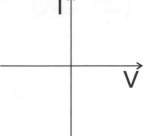

(ii)   Explain why the resistance of the filament lamp increases as the temperature of the filament increases.

(3 marks)

2   The graph below shows current against potential difference (P.D.) for a diode.

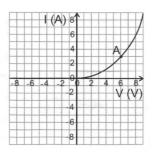

(a)   Explain why the graph shows zero current for negative P.D.s.

(1 mark)

(b)   Calculate the resistance of the diode at the point marked A.

(2 marks)

(c)   Light emitting diodes (LEDs) are often used for lighting. Give **one** advantage of using LEDs instead of filament lamps.

(1 mark)

Series Circuits

You need to be able to tell the difference between series and parallel circuits <u>just by looking at them</u>. You also need to know the <u>rules</u> about what happens with both types. Read on.

Series circuits — *all or nothing*

1) In <u>series circuits</u>, the different components are connected <u>in a line, end to end</u>, between the +ve and –ve of the power supply (except for <u>voltmeters</u>, which are always connected <u>in parallel</u>, but they don't count as part of the circuit).

2) If you remove or disconnect <u>one</u> component, the circuit is <u>broken</u> and they all <u>stop</u>.

3) This is generally <u>not very handy</u>, and in practice <u>very few things</u> are connected in series.

1) Potential difference is **shared**:

In series circuits the <u>total P.D.</u> of the <u>supply</u> is <u>shared</u> between the various <u>components</u>. So the <u>voltages</u> round a series circuit <u>always add up</u> to equal the <u>source voltage</u>:

$$V = V_1 + V_2 + ...$$

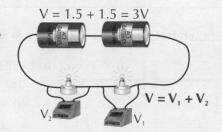

$V = 1.5 + 1.5 = 3V$

$V = V_1 + V_2$

2) Current is the **same** everywhere:

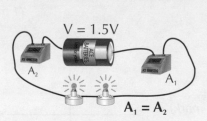

$V = 1.5V$

A_2 A_1

$A_1 = A_2$

1) In series circuits the <u>same current</u> flows through <u>all parts</u> of the circuit, i.e:

$$A_1 = A_2$$

2) The <u>size</u> of the current is determined by the <u>total P.D.</u> of the cells and the <u>total resistance</u> of the circuit: i.e. $I = V/R$

3) Resistance **adds up**:

1) In series circuits the <u>total resistance</u> is just the <u>sum</u> of all the resistances:

$$R = R_1 + R_2 + R_3$$

2) The <u>bigger</u> the <u>resistance</u> of a component, the bigger its <u>share</u> of the <u>total P.D.</u>

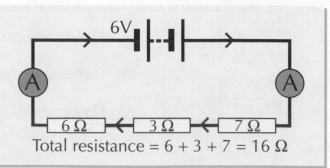

6V

$6\,\Omega$ $3\,\Omega$ $7\,\Omega$

Total resistance = 6 + 3 + 7 = 16 Ω

Series Circuits

It's <u>not enough</u> to know how circuits work in theory, it's important that you can calculate the currents, potential differences and resistances in a <u>range of examples</u>. There's a nice example on this page to help you see how all the theory from the last page can be <u>put into practice</u>.

Cell voltages **add up**:

1) There is a bigger potential difference when more cells are in series, provided the cells are all <u>connected</u> the <u>same way</u>.

2) For example when two batteries of voltage 1.5 V are <u>connected in series</u> they supply 3 V <u>between them</u>.

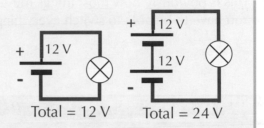

Example on **series circuits**

<u>Potential differences</u> add to equal the <u>source P.D.</u>:
1.5 + 2 + 2.5 = 6 V

<u>Total resistance</u> is the sum of the resistances in the circuit: 3 + 4 + 5 = 12 Ω

<u>Current</u> flowing through all parts of the circuit = V/R = 6/12 = 0.5 A

(If an extra cell was added of P.D. 3 V then the P.D. across each resistor would increase and the current would increase too.)

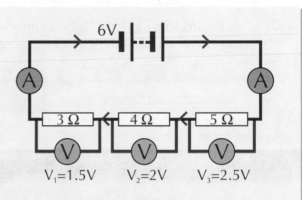

Christmas **fairy lights** are sometimes wired in **series**

1) <u>Christmas fairy lights</u> are about the <u>only</u> real-life example of things connected in <u>series</u>, and it can be a real <u>pain</u> when the <u>whole lot go out</u> just because <u>one</u> of the bulbs breaks.

2) The only <u>advantage</u> is that the bulbs can be <u>very small</u> because the total 230 V is <u>shared out</u> between them, so each bulb only has a <u>small</u> potential difference across it.

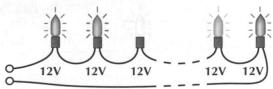

Mains voltage is 230 V.

Series circuits aren't used very much in the real world

A lot of fairy lights are actually done on a <u>parallel circuit</u> (see next page) these days — they have an adapter that lowers the voltage, so the lights can still be diddy but it doesn't matter if one of them blows.

Parallel Circuits

Parallel circuits are much more <u>sensible</u> than series circuits. First up, the reason why...

Parallel circuits — independence and isolation

1) In <u>parallel circuits</u>, each component is <u>separately</u> connected to the +ve and –ve of the <u>supply</u>.

2) If you remove or disconnect <u>one</u> of them, it will <u>hardly affect</u> the others at all.

3) This is <u>obviously</u> how <u>most</u> things must be connected, for example in <u>cars</u> and in <u>household electrics</u>. You have to be able to switch everything on and off <u>separately</u>.

1) P.D. is the **same** across **all** components:

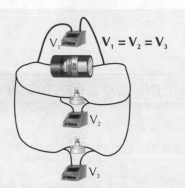

1) In parallel circuits <u>all</u> components get the <u>full source P.D.</u>, so the voltage is the <u>same</u> across all components:

$$V_1 = V_2 = V_3$$

2) This means that <u>identical bulbs</u> connected in parallel will all be at the <u>same brightness</u>.

2) Current is **shared** between branches:

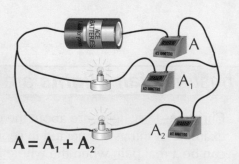

1) In parallel circuits the <u>total current</u> flowing around the circuit is equal to the <u>total of all</u> the currents through the <u>separate components</u>.

$$A = A_1 + A_2 + ...$$

2) In a parallel circuit, there are <u>junctions</u> where the current either <u>splits</u> or <u>rejoins</u>. The total current going <u>into</u> a junction has to equal the total current <u>leaving</u>.

3) If two <u>identical components</u> are connected in parallel then the <u>same current</u> will flow through each component.

All the electrics in your house will be wired in parallel circuits

Parallel circuits might look a bit scarier than series ones, but they're much <u>more useful</u> — and you don't have to learn as many equations for them. Remember: each branch has the <u>same voltage</u> across it, and the <u>total current</u> is equal to the <u>sum</u> of the currents through each of the branches.

Parallel Circuits

This page covers some useful examples of <u>parallel circuits</u>.

Voltmeters and ammeters are exceptions to the rule:

1) Ammeters and voltmeters are <u>exceptions</u> to the series and parallel rules.
2) Ammeters are <u>always</u> connected in <u>series</u> even in a parallel circuit.
3) Voltmeters are <u>always</u> connected in <u>parallel with a component</u> even in a series circuit.

Example on parallel circuits

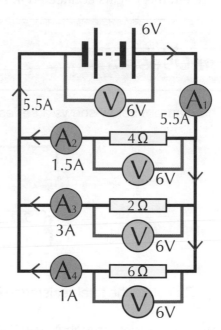

1) The <u>P.D.</u> across each resistor in the circuit is the same as the <u>supply P.D.</u> Each voltmeter will read 6 V.

2) The <u>current</u> through each <u>resistor</u> will be <u>different</u> because they have different values of <u>resistance</u>.

3) The current through the <u>battery</u> is the same as the <u>sum</u> of the other currents in the branches.
i.e. $A_1 = A_2 + A_3 + A_4 \Rightarrow A_1 = 1.5 + 3 + 1 = 5.5$ A

Everything electrical in a car is connected in parallel

<u>Parallel connection</u> is <u>essential</u> in a car to give these <u>two features</u>:

1) Everything can be <u>turned on and off separately</u>.
2) Everything always gets the <u>full voltage</u> from the battery.

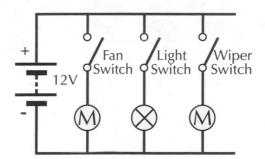

$\textcircled{M}$ *is the symbol for a motor.*

The only <u>slight effect</u> is that when you turn <u>lots of things on</u> the lights may go <u>dim</u> because the battery can't provide <u>full voltage</u> under <u>heavy load</u>. This is normally a <u>very slight</u> effect.

You can spot the same thing at home when you turn a kettle on, if you watch very carefully.

Warm-Up and Exam Questions

Those last few pages had lots more stuff on circuits and electricity.
Try these out to see what you can remember...

Warm-Up Questions

1) Give one disadvantage of series circuits.
2) How do you work out the total resistance in a series circuit?
3) In an electrical circuit, would you put an ammeter in series or parallel?
4) In a parallel circuit, is the p.d. across all the components the same or different?
5) Are circuits in cars connected in series or parallel?

Exam Questions

1   The diagram below shows a series circuit.

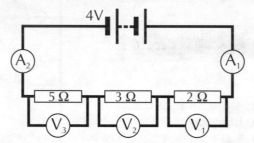

(a) Calculate the total resistance in the circuit.

(2 marks)

(b) The current through A_1 is 0.4 A. What is the current through A_2?
Explain your answer.

(2 marks)

(c) V_1 reads 0.8 V and V_2 reads 1.2 V.
Calculate the reading on V_3.

(2 marks)

2   A parallel circuit is connected as shown.

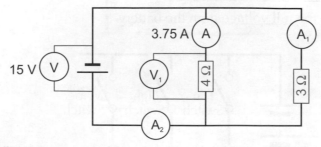

Calculate the readings on:
(a) Voltmeter V_1.

(1 mark)

(b) Ammeter A_1.

(2 marks)

(c) Ammeter A_2.

(2 marks)

Revision Summary for Physics 2a

Well done — you've made it to the end of another section. There are loads of bits and bobs about forces, motion and electricity which you have to learn. The best way to find out what you know is to get stuck in to these revision questions...

1) What's the difference between speed and velocity?

2)* Write down the formula for acceleration. What's the acceleration of a object that starts off from rest and reaches a speed of 14 m/s in 0.4 seconds?

3) Explain how to find speed, distance and acceleration from a velocity-time graph.

4) Explain the difference between mass and weight.

5) Explain what is meant by a "resultant force".

6) If an object has zero resultant force on it, can it be moving? Can it be accelerating?

7)* Write down the formula relating resultant force and acceleration.
A resultant force of 30 N pushes a trolley of mass 4 kg. What will be its acceleration?

8)* A skydiver has a mass of 75 kg. At 80 mph, the drag force on the skydiver is 650 N.
Find the acceleration of the skydiver at 80 mph (take g = 10 N/kg).

9)* A man pushes a tree with a force of 120 N. What is the size of the reaction force that the man feels pushing back at him?

10) What is "terminal velocity"?

11) What are the two different parts of the overall stopping distance of a car?

12)* Write down the formula for work done. A dog drags a big branch 12 m over the next-door neighbour's front lawn, pulling with a force of 535 N. How much work was done?

13)* A 4 kg cheese is taken 30 m up a hill before being rolled back down again. If g = 10 N/kg, how much gravitational potential energy does the cheese have at the top of the hill?

14)* What's the formula for kinetic energy? Find the kinetic energy of a 78 kg object moving at 23 m/s.

15)* Calculate the kinetic energy of the same 78 kg object just as it hits the floor after falling through 20 m.

16)* A car of mass 1000 kg is travelling at a velocity of 2 m/s when a sheep runs out 5 m in front.
If the driver immediately applies the maximum braking force of 395 N, can he avoid hitting it?

17) Write down the equation that relates the force on a spring and its extension.

18)* Calculate the power output of a 78 kg runner when she runs 20 m up a staircase in 16.5 seconds.

19) If the total momentum of a system before a collision is zero, what is the total momentum of the system after the collision?

20) Explain how seat belts, crumple zones, side impact bars and air bags are useful in a crash.

21) What is the advantage of using regenerative braking systems?

22) What causes the build-up of static electricity? Which particles move when static builds up?

23) True or false: the greater the resistance of a component, the smaller the current that flows through it?

24)* 240 C of charge is carried though a wire in a circuit in one minute.
How much current has flowed through the wire?

25) Draw a diagram of the circuit that you would use to find the resistance of a motor.

26) Sketch typical potential difference-current graphs for:
a) a resistor, b) a filament lamp, c) a diode. Explain the shape of each graph.

27) Explain how resistance of a component changes with its temperature in terms of ions and electrons.

28)* What potential difference is required to push 2 A of current through a 0.6 Ω resistor?

29) Describe how the resistance of an LDR varies with light intensity. Give an application of an LDR.

30)* A 4 Ω bulb and a 6 Ω bulb are connected in series with a 12 V battery.
a) How much current flows through the 4 Ω bulb?
b) What is the P.D over the 6 Ω bulb?
c) What would the P.D. over the 6 Ω bulb be if the two bulbs were connected in parallel?

*Answers on page 249.

Mains Electricity

Electric current is the <u>movement of charge carriers</u>. To transfer energy, it <u>doesn't matter which way</u> the charge carriers are going. That's why an <u>alternating current</u> works. Read on to find out more...

Mains supply is **AC**, battery supply is **DC**

1) The UK mains supply is approximately <u>230 volts</u>.   ← Important

2) It is an <u>AC supply</u> (alternating current), which means the current is <u>constantly</u> changing direction.

3) The frequency of the AC mains supply is <u>50 cycles per second</u> or <u>50 Hz</u> (hertz).

4) By contrast, cells and batteries supply <u>direct current</u> (DC).
   This just means that the current always keeps flowing in the <u>same direction</u>.

Electricity supplies can be shown on an *oscilloscope* screen

1) A <u>cathode ray oscilloscope</u> (CRO) is basically a <u>voltmeter</u>.

2) If you plug an <u>AC supply</u> into an oscilloscope, you get a '<u>trace</u>' on the screen that shows how the voltage of the supply changes with <u>time</u>. The trace goes up and down in a <u>regular pattern</u> — some of the time it's positive and some of the time it's negative.

3) If you plug in a <u>DC supply</u>, the trace you get is just a <u>straight line</u>.

4) The <u>vertical height</u> of the AC trace at any point shows the <u>input voltage</u> at that point.
   By measuring the height of the trace you can find the potential difference of the AC supply.

5) For DC it's a <u>lot simpler</u> — the voltage is just the distance from the <u>straight line trace</u> to the centre line.

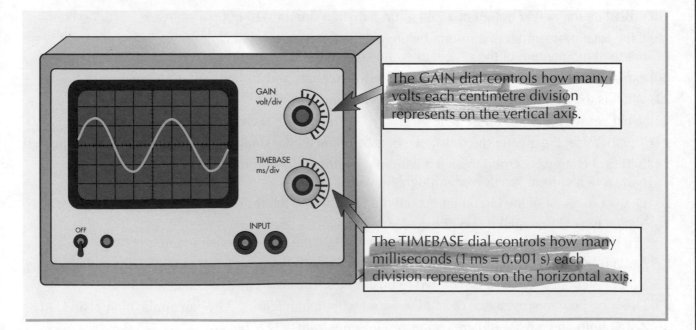

The GAIN dial controls how many volts each centimetre division represents on the vertical axis.

The TIMEBASE dial controls how many milliseconds (1 ms = 0.001 s) each division represents on the horizontal axis.

Mains Electricity

Learn how to *read* an *oscilloscope trace*

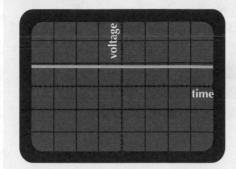

A DC source is always at the same voltage, so you get a straight line.

An AC source gives a regularly repeating wave. From that, you can work out the period and the frequency of the supply.

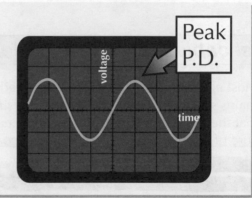

Peak P.D.

You work out the frequency using:

$$\text{Frequency (Hz)} = \frac{1}{\text{Time period (s)}}$$

Example

The trace to the right comes from an oscilloscope with the timebase set to 5 ms/div. Find:
a) the time period, and b) the frequency of the AC supply.

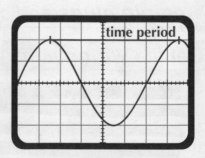

Time period = the time to complete one cycle.
1 ms = 0.001 s.

ANSWER:

a) To find the time period, measure the horizontal distance between two peaks. The time period of the signal is 6 divisions. Multiply by the timebase:
Time period = 5 ms × 6 = 0.03 s

b) Using the frequency formula:
Frequency = 1/0.03 = 33 Hz

Be prepared to use traces like these to do calculations

Because mains power is AC, its current can be increased or decreased using a device called a transformer. The lower the current in power transmission lines, the less energy is wasted as heat.

Electricity in the Home

It's important to know how to correctly <u>wire a plug</u> — plugs that aren't wired correctly are <u>dangerous</u>.

Hazards *in the* home *— eliminate them before they* eliminate you

A likely <u>exam question</u> will show you a picture with various <u>electrical hazards</u>, and then ask you to <u>list all the hazards</u>. This should be mostly <u>common sense</u>, but it'll help if you already know some of the likely hazards, so learn these 9 examples:

1) <u>Long cables</u>.
2) <u>Frayed cables</u>.
3) <u>Cables</u> in contact with something <u>hot or wet</u>.
4) <u>Water near sockets</u>.
5) <u>Shoving</u> things into sockets.

6) <u>Damaged plugs</u>.
7) <u>Too many</u> plugs into one socket.
8) Lighting sockets <u>without bulbs in</u>.
9) Appliances without their <u>covers</u> on.

Most cables *have* three *separate wires*

1) Most electrical appliances are connected to the mains supply by <u>three-core</u> cables. This means that they have <u>three wires</u> inside them, each with a <u>core of copper</u> and a <u>coloured plastic coating</u>.

2) The brown <u>LIVE WIRE</u> in a mains supply alternates between a <u>HIGH +VE AND −VE VOLTAGE</u>.

3) The blue <u>NEUTRAL WIRE</u> is always at <u>0V</u>. Electricity normally flows in and out through the live and neutral wires only.

4) The green and yellow <u>EARTH WIRE</u> is for protecting the wiring, and for safety — it works together with a fuse to prevent fire and shocks. It is attached to the metal casing of the appliance and <u>carries the electricity to earth</u> (and away from you) should something go wrong and the live or neutral wires touch the metal case.

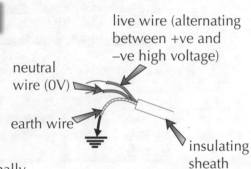

live wire (alternating between +ve and −ve high voltage)

neutral wire (0V)

earth wire

insulating sheath

Three-pin plugs *and* cables *— learn the* safety features

Get the wiring *right*

1) The <u>right coloured wire</u> is connected to each pin, and <u>firmly screwed</u> in.
2) <u>No bare wires</u> showing inside the plug.
3) <u>Cable grip</u> tightly fastened over the cable <u>outer layer</u>.
4) Different appliances need <u>different</u> amounts of electrical energy. <u>Thicker</u> cables have <u>less resistance</u>, so they carry <u>more current</u>.

Rubber or plastic case

Earth Wire Green/Yellow

Fuse

Neutral Wire Blue

Live Wire Brown

Cable grip

Brass Pins

Plug *features*

1) The <u>metal parts</u> are made of copper or brass because these are <u>very good conductors</u>.
2) The case, cable grip and cable insulation are made of <u>rubber</u> or <u>plastic</u> because they're really good <u>insulators</u>, and <u>flexible</u> too.
3) This all keeps the electricity flowing <u>where it should</u>.

Fuses and Earthing

Questions about fuses are an exam favourite because they <u>cover lots of stuff</u> — electrical current, resistance, energy transfers and electrical safety. Learn this page and make sure you've got it sussed.

Earthing and *fuses* prevent **electrical overloads**

The earth wire and fuse (or circuit breaker) are included in electrical appliances for safety and work together like this:

1) If a <u>fault</u> develops in which the <u>live wire</u> somehow touches the <u>metal case</u>, then because the case is <u>earthed</u>, <u>too great a current</u> flows in through the <u>live wire</u>, through the <u>case</u> and out down the <u>earth wire</u>.

2) This <u>surge</u> in current <u>melts the fuse</u> (or trips the circuit breaker in the live wire) when the amount of current is greater than the fuse rating. This <u>cuts off</u> the <u>live supply</u> and <u>breaks the circuit</u>.

3) This <u>isolates</u> the <u>whole appliance</u>, making it <u>impossible</u> to get an electric <u>shock</u> from the case. It also prevents the risk of <u>fire</u> caused by the heating effect of a large current.

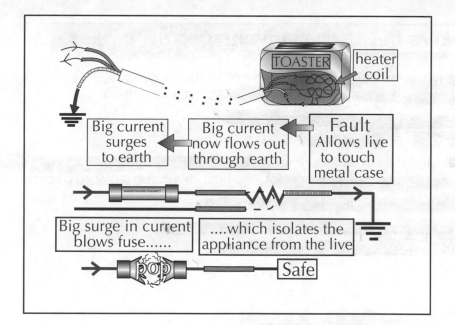

4) As well as people, fuses and earthing are there to <u>protect the circuits and wiring</u> in your appliances from getting <u>fried</u> if there is a <u>current surge</u>.

5) <u>Fuses</u> should be <u>rated</u> as near as possible but <u>just higher</u> than the <u>normal operating current</u>.

6) The <u>larger the current</u>, the <u>thicker the cable</u> you need to carry it. That's why the <u>fuse rating</u> needed for cables usually <u>increases</u> with <u>cable thickness</u>.

Fuses — you'll find them in exams and kettles

<u>Safety precautions</u> on modern appliances mean it's pretty difficult to get electrocuted by them. But that's only so long as they are in <u>good condition</u> and you're not doing <u>something really stupid</u>. Watch out for frayed wires, don't overload plugs, and for goodness sake don't use a knife to get toast out of a toaster when it is switched on. Turn over to the next page to find out more about safety precautions that you might find in your home.

Fuses and Earthing

Earthing is another way in which we can prevent appliances giving us an electric shock.

Insulating materials make appliances "double insulated"

1) All appliances with metal cases are usually "earthed" to reduce the danger of electric shock.

2) "Earthing" just means the case must be attached to an earth wire.

3) An earthed conductor can never become live.

4) If the appliance has a plastic casing and no metal parts showing then it's said to be double insulated.

5) Anything with double insulation like that doesn't need an earth wire — just a live and neutral.

6) Cables that only carry the live and neutral wires are known as two-core cables.

Circuit breakers have some advantages over fuses

1) Circuit breakers are an electrical safety device used in some circuits. Like fuses, they protect the circuit from damage if too much current flows.

2) When circuit breakers detect a surge in current in a circuit, they break the circuit by opening a switch.

3) A circuit breaker (and the circuit they're in) can easily be reset by flicking a switch on the device. This makes them more convenient than fuses — which have to be replaced once they've melted.

4) They are, however, a lot more expensive to buy than fuses.

5) One type of circuit breaker used instead of a fuse and an earth wire is a Residual Current Circuit Breakers (RCCBs):

Residual Current Circuit Breakers

1) Normally exactly the same current flows through the live and neutral wires. If somebody touches the live wire, a small but deadly current will flow through them to the earth. This means the neutral wire carries less current than the live wire. The RCCB detects this difference in current and quickly cuts off the power by opening a switch.

2) They also operate much faster than fuses — they break the circuit as soon as there is a current surge — no time is wasted waiting for the current to melt a fuse. This makes them safer.

3) RCCBs even work for small current changes that might not be large enough to melt a fuse. Since even small current changes could be fatal, this means RCCBs are more effective at protecting against electrocution.

Energy and Power in Circuits

Electricity is just another form of <u>energy</u> — which means that it is always <u>conserved</u>.

Energy is transferred from cells and other sources

Anything which <u>supplies electricity</u> is also supplying <u>energy</u>.
So cells, batteries, generators, etc. all <u>transfer energy</u> to components in the circuit:

| <u>Motion</u>: motors | <u>Light</u>: light bulbs | <u>Heat</u>: Hair dryers/kettles | <u>Sound</u>: speakers |

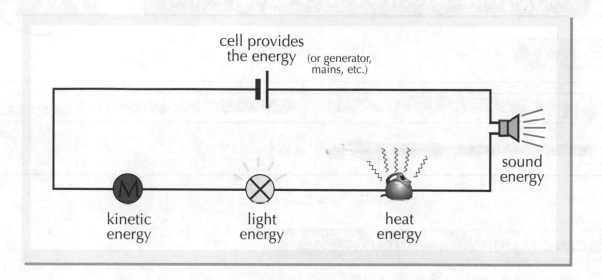

cell provides
the energy (or generator,
mains, etc.)

kinetic
energy

light
energy

heat
energy

sound
energy

All resistors produce heat when a current flows through them

1) Whenever a <u>current</u> flows through anything with <u>electrical resistance</u> (which is pretty much everything) then <u>electrical energy</u> is converted into <u>heat energy</u>.

2) The <u>more current</u> that flows, the more heat is produced.

3) A <u>bigger voltage</u> means more heating because it pushes more current through.

4) <u>Filament bulbs</u> work by passing a current through a very <u>thin wire</u>, heating it up so much that it glows. Rather obviously, they waste a lot of energy as <u>heat</u>.

If an appliance is efficient it wastes less energy

All this energy wasted as heat can get a little <u>depressing</u> — but there is a solution.

1) When you buy electrical appliances you can choose to buy ones that are more <u>energy efficient</u>.

2) These appliances transfer more of their <u>total electrical energy output to useful energy</u>.

3) For example, less energy is wasted as heat in power-saving lamps such as <u>compact fluorescent lamps</u> (CFLs) and <u>light-emitting diodes</u> (page 164) than in ordinary filament bulbs.

4) Unfortunately, they do <u>cost more to buy</u>, but over time the money you <u>save</u> on your electricity bills pays you back for the initial investment.

Energy and Power in Circuits

Power ratings tell you how much energy a device transfers per second.

Appliances have power ratings

1) The total energy transferred by an appliance depends on how long the appliance is on and its power rating.

2) The power of an appliance is the energy that it uses per second.

Energy Transferred = Power rating × time

Example

> A 2.5 kW kettle is on for 5 minutes. Calculate the energy transferred by the kettle in this time.
>
> ANSWER: 2500 × 300 = 750 000 J = 750 kJ. (5 minutes = 300 s).

Electrical power and fuse ratings

1) The formula for electrical power is:

POWER = CURRENT × POTENTIAL DIFFERENCE

 $P = I \times V$

2) Most electrical goods show their power rating and voltage rating. To work out the size of the fuse needed, you need to work out the current that the item will normally use.

Example

> A hair dryer is rated at 230 V, 1 kW. Find the fuse needed.
>
> ANSWER: I = P/V = 1000/230 = 4.3 A. Normally, the fuse should be rated just a little higher than the normal current, so a 5 amp fuse is ideal for this one.

Use fuses with a rating just above the usual current

In the UK, you can usually get fuses rated at 3 A, 5 A or 13 A, and that's about it.
You should bear that in mind when you're working out fuse ratings.
If you find you need a 10.73 A fuse — tough. You'll have to use a 13A one.

Power and Energy Change

You can think about <u>electrical circuits</u> in terms of <u>energy transfer</u> — the charge carriers take charge around the circuit, and when they go through an electrical component energy is transferred to make the component work. Read on for more...

Potential difference is the energy transferred per charge passed

1) When an electrical <u>charge</u> (Q) goes through a <u>change</u> in potential difference (V), then <u>energy</u> (E) is <u>transferred</u>.

2) Energy is <u>supplied</u> to the charge at the <u>power source</u> to 'raise' it through a potential.

3) The charge <u>gives up</u> this energy when it 'falls' through any <u>potential drop</u> in <u>components</u> elsewhere in the circuit.

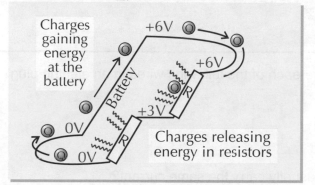

Charges gaining energy at the battery

Charges releasing energy in resistors

4) The formula is simple:

Energy transformed = Charge × Potential difference

5) The <u>bigger</u> the <u>change</u> in P.D. (or voltage.), the <u>more energy</u> is transferred for a <u>given amount of charge</u> passing through the circuit.

6) That means that a battery with a <u>bigger voltage</u> will supply <u>more energy</u> to the circuit for every <u>coulomb</u> of charge which flows round it, because the charge is raised up "<u>higher</u>" at the start — and as the diagram shows, <u>more energy</u> will be <u>dissipated</u> in the circuit too.

Example

> The motor in an electric toothbrush is attached to a 3 V battery.
> If a current of 0.8 A flows through the motor for 3 minutes:
>
> a) Calculate the total charge passed.
>
> b) Calculate the energy transformed by the motor.
>
> c) Explain why the kinetic energy output of the motor will be less than your answer to b).

<u>ANSWER:</u> a) Use the formula (page 160) Q = I × t = 0.8 × (3 × 60) = <u>144 C</u>

b) Use E = Q × V = 144 × 3 = <u>432 J</u>

c) The motor won't be 100% efficient.
Some of the energy will be transformed into <u>sound and heat</u>.

Warm-Up and Exam Questions

Check you can do the straightforward stuff with this warm-up, then have a go at the exam questions...

Warm-Up Questions

1) What is the frequency of UK mains electricity supply?
2) Which of the live, neutral or earth wires is always at 0 volts?
3) Why is the case of a plug usually made out of plastic?
4) Appliances with double insulation don't need which type of wire?
5) What energy transformation occurs when electric current flows through a resistor?
6) What is the equation linking Q, V and E?

Exam Questions

1   (a) What colour(s) are each of the following wires in an electric plug?

        (i)   live

        (ii) neutral

        (iii) earth

(3 marks)

    (b) Which two wires usually carry the same current?

(1 mark)

    (c) What type of safety device contains a wire that is designed to melt when the current passing through it goes above a certain value?

(1 mark)

2   *In this question you will be assessed on the quality of your English, the organisation of your ideas and your use of appropriate specialist vocabulary.*

    A domestic appliance has a plug containing live, neutral and earth wires and a fuse.
The appliance has a metal case.

    Describe how the earth wire and fuse work together to protect the appliance and to prevent the user getting an electric shock if there is a fault.

(6 marks)

3   A current of 0.5 A passes through a torch bulb. The torch is powered by a 3 V battery.

    (a) Calculate the power of the torch.

(2 marks)

    (b) In half an hour, 900 C of charge pass through the battery.
Calculate how much electrical energy the bulb transfers in half an hour.

(2 marks)

4   The diagram on the right shows a trace on a CRO.

    (a) Is the trace displaying the output from the mains or a battery? Explain your answer.

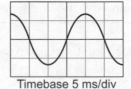

Timebase 5 ms/div

(1 mark)

    (b) What is the time period of the wave?

(1 mark)

    (c) What is the frequency of the wave?

(2 marks)

    (d) What will happen to the CRO trace if the voltage of the supply is reduced?

(1 mark)

Atomic Structure

Ernest Rutherford didn't just pick the nuclear model of the atom out of thin air. It all started with a Greek fella called Democritus in the 5th Century BC. He thought that all matter, whatever it was, was made up of identical lumps called "atomos". And that's about as far as the theory got until the 1800s...

Rutherford scattering and the demise of the plum pudding

1) In 1804 John Dalton agreed with Democritus that matter was made up of tiny spheres ("atoms") that couldn't be broken up, but he reckoned that each element was made up of a different type of "atom".

2) Nearly 100 years later, J J Thomson discovered that electrons could be removed from atoms. So Dalton's theory wasn't quite right (atoms could be broken up). Thomson suggested that atoms were spheres of positive charge with tiny negative electrons stuck in them like plums in a plum pudding.

3) That "plum pudding" theory didn't last very long though. In 1909 Rutherford and Marsden tried firing a beam of alpha particles (see page 184) at thin gold foil. They expected that the positively charged alpha particles would be slightly deflected by the electrons in the plum pudding model.

4) However, most of the alpha particles just went straight through, but the odd one came straight back at them, which was frankly a bit of a shocker for Rutherford and his pal.

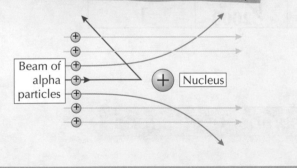

5) Being pretty clued-up guys, Rutherford and Marsden realised this meant that most of the mass of the atom was concentrated at the centre in a tiny nucleus. They also realised that the nucleus must have a positive charge, since it repelled the positive alpha particles.

6) It also showed that most of an atom is just empty space, which is also a bit of a shocker when you think about it.

Atomic Structure

Rutherford and Marsden used the results from their scattering experiment (see previous page) to produce a model for the atom.

Rutherford and Marsden came up with the nuclear model of the atom

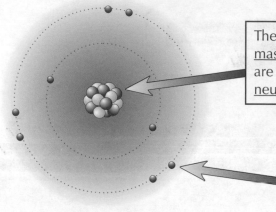

The nucleus is tiny but it makes up most of the mass of the atom. It contains protons (which are positively charged) and neutrons (which are neutral) — which gives it an overall positive charge.

The rest of the atom is mostly empty space. The negative electrons whizz round the outside of the nucleus really fast. They give the atom its overall size — the radius of the atom's nucleus is about 10 000 times smaller than the radius of the atom.

We can use relative charges and masses to compare particles

Learn the relative charges and masses of each particle:

PARTICLE	MASS	CHARGE
Proton	1	+1
Neutron	1	0
Electron	1/2000	-1

Number of protons equals number of electrons

1) Atoms have no charge overall.
2) The charge on an electron is the same size as the charge on a proton — but opposite.
3) This means the number of protons always equals the number of electrons in a neutral atom.
4) If some electrons are added or removed, the atom becomes a charged particle called an ion.

The nuclear model is just one way of thinking about the atom

Rutherford and Marsden's nuclear model works really well for explaining a lot of physical properties of different elements — but it's certainly not the whole story. Other bits of science are explained using different models of the atom. The beauty of it though is that no one model is more right than the others.

Radioactivit...

You have just entered the subatomic...

Isotopes are different f...

1) <u>Isotopes</u> are atoms with the <u>same</u>...
2) Hence they have the <u>same atomic</u>...
3) Atomic number is the <u>number of pr</u>...
4) Mass number is the <u>number of proto</u>...
5) <u>Carbon-12</u> and <u>carbon-14</u> are good e...

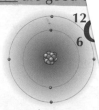

6) <u>Most elements</u> have different isotopes, bu...
7) The other isotopes tend to be <u>radioactive</u>, w...
   <u>decay</u> into <u>other elements</u> and give out radi...

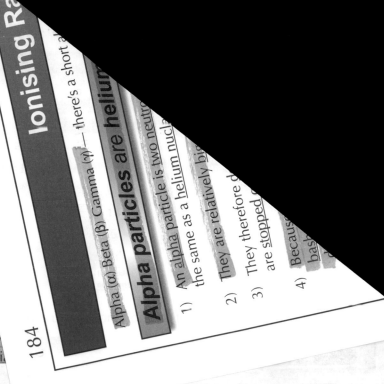

Ionising Ra...

184

Alpha (α) Beta (β) Gamma (γ) — there's a short a...

Alpha particles are heliu...

1) An <u>alpha</u> particle is two neutro...
   the same as a <u>helium nucle</u>...
2) They are relatively bi...
3) They therefore...
   are <u>stopped</u>...
4) Becaus...
   bas...

Radioactivity is a totally random process

1) <u>Radioactive substances</u> give out radiation from the nuclei of their atoms —
   <u>no matter what is done to them</u>.

2) This process is entirely <u>random</u>. This means that if you have 1000 unstable nuclei, you can't say when
   <u>any one of them</u> is going to decay, and neither can you do anything at all <u>to make a decay happen</u>.

3) It's completely unaffected by <u>physical</u> conditions like <u>temperature</u>
   or by any sort of <u>chemical bonding</u> etc.

4) Radioactive substances <u>spit out</u> one or more of the three
   types of radiation, <u>alpha</u>, <u>beta</u> or <u>gamma</u> (see next page).

Background radiation comes from many sources

<u>Background radiation</u> is radiation that is present at all times, all around us,
wherever you go. The background radiation we receive comes from:

1) Radioactivity of naturally occurring <u>unstable isotopes</u> which are <u>all around us</u> —
   in the <u>air</u>, in <u>food</u>, in <u>building materials</u> and in the <u>rocks</u> under our feet.
2) Radiation from <u>space</u>, which is known as <u>cosmic rays</u>. These come mostly from the <u>Sun</u>.
3) Radiation due to <u>man-made sources</u>, e.g. <u>fallout</u> from <u>nuclear weapons tests</u>,
   <u>nuclear accidents</u> (such as Chernobyl) or <u>dumped nuclear waste</u>.

The <u>RELATIVE PROPORTIONS</u> of
<u>background radiation</u>:

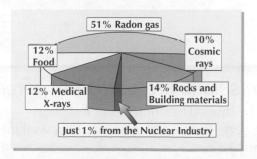

51% Radon gas
12% Food
10% Cosmic rays
12% Medical X-rays
14% Rocks and Building materials
Just 1% from the Nuclear Industry

...phabet of radiation for you to learn. And it's all <u>ionising</u>.

... nuclei

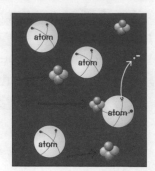

... ...ns and <u>two protons</u> —
... ...us.

... ...g and <u>heavy</u> and <u>slow moving</u>.

...on't penetrate very far into materials and
... ...quickly, even when travelling through <u>air</u>.

... ...e of their size they are <u>strongly ionising</u>, which just means they
... ...into a lot of atoms and <u>knock electrons off them</u> before they slow
... ...own, which creates lots of ions — hence the term "<u>ionising</u>".

Beta particles are electrons

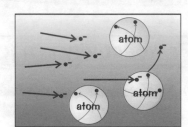

1) Beta particles are <u>in between</u> alpha and gamma in terms of their <u>properties</u>.

2) They move <u>quite</u> fast and they are <u>quite</u> small (they're electrons).

3) They <u>penetrate moderately</u> into materials before colliding, have a <u>long range</u> in air, and are <u>moderately ionising</u> too.

4) For every β-particle emitted, a <u>neutron</u> turns to a <u>proton</u> in the nucleus.

5) A <u>β-particle</u> is simply an <u>electron</u>, with virtually no mass and a charge of −1.

Gamma rays are very short wavelength EM waves

1) Gamma rays are the <u>opposite</u> of alpha particles in a way.

2) They <u>penetrate far into materials</u> without being stopped and pass <u>straight through air</u>.

3) This means they are <u>weakly ionising</u> because they tend to <u>pass through</u> rather than collide with atoms. Eventually they <u>hit something</u> and do <u>damage</u>.

4) Gamma rays have <u>no mass</u> and <u>no charge</u>.

Alpha and beta emissions are particles, gamma emissions are rays

Learn <u>all the details</u> about the three different types of radiation — alpha, beta and gamma. You need to know what they are, their ionising power, how well they penetrate through materials and their range in the air.

Ionising Radiation

When nuclei decay by <u>alpha</u> or <u>beta</u> emission, they change from one element into a different one.

You need to be able to **balance nuclear equations**

1) You can write alpha and beta decays as <u>nuclear equations</u>.

2) Watch out for the <u>mass and atomic numbers</u> — they have to <u>balance up</u> on both sides.

Alpha decay:

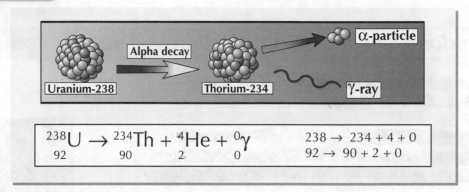

$$^{238}_{92}U \rightarrow \, ^{234}_{90}Th + \, ^{4}_{2}He + \, ^{0}_{0}\gamma$$

$$238 \rightarrow 234 + 4 + 0$$
$$92 \rightarrow 90 + 2 + 0$$

Beta decay:

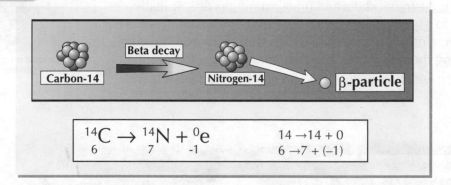

$$^{14}_{6}C \rightarrow \, ^{14}_{7}N + \, ^{0}_{-1}e$$

$$14 \rightarrow 14 + 0$$
$$6 \rightarrow 7 + (-1)$$

Alpha and *beta* are *deflected* by *electric* and *magnetic fields*

1) Alpha particles have a <u>positive charge</u>, beta particles have a <u>negative charge</u>.

2) When travelling through a <u>magnetic</u> or <u>electric field</u>, both alpha and beta particles will be <u>deflected</u>.

3) They're deflected in <u>opposite directions</u> because of their <u>opposite charge</u>.

4) Alpha particles have a <u>larger charge</u> than beta particles, and feel a <u>greater force</u> in magnetic and electric fields. But they're <u>deflected less</u> because they have a <u>much greater mass</u>.

5) <u>Gamma radiation</u> is an electromagnetic (EM) wave and has <u>no charge</u>, so it <u>doesn't get deflected</u> by electric or magnetic fields.

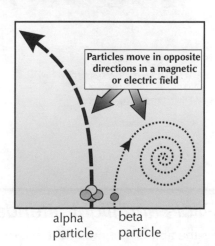

Particles move in opposite directions in a magnetic or electric field

alpha particle   beta particle

Radiation Dose

This page is all about what <u>affects</u> the amount of <u>radiation</u> we're <u>exposed</u> to, and the damage it does.

The **damage** caused by **radiation depends** on the **radiation dose**

How likely you are to <u>suffer damage</u> if you're exposed to nuclear radiation depends on the <u>radiation dose</u>.

1) Radiation dose depends on the <u>type</u> and <u>amount of radiation</u> you've been exposed to.

2) The <u>higher</u> the radiation dose, the <u>more at risk</u> you are of <u>developing cancer</u>.

Radiation dose can depend on **location** and **occupation**

The amount of radiation you're exposed to (and hence your radiation dose) can be affected by your <u>location</u> and <u>occupation</u>:

1) Certain <u>underground rocks</u> (e.g. granite) can cause higher levels at the <u>surface</u>, especially if they release <u>radioactive radon gas</u>, which tends to get <u>trapped inside people's houses</u>.

Coloured bits indicate more radiation from rocks

2) <u>Nuclear industry</u> workers and <u>uranium miners</u> are typically exposed to <u>10 times</u> the normal amount of radiation. They wear <u>protective clothing</u> and <u>face masks</u> to stop them from <u>touching</u> or <u>inhaling</u> the radioactive material, and <u>monitor</u> their radiation doses with <u>special radiation badges</u> and <u>regular check-ups</u>.

3) <u>Radiographers</u> work in hospitals using ionising radiation and so have a higher risk of radiation exposure. They wear <u>lead aprons</u> and stand behind <u>lead screens</u> to protect them from <u>prolonged exposure</u> to radiation.

4) At <u>high altitudes</u> (e.g. in <u>jet planes</u>) the background radiation <u>increases</u> because of more exposure to <u>cosmic rays</u>. That means <u>commercial pilots</u> have an increased risk of getting some types of cancer.

5) <u>Underground</u> (e.g. in <u>mines</u>, etc.) it increases because of the <u>rocks</u> all around, posing a risk to <u>miners</u>.

Pilots and flight attendants have a greater exposure to cosmic rays

So the amount of radiation you're <u>exposed</u> to depends on your <u>job</u> and your <u>location</u>. Don't forget that some places have higher levels of background radiation than others — so the people there'll get a <u>higher radiation dose</u>.

Warm-Up and Exam Questions

It's time again to test what you've learnt from the last few pages. Have a go at these...

Warm-Up Questions

1) In the 'plum pudding' model of the atom, what are the 'plums'?
2) Give one man-made source of background radiation.
3) Which are the most ionising — alpha particles or gamma rays?
4) Give two factors that affect a person's average yearly radiation dose.
5) Which type of background radiation are pilots more exposed to than the average person?

Exam Questions

1   (a)   Give the relative charge of the following particles:
        (i)   electron
        (ii)   proton
        (iii) neutron

(3 marks)

    (b)   Name the two types of particle that the nucleus of an atom contains.

(2 marks)

    (c)   Describe how the atomic number of a nucleus changes when a beta particle is emitted.

(1 mark)

    (d)   Describe how the mass number of a nucleus changes after alpha emission.

(1 mark)

    (e)   The table below contains information about three atoms.

	Mass number	Atomic number
Atom A	32	17
Atom B	33	17
Atom C	32	16

        (i)   What is meant by the mass number of an atom?

(1 mark)

        (ii)   Which of the two atoms are isotopes of the same element? Explain your answer.

(2 marks)

    (f)   Alpha and beta particles are deflected in electric and magnetic fields.
        (i)   Explain why alpha and beta particles are deflected in opposite directions.

(1 mark)

        (ii)   Explain why alpha particles are deflected less than beta particles.

(1 mark)

2   Rutherford and Marsden's scattering experiment led to their nuclear model of the atom.
    (a)   Describe what Rutherford and Marsden saw when they fired a beam of alpha particles at thin gold foil.

(2 marks)

    (b)   Describe the main features of their nuclear model of the atom.

(4 marks)

Half-Life

The <u>unit</u> for measuring <u>radioactivity</u> is the <u>becquerel</u> (Bq). 1 Bq means <u>one nucleus decaying per second</u>.

The radioactivity of a sample always decreases over time

1) This is <u>pretty obvious</u> when you think about it. Each time a <u>decay</u> happens and an alpha, beta or gamma is given out, it means one more <u>radioactive nucleus</u> has <u>disappeared</u>.

2) Obviously, as the <u>unstable nuclei</u> all steadily disappear, the <u>activity</u> (the number of nuclei that decay per second) will <u>decrease</u>. So the <u>older</u> a sample becomes, the <u>less radiation</u> it will emit.

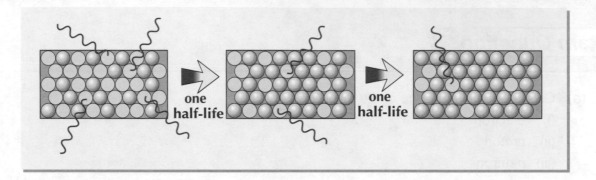

3) <u>How quickly</u> the activity <u>drops off</u> varies a lot. For <u>some</u> substances it takes <u>just a few microseconds</u> before nearly all the unstable nuclei have <u>decayed</u>, whilst for others it can take <u>millions of years</u>.

4) The problem with trying to <u>measure</u> this is that <u>the activity never reaches zero</u>, which is why we have to use the idea of <u>half-life</u> to measure how quickly the activity <u>drops off</u>.

5) Learn this <u>definition</u> of <u>half-life</u>:

> ### <u>HALF-LIFE</u> is the <u>AVERAGE TIME</u> it takes for the <u>NUMBER OF NUCLEI</u> in a <u>RADIOACTIVE ISOTOPE SAMPLE</u> to <u>HALVE</u>.

6) In other words, it is the <u>time it takes</u> for the <u>count rate</u> (the number of radioactive emissions detected per unit of time) from a sample containing the isotope to <u>fall to half its initial level</u>.

7) A <u>short half-life</u> means the <u>activity falls quickly</u>, because <u>lots</u> of the nuclei decay <u>quickly</u>.

8) A <u>long half-life</u> means the activity <u>falls more slowly</u> because <u>most</u> of the nuclei don't decay <u>for a long time</u> — they just sit there, <u>basically unstable</u>, but kind of <u>biding their time</u>.

Half-life measures how quickly the activity of a source drops off

For <u>medical applications</u>, you need to use isotopes that have a <u>suitable half-life</u>.
A radioactive tracer needs to have a short half-life to minimise the risk of damage to the patient.
A radioactive source for sterilising equipment needs to have a long half-life, so you don't have to replace it too often (see page 190 for more). Don't forget that some places have higher levels of background radiation than others — so the people there'll get a <u>higher radiation dose</u>.

Half-Life

Calculating half-life is bound to come up on the exam. So this page is about how to tackle the two main types of half-life questions.

Do *half-life* questions *step by step*

Half-life is maybe a little confusing, but exam calculations are straightforward so long as you do them slowly, STEP BY STEP. Like this one:

> The activity of a radioisotope is 640 cpm (counts per minute).
> Two hours later it has fallen to 80 cpm. Find the half-life of the sample.

ANSWER: You must go through it in short simple steps like this:

INITIAL count:		after ONE half-life:		after TWO half-lives:		after THREE half-lives:
640	(÷2)→	320	(÷2)→	160	(÷2)→	80

Notice the careful step-by-step method, which tells us it takes three half-lives for the activity to fall from 640 to 80. Hence two hours represents three half-lives, so the half-life is 120 mins ÷ 3 = 40 minutes.

(handwritten) 2 hours

(handwritten) Has to be in minutes

Finding *the* half-life *of a sample using a* graph

1) The data for the graph will usually be several readings of count rate taken with a G-M tube and counter.

2) The graph will always be shaped like the one shown.

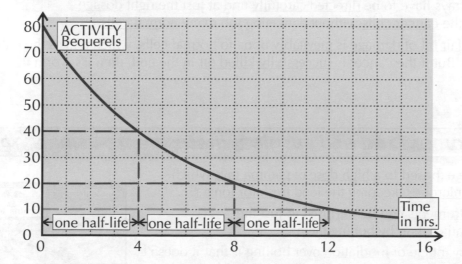

The half-life is found from the graph by finding the time interval on the bottom axis corresponding to a halving of the activity on the vertical axis. Easy peasy really.

So the half-life of the sample is 4 hours.

Uses of Radiation

Radiation gets a lot of bad press, but the fact is it's essential for things like <u>modern medicine</u>.

Smoke detectors — use α-radiation

1) A <u>weak</u> source of <u>alpha</u> radiation is placed in the detector, close to <u>two electrodes</u>.

2) The source causes <u>ionisation</u>, and a <u>current</u> flows between the electrodes.

3) If there is a fire then smoke will <u>absorb</u> the radiation — so the current stops and the <u>alarm sounds</u>.

Tracers in medicine — always short half-life β or γ-emitters

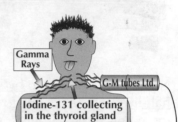

1) Certain <u>radioactive isotopes</u> can be <u>injected</u> into people (or they can just <u>swallow</u> them) and their progress <u>around the body</u> can be followed using an external <u>detector</u>. A computer converts the reading to a <u>display</u> showing where the <u>strongest reading</u> is coming from.

2) A well-known example is the use of <u>iodine-131</u>, which is absorbed by the <u>thyroid gland</u> just like normal iodine-127, but it gives out <u>radiation</u> which can be <u>detected</u> to indicate whether the thyroid gland is <u>taking in iodine</u> as it should.

3) <u>All isotopes</u> which are taken <u>into the body</u> must be <u>GAMMA or BETA</u> emitters (never alpha), so that the radiation <u>passes out of the body</u> — and they should only last <u>a few hours</u>, so that the radioactivity inside the patient <u>quickly disappears</u> (i.e. they should have a <u>short half-life</u>).

Radiotherapy — the treatment of cancer using γ-rays

1) Since high doses of gamma rays will <u>kill all living cells</u>, they can be used to <u>treat cancers</u>.

2) The gamma rays have to be <u>directed carefully</u> and at just the right <u>dosage</u> so as to kill the <u>cancer cells</u> without damaging too many <u>normal cells</u>.

3) However, a <u>fair bit of damage</u> is <u>inevitably</u> done to <u>normal cells</u>, which makes the patient feel <u>very ill</u>. But if the cancer is <u>successfully killed off</u> in the end, then it's worth it.

Sterilisation of food and surgical instruments using γ-rays

1) <u>Food</u> can be exposed to a <u>high dose</u> of <u>gamma rays</u> which will <u>kill</u> all <u>microbes</u>, keeping the food <u>fresh for longer</u>.

2) <u>Medical instruments</u> can be <u>sterilised</u> in just the same way, rather than by <u>boiling them</u>.

3) The great <u>advantage</u> of <u>irradiation</u> over boiling is that it doesn't involve <u>high temperatures</u>, so things like <u>fresh apples</u> or <u>plastic instruments</u> can be totally <u>sterilised</u> without <u>damaging</u> them.

4) The food is <u>not</u> radioactive afterwards, so it's <u>perfectly safe</u> to eat.

5) The isotope used for this needs to be a <u>very strong</u> emitter of <u>gamma rays</u> with a <u>reasonably long half-life</u> (at least several months) so that it doesn't need <u>replacing</u> too often.

Radioactivity Safety

When <u>Marie Curie</u> discovered the radioactive properties of <u>radium</u> in 1898, nobody knew about its dangers. Radium was used to make glow-in-the-dark watches and many <u>watch dial painters</u> developed cancer as a result. We now know lots more about the dangers of radiation...

Radiation harms living cells

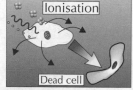
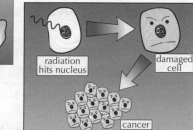

1) <u>Alpha</u>, <u>beta</u> and <u>gamma</u> radiation will cheerfully <u>enter living cells</u> and <u>collide with molecules</u>.

2) These collisions cause <u>ionisation</u>, which <u>damages or destroys</u> the <u>molecules</u>.

3) <u>Lower doses</u> tend to cause <u>minor damage</u> without <u>killing</u> the cell.

4) This can give rise to <u>mutant cells</u> which <u>divide</u> <u>uncontrollably</u>. This is <u>cancer</u>.

5) <u>Higher doses</u> tend to <u>kill cells completely</u>, which causes <u>radiation</u> <u>sickness</u> if a lot of body cells <u>all get hit at once</u>.

6) The <u>extent</u> of the harmful effects depends on <u>two things</u>:

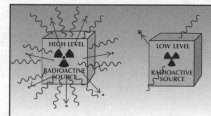

   a) How <u>much exposure</u> you have to the radiation.

   b) The <u>energy and penetration</u> of the radiation, since <u>some types</u> are <u>more hazardous</u> than others, of course.

Outside the body, β and γ–sources are the most dangerous

This is because <u>beta and gamma</u> can get <u>inside</u> to the delicate <u>organs</u>, whereas alpha is much less dangerous because it <u>can't penetrate the skin</u>.

Inside the body, an α-source is the most dangerous

<u>Inside the body</u> alpha sources do all their damage in a <u>very localised area</u>. Beta and gamma sources on the other hand are <u>less dangerous</u> inside the body because they mostly <u>pass straight out</u> without doing much damage.

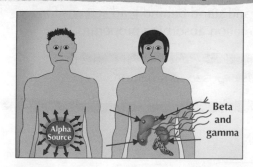

Nuclear radiation + living cells = cell damage, cell death or cancer

Sadly, much of our knowledge of the harmful effects of radiation has come as a result of devastating events such as the <u>atomic bombing</u> of Japan in 1945. In the months following the bombs, <u>thousands</u> suffered from <u>radiation sickness</u> — the symptoms of which include nausea, fatigue, skin burns, hair loss and, in serious cases, death. In the long term, the area has experienced <u>increased rates</u> of cancer.

Radioactivity Safety

The last page was all about the damage that radiation can do to your body. Now here are some ways you can <u>protect</u> yourself <u>against exposure</u> to radiation.

You need to **learn** about these **safety precautions**

Obviously radioactive materials need to be handled <u>carefully</u>.
But in the exam they might ask you to <u>evaluate some specific precautions</u> that should be taken when <u>handling radioactive materials</u>.

1) When conducting experiments, use radioactive sources for as <u>short a time</u> as possible so your <u>exposure</u> is kept to a <u>minimum</u>.

2) <u>Never</u> allow <u>skin contact</u> with a source. Always handle with <u>tongs</u>.

3) Hold the source at <u>arm's length</u> to keep it <u>as far</u> from the body <u>as possible</u>. This will decrease the amount of radiation that hits you, especially for alpha particles as they <u>don't travel far in air</u>.

4) Keep the source <u>pointing away</u> from the body and <u>avoid looking directly at it</u>.

Lead can help **protect** us from **exposure** to **radiation**

1) <u>Lead</u> absorbs all three types of radiation (though a lot of it is needed to stop gamma radiation completely). <u>Always</u> store radioactive sources in a <u>lead box</u> and put them away <u>as soon</u> as the experiment is <u>over</u>.

2) Medical professionals who work with radiation <u>every day</u> (such as radiographers) wear <u>lead aprons</u> and stand behind <u>lead screens</u> for extra protection because of its radiation absorbing properties.

3) When someone needs an X-ray or radiotherapy, only the area of the body that <u>needs to be treated</u> is exposed to radiation.

4) The rest of the body is <u>protected with lead</u> or other <u>radiation absorbing</u> materials.

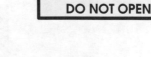

Radiation's dangerous stuff — safety precautions are crucial

Radiation can be harmful to us (see previous page) but following the safety precautions above can <u>minimise</u> our exposure to radiation. Learn all the points above about how to <u>protect</u> yourself in the laboratory, and make sure you can give examples of how <u>medical workers</u> can protect themselves from radiation too.

Warm-Up and Exam Questions

There's no point in skimming through the section and glancing over the questions. Do the warm-up questions and go back over any bits you don't know. Then try the exam questions — without cheating.

Warm-Up Questions

1) How do smoke detectors work?
2) Why is nuclear radiation dangerous?
3) Which type of radiation is most dangerous inside the body — alpha particles or beta particles?
4) Describe two precautions that should be taken when handling radioactive sources in the lab.
5) Give one way in which people who work with radiation can be protected from it.

Exam Questions

1   Which of the following is not a use of gamma radiation? Circle the correct answer.

| treatment of cancer | smoke detectors | sterilising machines | medical tracers |

(1 mark)

2   Nuclear radiation has many uses within medicine.

(a) Suggest **two** reasons why alpha sources aren't used as medical tracers.

(2 marks)

(b) Suggest **one** reason why it is important that radioactive sources used in hospital sterilising machines have a long half-life.

(1 mark)

(c) Explain why the dose of radiation given in radiotherapy is directed only at the tumour.

(1 mark)

3   Nuclear radiation can have harmful effects on the human body.

(a) Briefly explain how a low dose of nuclear radiation can cause cancer.

(2 marks)

(b) Describe what can happen to the body if it receives a very high dose of nuclear radiation.

(1 mark)

4   A sample of a highly ionising radioactive gas has a half-life of two minutes.

(a) Describe what is meant by the term 'half-life'.

(1 mark)

(b) The sample contains a number of unstable atoms.
Calculate the fraction of these atoms that will be present after four minutes.

(1 mark)

(c) A worker holds a sample of the gas in a container using tongs.
Suggest **two** other ways she could protect herself against exposure to radiation from the gas.

(2 marks)

Nuclear Fission

Unstable isotopes aren't just good for medicine — with the right set-up you can generate some <u>serious energy</u>. Read on for how we can use that energy in power stations...

Nuclear fission — the splitting up of big atomic nuclei

1) <u>Nuclear power stations</u> generate electricity using <u>nuclear reactors</u>.

2) In a nuclear reactor, a controlled <u>chain reaction</u> takes place in which atomic nuclei <u>split up</u> and <u>release energy</u> in the form of <u>heat</u>. This heat is then simply used to <u>heat water</u> to make steam, which is used to drive a <u>steam turbine</u> connected to an <u>electricity generator</u>.

3) The "<u>fuel</u>" that's split is usually <u>uranium-235</u>, though sometimes it's <u>plutonium-239</u> (or both).

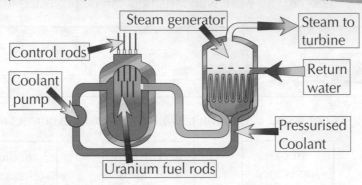

The chain reactions:

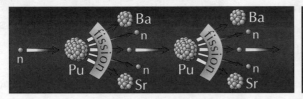 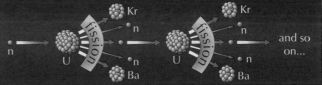

1) For nuclear fission to happen, a <u>slow moving neutron</u> must be <u>absorbed</u> into a uranium or plutonium nucleus. This addition of a neutron makes the nucleus unstable, causing it to <u>split</u>.

2) Each time a <u>uranium</u> or <u>plutonium</u> nucleus <u>splits up</u>, it spits out <u>two or three neutrons</u>, one of which might hit <u>another</u> nucleus, causing it to <u>split</u> also, and thus keeping the <u>chain reaction</u> going.

3) When a large atom splits in two it will form <u>two new smaller nuclei</u>. These new nuclei are usually <u>radioactive</u> because they have the "<u>wrong</u>" number of neutrons in them.

4) A nucleus <u>splitting</u> (called a <u>fission</u>) gives out <u>a lot of energy</u> — lots more energy than you get from any <u>chemical</u> reaction. <u>Nuclear processes</u> release <u>much more energy</u> than chemical processes do. That's why <u>nuclear bombs</u> are <u>so much</u> more <u>powerful</u> than ordinary bombs (which rely on <u>chemical</u> reactions).

5) The <u>main problem</u> with <u>nuclear power</u> is with the disposal of <u>waste</u>. The products left over after nuclear fission are highly <u>radioactive</u>, so they can't just be thrown away. They're very <u>difficult</u> and <u>expensive</u> to dispose of <u>safely</u>.

6) Nuclear <u>fuel</u> is <u>cheap</u> but the <u>overall cost</u> of nuclear power is <u>high</u> due to the cost of the <u>power plant</u> and final <u>decommissioning</u>. Dismantling a nuclear plant safely takes <u>decades</u>.

7) Nuclear power also carries the risk of radiation <u>leaks</u> from the plant or a <u>major catastrophe</u> like <u>Chernobyl</u>.

Nuclear Fusion

Scientists have been looking into producing energy the same way stars do — through <u>fusion</u>.

Nuclear fusion — *the joining of small atomic nuclei*

1) Two <u>light nuclei</u> (e.g. hydrogen) can <u>join</u> to create a larger nucleus — this is called <u>nuclear fusion</u>.

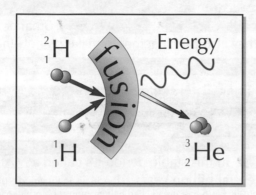

2) Fusion releases <u>a lot</u> of energy (<u>more</u> than fission for a given mass) — all the energy released in <u>stars</u> comes from fusion (see next page). So people are trying to develop <u>fusion reactors</u> to generate <u>electricity</u>.

3) Fusion <u>doesn't</u> leave behind a lot of radioactive <u>waste</u> like fission, and there's <u>plenty</u> of hydrogen knocking about to use as <u>fuel</u>.

4) The <u>big problem</u> is that fusion can only happen at <u>really high temperatures</u> — about <u>10 000 000 °C</u>.

5) You can't hold the hydrogen at the <u>high temperatures</u> and <u>pressures</u> required for fusion in an ordinary container — you need an <u>extremely strong magnetic field</u>.

6) There are a few <u>experimental</u> reactors around, but none of them are generating electricity yet. At the moment it takes <u>more power</u> to get up to temperature than the reactor can <u>produce</u>.

Ten million degrees — *that's hot...*

It'd be great if we could get nuclear fusion to work — there's loads of fuel available and it doesn't create much radioactive waste compared with fission. It's a shame that at the moment we need to use more energy to create the conditions for fusion than we can get out of it. Make sure you know the <u>pros</u> and <u>cons</u> of fission and fusion.

The Life Cycle of Stars

Stars go through <u>many traumatic stages</u> in their lives — just like teenagers.

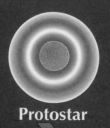

Protostar

1) Stars <u>initially form</u> from <u>clouds of DUST AND GAS</u>. The <u>force of gravity</u> makes the gas and dust <u>spiral in together</u> to form a <u>protostar</u>.

2) <u>Gravitational energy</u> is converted into <u>heat energy</u>, so the <u>temperature rises</u>. When the temperature gets <u>high enough</u>, <u>hydrogen nuclei</u> undergo <u>nuclear fusion</u> to form <u>helium nuclei</u> and give out massive amounts of <u>heat and light</u>. A star is born. Smaller masses of gas and dust may also pull together to make <u>planets</u> that orbit the star.

Main Sequence Star

3) The star immediately enters a <u>long stable period</u>, where the <u>heat created</u> by the nuclear fusion provides an <u>outward pressure</u> to <u>balance the force of gravity</u> pulling everything <u>inwards</u>. The star maintains its energy output for <u>millions of years</u> due to the <u>massive amounts of hydrogen</u> it consumes. In this <u>stable</u> period it's called a <u>MAIN SEQUENCE STAR</u> and it lasts <u>several billion years</u>. (The Sun is in the middle of this stable period — or to put it another way, the <u>Earth</u> has already had <u>half its innings</u> before the Sun <u>engulfs</u> it!)

Stars much bigger than the Sun

Stars about the same size as the Sun

4) Eventually the <u>hydrogen</u> begins to <u>run out</u>. <u>Heavier elements</u> such as iron are made by nuclear fusion of <u>helium</u>. The star then <u>swells</u> into a <u>RED GIANT</u>, if it's a small star, or a <u>RED SUPER GIANT</u> if it's a big star. It becomes <u>red</u> because the surface <u>cools</u>.

Red Giant

Red Super Giant

White Dwarf

5) A <u>small-to-medium</u>-sized star like the Sun then becomes unstable and <u>ejects</u> its <u>outer layer</u> of <u>dust and gas</u> as a <u>PLANETARY NEBULA</u>.

6) This leaves behind a hot, dense solid core — a <u>WHITE DWARF</u>, which just cools down to a <u>BLACK DWARF</u> and eventually disappears.

Neutron Star...

...or Black Hole

Supernova

7) <u>Big stars</u>, however, start to <u>glow brightly again</u> as they undergo more <u>fusion</u> and <u>expand and contract several times</u>, forming elements as <u>heavy as iron</u> in various <u>nuclear reactions</u>. Eventually they <u>explode</u> in a <u>SUPERNOVA</u>, forming elements <u>heavier than iron</u> and ejecting them into the universe to <u>form new planets and stars</u>.

8) The <u>exploding supernova</u> throws the outer layers of <u>dust and gas</u> into space, leaving a <u>very dense core</u> called a <u>NEUTRON STAR</u>. If the star is <u>big enough</u> this will become a <u>BLACK HOLE</u>.

Only big stars become black holes

The early universe contained <u>only hydrogen</u>, the simplest and lightest element. It's only thanks to nuclear fusion inside stars that we have any of the other <u>naturally occurring elements</u>. Remember — the heaviest element produced in stable stars is iron, but it takes a <u>supernova</u> (or a lab) to create <u>the rest</u>.

Warm-Up and Exam Questions

The end of the last section — sad times. Make sure you've understood it all by doing these questions (and the revision summary on the next page).

Warm-Up Questions

1) Name two elements often used as nuclear fuel.
2) What does nuclear fission produce in addition to energy? Why is this a problem?
3) What are stars formed from?
4) Will our Sun become a black hole? Explain your answer.
5) At the end of its main sequence phase, what does a small star become?

Exam Questions

1   Nuclear reactors often use uranium-235.

(a) Describe how a chain reaction is set up in a nuclear reactor.

(4 marks)

(b) Describe how the heat energy released by nuclear fission is used to generate electricity.

(2 marks)

2   The table shows some information about various elements and isotopes.

Element/isotope	Deuterium	Hydrogen	Krypton	Plutonium	Thorium	Tin
Relative mass	2	1	84	239	232	119

(a) Name the **two** substances in the table that would be most likely to be used in a fusion reaction.

(2 marks)

(b) Explain why scientists are interested in developing fusion power.

(2 marks)

(c) Explain why fusion is not used to generate electricity at present.

(1 mark)

3   Stars go through many stages in their lives.

(a) Describe how a star is formed.

(3 marks)

(b) The stable period of a main sequence star can last millions of years.
Explain why main sequence stars undergo a stable period.

(2 marks)

(c) When main sequence stars begin to run out of hydrogen in their core, they swell and become either a red giant or a super red giant depending on their size.

(i)   Describe what happens to small stars after their red giant phase.

(3 marks)

(ii) Describe what happens to big stars after their super red giant phase.

(3 marks)

Revision Summary for Physics 2b

There's some pretty heavy physics in this section. But just take it one page at a time and it's really not so bad. You're even allowed to go back through the pages for a sneaky peak if you get stuck on any of the questions below...

1)* An AC supply of electricity has a time period of 0.08 s. What is its frequency?

2) Name the three wires in a three-core cable.

3) Sketch and label a properly wired three-pin plug.

4) Explain fully how a fuse and earth wire work together.

5) How does an RCCB stop you from getting electrocuted?

6)* Which uses more energy, a 45 W pair of hair straighteners used for 5 minutes, or a 105 W hair dryer used for 2 minutes?

7)* Find the appropriate fuse (3 A, 5 A or 13 A) for these appliances:
   a) a toaster rated at 230 V, 1100 W   b) an electric heater rated at 230 V, 2000 W

8)* Calculate the energy transformed by a torch using a 6 V battery when 530 C of charge pass through.

9) Explain how the experiments of Rutherford and Marsden led to the nuclear model of the atom.

10) Draw a table stating the relative mass and charge of the three basic subatomic particles.

11) True or false: radioactive decay can be triggered by certain chemical reactions?

12) What type of subatomic particle is a beta particle?

13) Sketch the paths of an alpha particle and a beta particle travelling through an electric field.

14) List two places where the level of background radiation is increased and explain why.

15) Name three occupations that have an increased risk of exposure to radiation.

16) What is the definition of half-life?

17) Give an example of how gamma radiation can be used in medicine.

18) Which is the most dangerous form of radiation if you eat it? Why?

19) Draw a diagram to illustrate the fission of uranium-235 and explain how the chain reaction works.

20) What is the main environmental problem associated with nuclear power?

21) What is nuclear fusion? Why is it difficult to construct a working fusion reactor?

22) Describe the steps that lead to the formation of a main sequence star (like our Sun).

*Answers on page 250.

GCSE AQA Additional Science

Unit Biology 2

Higher Tier

In addition to this paper you should have:
- A ruler.
- A calculator.

Centre name				
Centre number				
Candidate number				

Time allowed:
- 60 minutes

Surname	
Other names	
Candidate signature	

Instructions to candidates
- Write your name and other details in the spaces provided above.
- Answer **all** questions in the spaces provided.
- Do all rough work on the paper.

Information for candidates
- The marks available are given in brackets at the end of each question.
- There are 7 questions in this paper.
- There are 60 marks available for this paper.
- You are allowed to use a calculator.
- You should answer Question 4(b) and Question 7(c) with continuous prose. You will be assessed on the quality of your English, the organisation of your ideas and your use of appropriate specialist vocabulary.

For examiner's use

Q	Attempt Nº			Q	Attempt Nº		
	1	2	3		1	2	3
1				5			
2				6			
3				7			
4				Total			

Advice to candidates
- In calculations show clearly how you worked out your answers.

Answer **all** questions in the spaces provided

1   Jeremy and Trisha investigated the organisms that live in a field next to their school.

1 (a)   They each counted the number of plants in the area of the field they were standing in using a 1 m² quadrat. They got the following results.

| Plant | Number counted per m² | | Mean per m² |
	Jeremy	Trisha	
Dandelions	5	7	6
Clover		96	89
Nettles	23	19	21
Buttercups	57	63	

1 (a) (i)   Fill in the missing numbers in the results table above.

(2 marks)

1 (a) (ii)   The field measures 50 m by 70 m. Use the data in the table to estimate the total population of dandelions in the field.

....

....

....

(2 marks)

1 (b) Suggest how Jeremy and Trisha could improve their investigation.

....

....

....

....

(2 marks)

$\boxed{6}$

Turn over for the next question

Turn over ▶

2   Some pondweed was used to investigate how the amount of light available affects the rate of photosynthesis.

The apparatus that was used for this experiment is shown below.

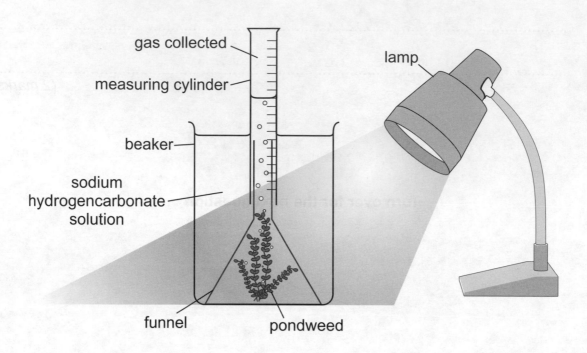

2 (a)   What gas is being collected in the measuring cylinder?

....

(1 mark)

2 (b)   What would happen to the volume of gas collected if the investigation was repeated with the lamp turned off? Give a reason for your answer.

....

....

....

(2 marks)

2 (c) Sodium hydrogen carbonate dissolves in water and releases carbon dioxide.

Suggest why sodium hydrogen carbonate was added to the water in this experiment.

....

....

....

(2 marks)

2 (d) Explain how temperature affects the rate of photosynthesis and suggest how this could be controlled in the experiment.

....

....

....

....

....

....

(3 marks)

2 (e) When plants photosynthesise they produce glucose.
Give **three** ways plants use the glucose they produce.

1. ....

2. ....

3. ....

(3 marks)

11

Turn over for the next question

Turn over ▶

3   The diagram below shows the stomach. The stomach is an organ.
It is an important part of the digestive system.

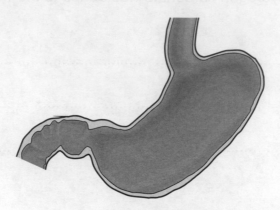

3 (a)   State what is meant by the term **organ**.

....

....
(1 mark)

3 (b)   The stomach contains different tissues.
Name **two** types of tissue found in the stomach and describe the role of each.

Tissue: ....

Role: ....

....

Tissue: ....

Role: ....

....
(4 marks)

5

4 The diagram below shows a single celled organism called *Euglena*, found in pond water.

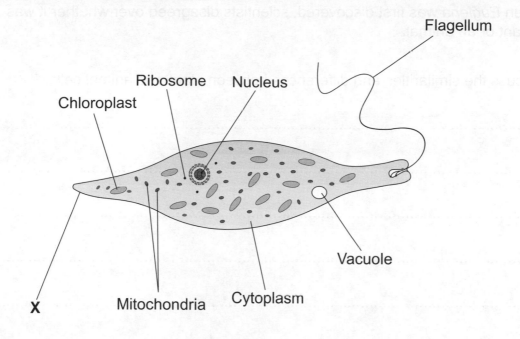

4 (a) Name part **X** and state its function.

....

....

(2 marks)

Question 4 continues on the next page

Turn over ▶

4 (b) *In this question you will be assessed on the quality of your English, the organisation of your ideas and your use of appropriate specialist vocabulary.*

When *Euglena* was first discovered, scientists disagreed over whether it was a plant or an animal.

Discuss the similarities and differences between plant and animal cells.

....

....

....

....

....

....

....

....

....

(6 marks)

8

5   Gregor Mendel proposed the idea of separate 'hereditary units'.
In one experiment he investigated the inheritance of round or wrinkled seed coats
in pea plants. The allele for round seed coats (R) is dominant over the allele for
wrinkled seed coats (r).

Mendel first crossed pure-breeding round seed plants (RR) with pure-breeding
wrinkled seed plants (rr). All the offspring had round seeds.

5 (a)   Explain how the experiment shows that the allele for round seeds is dominant.

....

....
(2 marks)

5 (b)   He then crossed the offspring together.

5 (b)(i)   Draw a genetic diagram to show the predicted results of this cross.

(3 marks)

Question 5 continues on the next page

Turn over ▶

5 (b) (ii) When Mendel crossed the offspring, 7324 plants were produced. 5474 of these had round seed coats and the other 1850 had wrinkled seed coats.

Calculate the ratio of round to wrinkled seed coats in Mendel's results. Give your answer to **two** decimal places.

....

....

(2 marks)

5 (b) (iii) Explain why this ratio does not exactly match the ratio predicted by your genetic diagram.

....

....

(1 mark)

5 (c) Suggest **one** reason why Mendel's proposal was not recognised by scientists until after his death.

....

....

(1 mark)

6   Nancy is a cyclist. A sports physiologist has produced a graph to show how the concentration of lactic acid in her blood changes with different work rates.

6 (a) (i) Describe the trend shown by the graph.

....

....

....

(2 marks)

6 (a) (ii) Suggest a reason for the trend you have described above.

....

....

....

....

(3 marks)

Question 6 continues on the next page

Turn over ▶

6 (b) Nancy takes part in a sprint race. Describe what will happen to Nancy's pulse rate and breathing rate immediately after her race, and explain why.

....

....

....

....

....

....

(3 marks)

8

7 Enzymes have many uses in the home and in industry.

7 (a) The enzyme amylase is often used in biological washing powders.

Asif did an experiment on the effect of temperature on the action of amylase. The graph below shows Asif's results.

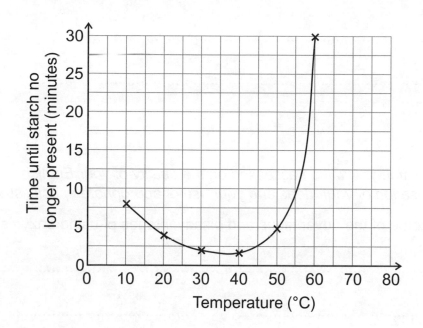

7 (a) (i) Use the graph to estimate the optimum temperature for this enzyme.

....
(1 mark)

7 (a) (ii) Explain the results between 50 °C and 60 °C.

....

....

....
(2 marks)

7 (a) (iii) Name **two** enzymes other than amylase that are often used in biological detergents.

1. ....

2. ....
(2 marks)

Question 7 continues on the next page

Turn over ▶

7 (b) Describe **two** ways that enzymes are used in the food industry.

1. ....

....

2. ....

....

(2 marks)

7 (c) *In this question you will be assessed on the quality of your English,*
the organisation of your ideas and your use of appropriate specialist vocabulary.

Discuss some of the advantages and disadvantages of using enzymes in industry.

....

....

....

....

....

....

....

....

....

....

(6 marks)

13

END OF QUESTIONS

CGP — Practice Exam Paper GCSE Additional Science

GCSE AQA Additional Science

Unit Chemistry 2

Higher Tier

In addition to this paper you should have:
• A ruler.
• A calculator.

Centre name				
Centre number				
Candidate number				

Time allowed:
• 60 minutes

Surname	
Other names	
Candidate signature	

Instructions to candidates
• Write your name and other details in the spaces provided above.
• Answer **all** questions in the spaces provided.
• Do all rough work on the paper.

Information for candidates
• The marks available are given in brackets at the end of each question.
• There are 9 questions in this paper.
• There are 60 marks available for this paper.
• You are allowed to use a calculator.
• You should answer Question 4(a) and 6 with continuous prose.
  You will be assessed on the quality of your English, the organisation
  of your ideas and your use of appropriate specialist vocabulary.

Advice to candidates
• In calculations show clearly how you worked out your answers.

For examiner's use						
Q	Attempt Nº			Q	Attempt Nº	
	1	2	3		1	2	3
1				6			
2				7			
3				8			
4				9			
5							
Total						

214

1   Read the information in the box and answer the questions that follow.

> Ammonium nitrate (NH_4NO_3) is an ionic substance.
>
> Relative atomic masses: H = 1, N = 14, O = 16.

1 (a)   Calculate the relative formula mass of ammonium nitrate.

Show clearly how you work out your answer.

....

....

Relative formula mass = ...

(2 marks)

1 (b)   Calculate the percentage of nitrogen in ammonium nitrate.

Show clearly how you work out your answer.

....

....

Percentage of nitrogen = ...%

(1 mark)

1 (c)   Describe the physical properties you would expect ammonium nitrate to have.

....

....

....

....

(4 marks)

7

2   Silver is a metallic element which occurs naturally as two isotopes, Ag-107 and Ag-109.

2 (a)   The relative atomic mass of silver is 108.

Explain what is meant by the term 'relative atomic mass'.

....

....

....
(2 marks)

2 (b)   All metallic elements have a similar structure that is determined by the way in which the atoms bond.

Draw a labelled diagram to represent the bonding within silver.

(1 mark)

Question 2 continues on the next page

Turn over ▶

2 (c) How does the structure of silver explain the following properties?

2 (c) (i) High thermal conductivity.

....

....

(1 mark)

2 (c) (ii) Ability to be bent and shaped.

....

....

(1 mark)

2 (d) Silver nanoparticles have been found to have an antibacterial action.

What are nanoparticles?

....

(1 mark)

$\boxed{\dfrac{}{6}}$

3 (a) Fullerenes are covalent substances that consist purely of carbon atoms.

Give **two** uses of fullerenes.

....

....

(2 marks)

3 (b)(i) Graphite is also a covalent substance that contains only carbon atoms.

Explain why graphite can conduct electricity.

....

....

(1 mark)

3 (b)(ii) Graphite is soft and slippery. Explain why.

....

....

(1 mark)

3 (c) Give **one** other covalent substance that only contains carbon atoms
and explain how its structure is different from graphite and from fullerenes.

....

....

....

....

....

(3 marks)

7

Turn over for the next question

4 (a) *In this question you will be assessed on the quality of your English, the organisation of your ideas and your use of appropriate specialist vocabulary.*

Thermosetting and thermosoftening polymers have different properties.

Describe and explain the properties of thermosetting and thermosoftening polymers.

....

....

....

....

....

....

....

....

....

....

....

(6 marks)

4 (b) The table below shows the properties of three different polymers, **A-C**.

Polymer	Properties of polymer
A	low melting point and flexible
B	high melting point and rigid
C	high melting point and flexible

4 (b)(i) Give the polymer that is most suitable for use for insulation around an electric lead.

....

(1 mark)

4 (b)(ii) Give the polymer that is most suitable to make a work surface.

....

(1 mark)

4 (b)(iii) Polymers **A-C** are made using a polymerisation reaction.

Give **two** factors that can be changed during the reaction to give polymers with different properties.

1. ....

2. ....

(2 marks)

10

Turn over for the next question

Turn over ▶

5   Self-heating cans use **exothermic** chemical reactions to heat up their contents.
When a seal is broken two chemicals mix and react, heating up the can.
Calcium oxide and water can be used to heat up drinks in this way.

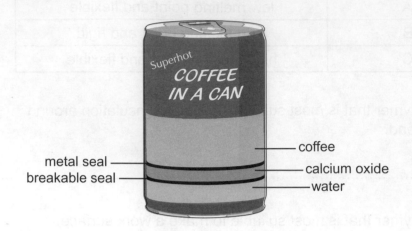

5 (a)   What is an exothermic reaction?

....

(1 mark)

5 (b)   A student wanted to test the reaction of different substances with water
to see if they could be used to cool drinks down.

Outline an experiment the student could carry out to test different substances.

....

....

....

....

(2 marks)

5 (c)   Describe what an endothermic reaction is.

....

....

(1 mark)

4

6

In this question you will be assessed on the quality of your English, the organisation of your ideas and your use of appropriate specialist vocabulary.

A chemicals business has just appointed a new director. The business has been making product X for 10 years without the use of a catalyst. The new director has decided to introduce a catalyst into the process.

Describe the advantages and disadvantages of this decision.

....

....

....

....

....

....

....

....

....

....

....

(6 marks)

6

Turn over for the next question

Turn over ▶

222

7   The graph shows the volume of gas produced over time when lumps of zinc
     are reacted with dilute sulfuric acid.

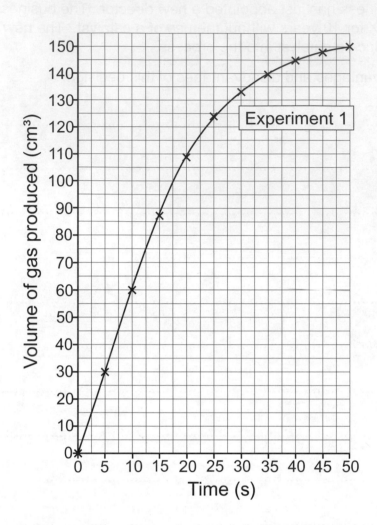

7 (a)   Calculate the rate of reaction (in cm³/s) for the reaction during the
         first ten seconds.

....

(1 mark)

In a second experiment, some copper sulfate catalyst was added to the acid.
The same amounts of zinc and dilute sulfuric acid were used as before.
The results are shown in the table.

Time (secs)	Volume of gas formed (cm³) Experiment 2
0	0
5	50
10	100
15	130
20	143
25	148
30	150
35	150
40	150
45	150
50	150

7 (b) Plot the results of the second experiment on the graph.

Draw a curve of best fit through the points. Label the line 'Experiment 2'.

(2 marks)

7 (c) How long does it take to form half of the total amount of gas collected in the second experiment?

....

(1 mark)

7 (d) What do the curves show about how the rate of reaction changes as the reaction proceeds?

....

(1 mark)

7 (e) How does the catalyst affect the reaction rate? ....

How can you tell this from the graph?

....

....

(1 mark)

6

Turn over for the next question

Turn over ▶

8   Tiffany is doing an experiment to investigate the electrolysis of
sodium chloride solution.

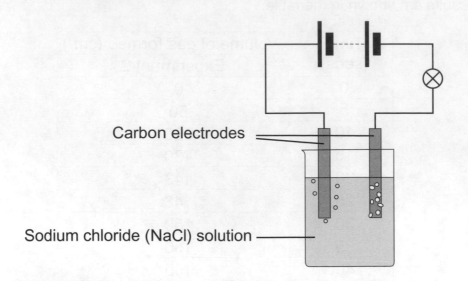

Carbon electrodes

Sodium chloride (NaCl) solution

8 (a)   The reaction at each electrode can be described by a half equation.

Complete the half equations for the reaction occurring at each electrode.

positive electrode   .... $Cl^- \rightarrow Cl_2 +$ ....

negative electrode   .... $H^+ +$ .... $\rightarrow H_2$

(2 marks)

8 (b)   At the end of her experiment, Tiffany is left with three products.

8 (b)(i)   Name the product that is left in the solution.

....

(1 mark)

8 (b)(ii) Give **one** industrial use for this product.

....

(1 mark)

8 (b)(iii) Give **two** industrial uses for the chlorine produced.

....

(2 marks)

8 (c)   Electrolysis can also be used in a process called electroplating.

What is electroplating?

....

(1 mark)

9   Soluble salts can be made by reacting an acid with an insoluble base or an alkali.

9 (a) (i) An excess of zinc oxide is added to a beaker of dilute hydrochloric acid.
The mixture is stirred and the acid is neutralised.

dilute hydrochloric acid

excess of zinc oxide

How could you tell when all the acid has been neutralised?

....
(1 mark)

9 (a) (ii) Give the products of this reaction.

....
(2 marks)

9 (b)   Describe how you could obtain pure, dry crystals of potassium chloride
from the alkali potassium hydroxide and dilute hydrochloric acid.

....

....

....

....
(4 marks)

7

END OF QUESTIONS

GCSE AQA Additional Science

Unit Physics 2

Higher Tier

In addition to this paper you should have:
* A ruler.
* A calculator.

Centre name				
Centre number				
Candidate number				

Time allowed:
* 60 minutes

Surname
Other names
Candidate signature

Instructions to candidates
* Write your name and other details in the spaces provided above.
* Answer **all** questions in the spaces provided.
* Do all rough work on the paper.
* You are allowed to use a calculator.

Information for candidates
* The marks available are given in brackets at the end of each question.
* You may get marks for method, even if your answer is incorrect.
* There are 9 questions in this paper.
* There are 60 marks available for this paper.
* You should answer Questions 5(b) and 8(d) with continuous prose.
  You will be assessed on the quality of your English, the organisation
  of your ideas and your use of appropriate specialist vocabulary.

For examiner's use

Q	Attempt Nº			Q	Attempt Nº		
	1	2	3		1	2	3
1				6			
2				7			
3				8			
4				9			
5							
Total							

Advice to candidates
* In calculations show clearly how you worked out your answers.

Answer **all** questions in the spaces provided

1   The diagram shows two children driving dodgem cars.

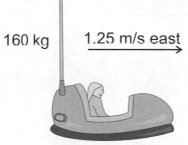

200 kg   2.5 m/s east   160 kg   1.25 m/s east

Dodgem Car P   Dodgem Car K
Momentum = 500 kg m/s   Momentum = 200 kg m/s

1 (a)   The two dodgem cars collide when **Car P** drives into the back of **Car K**.
Calculate the total momentum of the two cars:

1 (a) (i)   before the collision.

....

....

momentum = ... kg m/s to the east
(1 mark)

1 (a) (ii)   immediately after the collision. Include units and a direction in your answer.

momentum = ...
(1 mark)

1 (b)   Immediately after the collision, **Car P** dodgem car travels with a momentum of
200 kg m/s to the east.

Calculate the velocity of **Car K** dodgem car after the collision.
Include the direction of travel in your answer.

Clearly show how you work out your answer.

....

....

....

velocity = ... m/s to the ....
(4 marks)

Turn over for the next question

6

Turn over ▶

228

2   Terence drives along a flat, straight road before braking and stopping at a
     set of traffic lights. The velocity-time graph below shows Terence's motion.

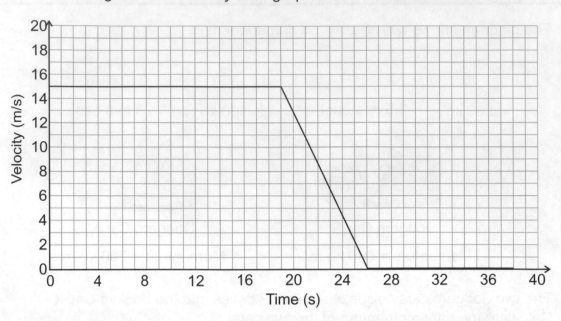

2 (a)   Use the graph to calculate Terence's acceleration between 19 s and 26 s.

     ....

     ....

                                        acceleration = ... m/s²
                                                                    (2 marks)

2 (b)   What happens to the temperature of the car brakes when they
         are applied to slow the car down? Explain why this happens.

     ....

     ....
                                                                    (2 marks)

2 (c) Terence's friend drives a car that has a regenerative braking system. Give **one** advantage of regenerative braking systems over traditional braking systems.

....

....

(1 mark)

2 (d) Both the thinking distance and braking distance of a car increase with speed. Describe **two** other factors that might increase the thinking distance.

....

....

(2 marks)

7

Turn over for the next question

3   The diagram shows a shopper walking around a supermarket pushing a trolley.

To push her empty trolley at a constant speed, she needs a force of 20 N.

3 (a)   Calculate how much work the shopper does if she pushes her empty trolley 300 m.

Clearly show how you work out your answer.

....

....

work done = ...J

(2 marks)

3 (b)   The shopper averages a power of 15 W.
Calculate how long it will take her to push the trolley 300 m.

Clearly show how you work out your answer.

....

....

time = ...s

(2 marks)

4

4   Modern cars have many safety features.

4 (a)   Air bags are one example of a safety feature found in many cars.
Explain how air bags help protect passengers during a crash.

....

....

(2 marks)

4 (b)   Seat belts are made from an elastic material. They stretch slightly during a
collision to reduce the risk of injury on the passengers.

The material used for one type of seat belt has a spring constant of 180 000 N/m.
Calculate the extension of the seat belt if the force on a passenger in a crash is
13 500 N.

Clearly show how you work out your answer and give the unit.

....

....

....

extension = ...

(3 marks)

5

Turn over for the next question

Turn over ▶

5   A free-fall skydiver jumps from an aeroplane and his motion is recorded.
     After his jump he looks at this velocity-time graph of his fall.

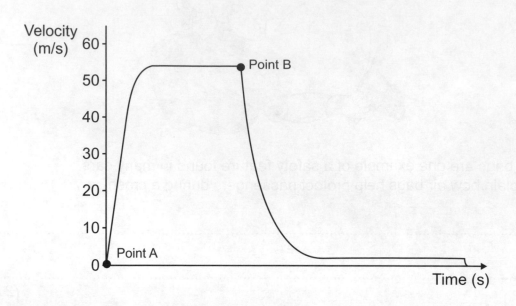

5 (a)   The skydiver has a mass of 83 kg. Calculate his weight.
        Use acceleration due to gravity = 10 N/kg.

        Clearly show how you work out your answer.

        ....

        ....

                              weight = ... N

                                                                      (2 marks)

5 (b)   *In this question you will be assessed on the quality of your English, the
        organisation of your ideas and your use of appropriate specialist vocabulary.*

        Describe the motion of the skydiver from **point A** to **point B** on the graph,
        in terms of the forces acting on him.

        ....

        ....

        ....

        ....

        ....

                                                                      (6 marks)

8

6 Two electric circuits are shown in the diagram below.

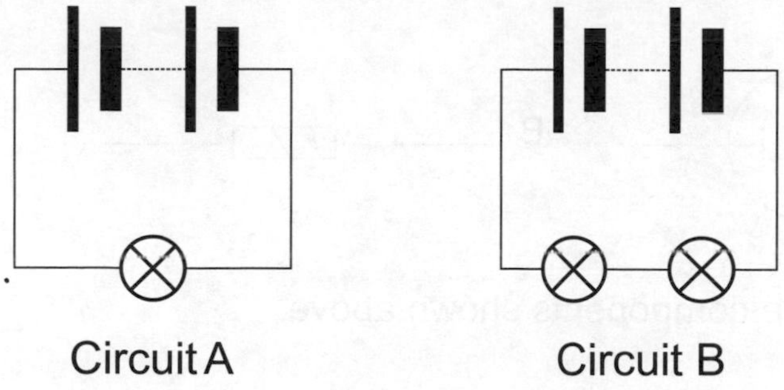

Circuit A   Circuit B

6 (a) All the lamps used are identical. Compare the resistance and current in **circuit B** with **circuit A**.

....

....
(2 marks)

6 (b) An ammeter and a voltmeter are added to **circuit A**.
They show readings of 0.5 A and 3 V respectively.

Calculate the power of the lamp.

Clearly show how you work out your answer.

....

....

power = ... W
(2 marks)

Question 6 continues on the next page

234

The following components are added to Circuit A.

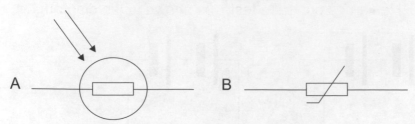

6 (c) (i) Name each of the components shown above.

A ....

B ....

(2 marks)

6 (c) (ii) Describe what happens to the resistance of component A as the intensity of the light that falls on it increases.

....

(1 mark)

7

7 Steven is carrying out an experiment to find out what types of radiation are emitted by a source. He carries out three tests, as shown in the diagram.

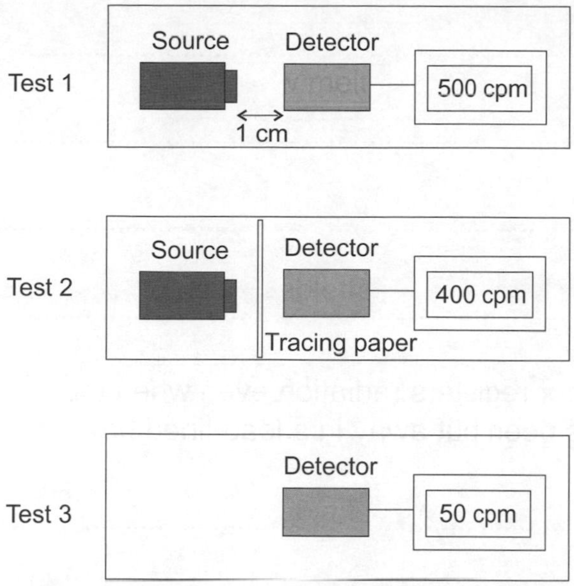

Steven's results show that the source is emitting more than one type of radiation.

7 (a) What type of radiation is the source definitely emitting?
Give a reason for your answer.

....

(1 mark)

7 (b) Steven points the source into a uniform electric field. He observes the paths of two types of nuclear radiation shown in the diagram below.

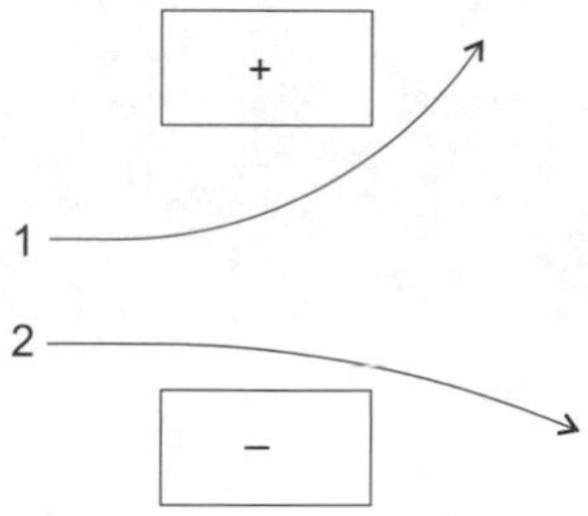

7 (b)(i) Name the **two** types of radiation detected in this experiment.

....

(1 mark)

Question 7 continues on the next page

Turn over ▶

7 (b)(ii) Explain why the two types of radiation are deflected in opposite directions and by different directions as they travel through the electric field.

....

....

....

....

(3 marks)

7 (c) Explain why the detector registers radiation even when the radioactive source has been put away in a lead-lined box.

....

(1 mark)

6

8 Nuclear reactors in power stations and submarines release energy through nuclear fission.

8 (a) Describe what is meant by the term nuclear fission.

....

....

(1 mark)

8 (b) Name **one** nuclear fuel commonly used in nuclear reactors.

....

(1 mark)

Scientists are trying to develop reactors in which energy is released through nuclear fusion.

8 (c) Describe what is meant by the term nuclear fusion.

....

....

(1 mark)

Question 8 continues on the next page

Turn over ▶

8 (d) *In this question you will be assessed on the quality of your English, the organisation of your ideas and your use of appropriate specialist vocabulary.*

Evaluate the advantages and disadvantages of nuclear fusion over nuclear fission as a method of generating electricity.

....

....

....

....

....

....

....

....

....

....

(6 marks)

9

9 A student wanted to know how the current flowing through a filament lamp changes with the potential difference across it. She set up this circuit.

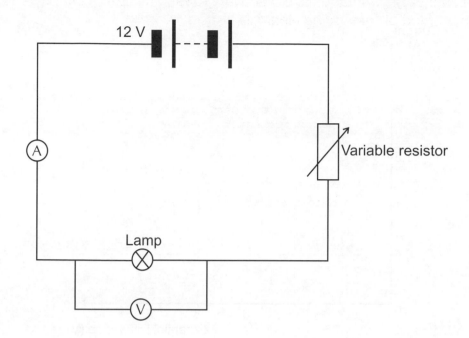

She used a variable resistor to change the potential difference across the lamp.

Here are the results the student got as she changed the potential difference across the lamp.

Voltmeter (V)	Ammeter (A)
0.0	0.0
3.0	1.0
5.0	1.4
7.0	1.7
9.0	1.9
11.0	2.1

Question 9 continues on the next page

9 (a) Use her results to draw a graph of current against potential difference for the lamp on the axes below. Draw a smooth curve through the points.

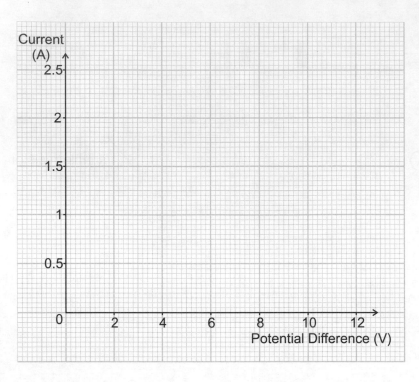

(2 marks)

9 (b) Describe and explain, in terms of particle collisions, what happens to the resistance of the lamp as the current through it increases.

....

....

....

....

(3 marks)

9 (c) Use your graph to find the current when the potential difference is 10 V.

current = ... A

(1 mark)

9 (d) Use your answer to **(c)** to calculate the resistance of the lamp when the potential difference is 10 V. Include units in your answer.

....

....

resistance = ...

(2 marks)

END OF QUESTIONS

Page 25

Warm-Up Questions

1) Plant cells have a rigid cell wall, they have a permanent vacuole and they contain chloroplasts.

2) Diffusion is the spreading out of particles from an area of high concentration to an area of low concentration.

3) (a) To carry oxygen.

(b) Any two of, e.g. concave shape gives the red blood cells a large surface area for absorbing oxygen / concave shape helps the red blood cells pass through capillaries to body cells / no nucleus maximises the space for haemoglobin.

4) differentiation

5) An organ system is a group of organs working together to perform a particular function.

6) Any five of, e.g. salivary glands / pancreas / liver / stomach / large intestine / small intestine.

Exam Questions

1 (a) C *(1 mark)*

(b) Chlorophyll *(1 mark)*

(c) E.g. it has a tall shape/a large surface area for absorbing carbon dioxide *(1 mark)*.

2 (a) B — it has a higher concentration of glucose outside the cell than inside *(1 mark)*, so glucose will diffuse into the cell *(1 mark)*.

(b) E.g. oxygen *(1 mark)*

Pages 31-32

Warm-Up Questions

1) Carbon dioxide, water, (sun)light, chlorophyll.

2) A limiting factor is something that stops photosynthesis from happening any faster.

3)

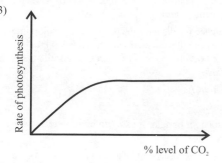

4) E.g. by using a paraffin heater.

5) respiration

Exam Questions

1 Making cell walls — cellulose *(1 mark)*
Making proteins — amino acids *(1 mark)*
Storing energy — starch *(1 mark)*

2 (a) epidermis/epidermal tissue *(1 mark)*

(b) Any two of, e.g. mesophyll tissue / xylem / phloem *(1 mark each)*

3 (a) (i) At the higher temperature the molecules/enzymes work more rapidly / there are more collisions and more energetic collisions between reacting molecules, so the rate of photosynthesis is quicker. *(1 mark)*

(ii) At 50 °C the enzymes are denatured/the plant dies. *(1 mark)*

(b) In the experiment the rate was highest at this temperature *(1 mark)*, but the optimum could actually be anywhere between 30 °C and 50 °C (where no measurements were made) *(1 mark)*.

4 (a) By counting the number of bubbles produced/measuring the volume of gas produced, in a given time/at regular intervals *(1 mark)*.

(b) (i) The rate of photosynthesis/number of bubbles/volume of gas *(1 mark)*.

(ii) The light intensity *(1 mark)*.

(c) E.g. carbon dioxide concentration in the water/temperature/the plant being used *(1 mark)*.

5 (a) A label anywhere on the sloping part of the graph, before it levels off *(1 mark)*.

(b) Carbon dioxide concentration / temperature / amount of chlorophyll / amount of water *(1 mark)*.

6 (a) Chlorophyll *(1 mark)*.

(b) (i)

(1 mark)

(ii) Plants need both chlorophyll and light to photosynthesise and produce starch — there is only chlorophyll in the green area of the plant *(1 mark)*, and light can only reach parts of the leaf not covered by black paper *(1 mark)*.

Page 36

Warm-Up Questions

1) Where an organism is found.

2) A quadrat is a square frame enclosing a known area.

3) The median is the middle value, in order of size, so it's 8.

4) transect

Exam Questions

1 (a) 21 *(1 mark)*

(b) (i) 6 + 15 + 9 + 14 + 20 + 5 + 3 + 11 + 10 + 7 = 100 *(1 mark)*
$100/10 = 10$ dandelions per m^2 *(1 mark)*

(ii) $90 \times 120 = 10\ 800\ m^2$ *(1 mark)*
$10 \times 10\ 800 = 108\ 000$ dandelions in field F *(1 mark)*

(c) Anna's, because she used a larger sample size (20 quadrats per field, whereas Paul only used 10) *(1 mark)*.

Page 42

Warm-Up Questions

1) A catalyst is a substance that increases the speed of a reaction, without being changed or used up in the reaction.

2) The optimum pH is the pH at which the enzyme works best.

3) They break down big molecules into smaller ones.

4) (a) amylase

(b) protease

(c) lipase

Proteases break down proteins, and lipases break down lipids (fats).

5) (a) sugars

(b) amino acids

(c) glycerol and fatty acids

Exam Questions

1 (a) The enzyme has a specific shape which will only fit with one type of substance *(1 mark)*.

(b) In the wrong conditions (e.g. high temperatures), the bonds in the enzyme are broken/the enzyme changes shape, so the substance can no longer fit into it/the enzyme won't work anymore *(1 mark)*.
If you heat a substance you supply it with energy and it moves about more. This helps things to react faster. But if you heat an enzyme too much, it jiggles about such a lot that it ends up breaking some of the bonds that hold it together and it loses its shape. A similar thing happens with pH — the wrong pH disrupts the bonds and the shape is changed.

2 (a)

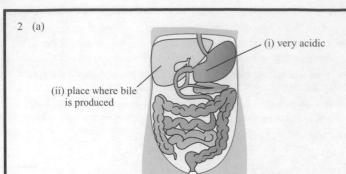

(i) very acidic

(ii) place where bile is produced

(1 mark for each)

The acidic part is the stomach.
The liver is where bile is produced.

(b) (i) It stores bile until it is ready to be released *(1 mark)*

(ii) It produces protease, amylase and lipase enzymes *(1 mark)* and releases them into the small intestine *(1 mark)*.

3 (a) Accept answers between 38 °C and 40 °C *(1 mark)*.

(b) Enzyme B, because it has an unusually high optimum temperature which it would need to work in the hot vent *(1 mark)*.

Page 47
Warm-Up Questions

1) Respiration is the process of breaking down glucose to release energy, which happens in every cell.

2) Any three of, e.g. the heart rate increases / the breathing rate increases / respiration rate increases / more energy is released in the muscles / anaerobic respiration may begin.

3) glycogen

4) Proteases are used to pre-digest the protein in some baby foods so it's easier for a baby to digest.

5) carbohydrases

Exam Questions

1 (a) During vigorous exercise the body can't supply enough oxygen to the muscles *(1 mark)*. It uses anaerobic respiration to provide energy without using oxygen, which keeps the muscles going for longer *(1 mark)*.

(b) glucose → lactic acid + energy *(1 mark)*

(c) It causes a build up of lactic acid, which is painful *(1 mark)* and it doesn't release as much energy as aerobic respiration *(1 mark)*.

2 (a) isomerase *(1 mark)*

(b) Fructose is sweeter than glucose *(1 mark)*. This means the food industry can use less of it in foods, which is good for making slimming foods *(1 mark)*.

3 (a) Because during exercise the muscles need more energy from respiration, and this respiration requires oxygen *(1 mark)*.

(b) Because there is an oxygen debt / oxygen is needed to break down the lactic acid that has built up *(1 mark)*.

Page 52
Warm-Up Questions

1) deoxyribose nucleic acid

2) mitosis

3) ovaries and testes / reproductive organs

4) 46

5) 23

Exam Questions

1 Before the cell starts to divide, the DNA is duplicated *(1 mark)*. The cell then divides twice, during which the chromosomes line up in pairs and are pulled apart *(1 mark)*. Four gametes are produced, each with a single set of chromosomes *(1 mark)*.

2 (a) The results suggest that Mr X was at the crime scene, because his DNA profile has the same pattern as the DNA profile from the blood at the crime scene *(1 mark)*.

(b) It is true that usually everyone's DNA is unique *(1 mark)*, but identical twins have the same DNA and so would have identical genetic fingerprints *(1 mark)*.

3 (a) (i) Each cell should contain only three chromatids *(1 mark)*, and there should be one of each type *(1 mark)* as shown:

Remember that there are two divisions in meiosis. In the first division, one chromosome from each pair goes into each of two new cells. In the second division, both those cells divide again, with one half of each chromosome going into each of the new cells.

(ii) They contain half the genetic material that the original cell contained *(1 mark)*.

(b) Any three of, e.g. it involves two divisions, instead of one / it halves the chromosome number, rather than keeping it constant / it produces genetically different cells, not genetically identical cells / it produces sex cells/gametes, not body cells *(1 mark for each)*.

Page 57
Warm-Up Questions

1) It's the process by which a cell changes to become specialised for its job.

2) E.g. paralysis

3) a) XY   b) XX

Exam Questions

1 (a) They are undifferentiated cells *(1 mark)* that can develop into different types of/specialised cells *(1 mark)*.

(b) They could be grown into a particular type of cell, which can then be used to replace faulty cells *(1 mark)*.

(c) Any one of: embryonic stem cells have the potential to develop into any kind of cell, whereas adult stem cells can only develop into certain types of cell / embryonic stem cells are more versatile than adult stem cells *(1 mark)*.

(d) E.g. bone marrow *(1 mark)*.

(e) How to grade your answer:

0 marks: No reasons for or against using embryos to create stem cells are given.

1-2 marks: There is a brief description of at least one reason for and one reason against using embryos to create stem cells for research.

3-4 marks: The answer gives at least two reasons for and two reasons against using embryos to create stem cells for research. The answer has a logical structure and spelling, grammar and punctuation are mostly correct.

5-6 marks: The answer gives at least three reasons for and three reasons against using embryos to create stem cells for research. The answer has a logical structure and uses correct spelling, grammar and punctuation.

Here are some points your answer may include:
Reasons for:
Some people believe that curing patients who already exist and are suffering is more important than the rights of embryos.
The embryos used in stem cell research are usually unwanted ones that would probably be destroyed if they weren't used for research.
Any research done on stem cells in the UK must follow strict guidelines.

Reasons against:
Some people feel that human embryos shouldn't be used for experiments since each one is a potential human life.
Some people think scientists should concentrate on finding and developing other sources of stem cells, so people could be helped without having to use embryos.

2 50% or 1/2 *(1 mark)*. The chances of the child being a boy are the same (50%) at each pregnancy *(1 mark)*.

Pages 64-65
Warm-Up Questions

1) They're different versions of the same gene.

2) The allele which causes cystic fibrosis is a recessive allele, so people can have one copy of the allele and not have the disorder/show any symptoms.

3) It's a genetic disorder where a baby is born with extra fingers or toes.

4) A cell is removed from the embryo and its genes are analysed so that genetic disorders can be detected.

5) 1:1

Exam Questions

1 (a) No, because polydactyly isn't a significant health issue / embryos are only screened for serious genetic disorders *(1 mark)*.

(b) Certain types of gene increase the risk of cancer, but they aren't a definite indication that the person will develop cancer *(1 mark)*. Also some types of cancer can be treated successfully *(1 mark)*. It can be argued that it isn't right to destroy an embryo because it might develop a disease which could be treatable *(1 mark)*.

(c) Any one of: e.g. it implies that people with genetic problems are undesirable. / The rejected embryos (which could have developed into humans) are destroyed. / They may be worried that it could lead to embryo screening being allowed for other traits. *(1 mark)*

Extracts can be a bit scary — all that scientific information in a big wodge. Try reading the extract once, then reading the questions and then reading the extract again, underlining any useful bits. The extract's there to help you with the questions — so use it.

2 (a) White flowers *(1 mark)*

(b) (i) FF *(1 mark)*

(ii) ff *(1 mark)*

(iii) Ff *(1 mark)*

3 (a)

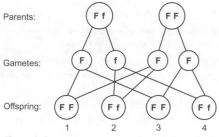

(1 mark for gametes correct, 1 mark for offspring correct)

(b) They will all be unaffected *(1 mark)*.

(c) (i) 1 in 2 / 50% *(1 mark)*

(ii) 2 and 4 *(1 mark)*

Page 69
Warm-Up Questions

1) Fossils are the remains of organisms from many years ago, which are found in rocks.

2) E.g. an animal's burrow / a plant's roots / a footprint

3) Some fossils are destroyed by geological activity, e.g. the movement of tectonic plates may have crushed fossils already formed in the rocks.

4) A species that doesn't exist anymore.

5) Isolation is where populations of a species are separated.

Exam Questions

1 (a) Inside the amber there is no oxygen or moisture *(1 mark)* so the insect remains can't decay / so decay microbes can't survive *(1 mark)*.

(b) E.g. a volcanic eruption / a collision with an asteroid *(1 mark)*.

2 (a) Teeth don't decay easily so they can last a long time when buried *(1 mark)*. They're eventually replaced by minerals as they decay (leaving a rock-like substance in the shape of the teeth) *(1 mark)*.

(b) Parts of Stegosaurus that were made of soft tissue will have decayed away completely, without being fossilised *(1 mark)*.

3 E.g. two populations of the original bird species became isolated/separated over the two islands due to a physical barrier (e.g. an earthquake) *(1 mark)*. Conditions on the two islands were slightly different *(1 mark)*. Each population showed genetic variation because they had a wide range of alleles *(1 mark)*. Different characteristics became more common in each population due to natural selection *(1 mark)*. Over time the two populations became so different that they couldn't interbreed any more *(1 mark)*.

Revision Summary for Biology 2b (page 70)

24) BB and bb

Pages 78-79
Warm-Up Questions

1) Mass number is the sum of the number of protons and the number of neutrons in an atom. Atomic number is the number of protons in an atom.

2) isotopes

3) A high boiling point.

4) When ionic compounds are dissolved the ions separate and are free to move in the solution. These free-moving charged particles allow the solution to carry electric current.

5) positive ions

6) negative ions

7) $Al(OH)_3$

Exam Questions

1 (a) An isotope is a different atomic form of the same element *(1 mark)*, which has the same number of protons *(1 mark)* but a different number of neutrons *(1 mark)*.

(b)

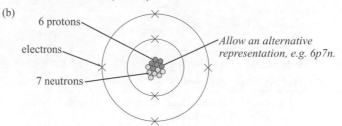

Allow an alternative representation, e.g. 6p7n.

(1 mark each for the correct number and placement of protons, neutrons and electrons)

(c) It has a different atomic number from carbon *(1 mark)*.

2 (a) 1 *(1 mark)*

(b) The relative mass of electrons is very small *(1 mark)*.

3 (a) lithium oxide *(1 mark)*

(b) (i) and (ii)

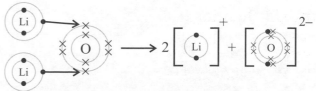

(1 mark for arrows shown correctly, 1 mark for correct electron arrangement and charge on lithium ion, 1 mark for correct electron arrangement and charge on oxygen ion).

244

4 (a)

(1 mark)   *(1 mark)*

(b) Mg^{2+} *(1 mark)* and F^- *(1 mark)*

(c) MgF_2 *(1 mark)*

(d) There are electrostatic forces of attraction between the ions *(1 mark)*.

(e) (i) There are strong electrostatic forces between the ions *(1 mark)* so a large amount of energy is needed to break these bonds/overcome these forces *(1 mark)*.

(ii) When the magnesium fluoride is molten the ions can move about and carry charge (i.e. conduct a current) through the liquid *(1 mark)*.

5 (a)

	Potassium atom, K	Potassium ion, K^+	Chlorine atom, Cl	Chloride ion, Cl^-
Number of electrons	19	18	17	18
Electron arrangement	2, 8, 8, 1	2, 8, 8	2, 8, 7	2, 8, 8

(1 mark for each correct column, maximum 3 marks)

(b)

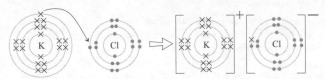

(2 marks — 1 mark for correct electron arrangements, 1 mark for correct arrow and charges on ions)

Page 86
Example

A is simple molecular, B is giant metallic,
C is giant covalent, D is giant ionic

Pages 87-88
Warm-Up Questions

1) In a covalent bond, the atoms share electrons. In an ionic bond, one of the atoms donates electrons to the other atom.

2) E.g. diamond is very hard and graphite is fairly soft. Graphite conducts electricity and diamond doesn't.

3) E.g. silicon dioxide/silica

4) Because the intermolecular forces between the chlorine molecules are very weak.

Exam Questions

1

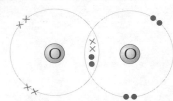

(1 mark for bonds shown correctly, 1 mark for correct number of atoms shown)

2 (a) (i) giant covalent *(1 mark)*

(ii) giant covalent *(1 mark)*

(iii) simple molecular *(1 mark)*

(b) It doesn't contain any ions to carry the charge *(1 mark)*.

(c) Each carbon atom has a delocalised electron that's able to carry the charge *(1 mark)*.

(d) All of the atoms in silicon dioxide and in graphite are held together by strong covalent bonds *(1 mark)*. In bromine, each molecule is held together with a strong covalent bond but the forces between these molecules are weak *(1 mark)*.

In order to melt, a substance has to overcome the forces holding its particles tightly together in the rigid structure of a solid. If the forces between the particles are weak, this is easy to do and doesn't take much energy at all. But if the forces are really strong, like in a giant covalent structure, you have to provide loads of heat to give the particles enough energy to break free.

3 (a) E.g:

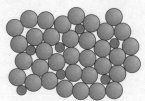

(1 mark for showing two different sizes of atoms, 1 mark for showing irregular arrangement)

(b) The regular arrangement of atoms in iron means that they can slide over each other meaning iron can be bent *(1 mark)*. Steel contains different sized atoms which distorts the layers of iron atoms *(1 mark)* making it more difficult for them to slide over each other *(1 mark)*.

4 (a) solid *(1 mark)*

(b) (i) giant covalent *(1 mark)*

(ii) giant ionic *(1 mark)*

(c) (i)

(1 mark for correct number of electrons in each shell, 1 mark for showing covalent bond correctly)

(ii) Oxygen has weak intermolecular forces between its molecules *(1 mark)*. It doesn't take much energy to separate the molecules *(1 mark)*.

(d) (i) It has delocalised electrons *(1 mark)* which are free to move through the whole structure and carry an electrical charge *(1 mark)*.

(ii) yes *(1 mark)*

Page 93
Warm-Up Questions

1) A shape memory alloy (about half nickel and half titanium) / a smart material

2) The higher the melting point the stronger the forces holding the polymer chains together.

3) crosslinks

4) E.g. the starting materials and the reaction conditions.

Exam Questions

1 (a) (i) nm *(1 mark)*

(ii) surface area *(1 mark)*, volume *(1 mark)*

(b) (i) The CNTs provide strength *(1 mark)* and lightness/low density *(1 mark)*.

(ii) fullerenes *(1 mark)*

(c) Any one of: e.g. in computer chips / in sensors / as catalysts / delivering drugs / in cosmetics / in lubricants *(1 mark)*.

2 (a) B *(1 mark)*

(b) C (accept A) *(1 mark)*

(c) A *(1 mark)*

Page 95
Top Tip
a) 30.0%

b) 88.9%

c) 48.0%

d) 65.3%

Page 96
Top Tip
CH_4

Page 98
Warm-Up Questions
1) The relative atomic mass.

2) The relative formula mass.

3) A mole is the relative formula mass of a substance, in grams.

4) One mole of O_2 weighs $16 \times 2 = 32$ g.

Exam Questions
1 (a) (i) Relative atomic mass *(1 mark)*.

(ii) Boron-11 has one more neutron in its nucleus than boron-10 *(1 mark)*.

(iii) Boron-11 must be the most abundant *(1 mark)*. The A_r value takes into account how much there is of each isotope, and in the case of boron it is closer to 11 than to 10 *(1 mark)*.

(b) (i) M_r of $BF_3 = 11 + (19 \times 3) = 68$ *(1 mark)*

(ii) M_r of $B(OH)_3 = 11 + (17 \times 3) = 62$ *(1 mark)*

2 (a) $100 - 60 = 40\%$ *(1 mark)*

(b) 40 g of sulfur combine with 60 g of oxygen.

$S = 40$ $O = 60$

$40 \div 32$ $60 \div 16$

$= 1.25$ $= 3.75$

$1.25 \div 1.25 = 1$ $3.75 \div 1.25 = 3$

Therefore, the formula of the oxide is SO_3 *(2 marks — 1 mark for correct working)*

3 (a) 100g .... reacts to give ... 56 g

1 g .... reacts to give ... $56 \div 100 = 0.56$ g

2 g .... reacts to give ... $0.56 \times 2 = 1.12$ g *(1 mark)*

(b) E.g. When transferring the $CaCO_3$ from the weighing apparatus to the test tube, or the CaO from the test tube to the weighing apparatus some of the solid may be left behind *(1 mark)*.

Page 103
Warm-Up Questions
1) Because a low product yield means that resources are wasted rather than being saved for future generations.

2) Instrumental methods are very sensitive, very fast and very accurate.

3) A gas chromatography machine can be attached to a mass spectrometer (GC-MS). The relative molecular mass of a substance can then be read off from the molecular ion peak on the graph the mass spectrometer draws.

Exam Questions
1 (a) From the equation, 4 moles of $CuO \rightarrow$ 4 moles of Cu
so 1 mole $CuO \rightarrow$ 1 mole Cu *(1 mark)*

$63.5 + 16 = 79.5$ g $CuO \rightarrow 63.5$ g Cu *(1 mark)*

1 g $CuO \rightarrow 63.5 \div 79.5 = 0.8$ g (1 d.p.)

4 g $CuO \rightarrow 0.8 \times 4 = 3.2$ g *(1 mark)*

(b) Percentage yield $= (2.8 \div 3.2) \times 100$ *(1 mark)* $= 87.5\%$ *(1 mark)*

(c) E.g. there may have been unexpected reactions (which used up the reactants so that there wasn't as much left to make the copper) *(1 mark)*. Some of the copper may have been left behind when it was scraped out into the beaker *(1 mark)*. Some of the copper may have been left on the filter paper *(1 mark)*.

2 (a) 4 *(1 mark)*

(b) 1 *(1 mark)*

(c) 3 *(1 mark)*

(d) 2 *(1 mark)*

Revision Summary for Chemistry 2a (page 104)
9) a) KCl   b) $CaCl_2$

10)

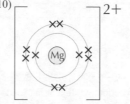

16) A: giant metallic, B: giant covalent, C: giant ionic

21) a) 40 b) 108 c) 44 d) 84 e) 106 f) 81 g) 56 h) 17

23) a) i) 12.0% ii) 27.3% iii) 75.0%

b) i) 74.2% ii) 70.0% iii) 52.9%

24) $MgSO_4$

25) 80.3 g

Page 112
Warm-Up Questions
1) E.g. the corrosion of iron is a reaction that happens very slowly. Explosions are very fast reactions.

2) Increase the temperature (of the acid).
Use smaller pieces of/powdered magnesium.
Increase the acid concentration.
Use a catalyst.

3) Measure the volume of gas given off by collecting it in a gas syringe/ monitor the mass of a reaction flask from which the gas escapes.

4) It would increase the time taken (i.e. reduce the rate of reaction).

5) By keeping the milk cool/storing it in a fridge.

Exam Questions
1 (a) Any two from: e.g. the concentration of sodium thiosulfate/hydrochloric acid / the person judging when the black cross is obscured / the black cross used (size, darkness etc.) *(1 mark each)*.

Judging when a cross is completely obscured is quite subjective — two people might not agree on exactly when it happens. You can try to limit this problem by using the same person each time, but you can't remove the problem completely. The person might have changed their mind slightly by the time they do the next experiment — or be looking at it from a different angle, be a bit more bored, etc.

(b)

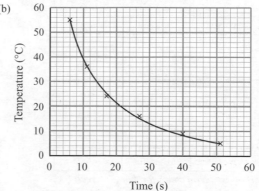

Time (s)
(1 mark for all points plotted correctly, 1 mark for best-fit curve)

(c) As the temperature increases the time decreases, meaning that the reaction is happening faster *(1 mark)*.

(d) Each of the reactions would happen more slowly *(1 mark)*, although they would still vary with temperature in the same way *(1 mark)*.

(e) E.g. by repeating the experiment and taking an average of the results *(1 mark)*.

2 (a) A gas/carbon dioxide is produced and leaves the flask *(1 mark)*.

(b) The same volume and concentration of acid was used each time, with excess marble *(1 mark)*.

(c) E.g. the marble chips were smaller/the temperature was higher *(1 mark)*.

(d) The concentration of the acid is greatest at this point, before it starts being converted into products *(1 mark)*.

Page 118
Warm-Up Questions

1) They must collide with enough energy.

2) There will be more frequent collisions so the rate of reaction will increase.

3) A catalyst is a substance which speeds up a reaction, without being used up in the reaction.

4) The temperature will decrease.

Exam Questions

1   How to grade your answer:

0 marks: No ways of increasing the rate given.

1-2 marks: One or two ways of increasing the rate are given. No discussion of collision theory is provided.

3-4 marks: At least two ways of increasing the rate are given. There is some relevant discussion of collision theory. The answer has a logical structure and spelling, grammar and punctuation are mostly correct.

5-6 marks: Detailed discussion of ways of increasing the rate and relevant collision theory is given. The answer has a logical structure and uses correct spelling, grammar and punctuation.

Here are some points your answer may include:

Collision theory says that the rate of reaction depends on how often and how hard the reacting particles collide with each other. If the particles collide hard enough (with enough energy) they will react.

Increasing the temperature makes particles move faster, so they collide more often and with greater energy. This will increase the rate of reaction.

If the surface area of the catalyst is increased then the particles around it will have more area to work on. This increases the frequency of successful collisions and will increase the rate of reaction.

Increasing the pressure of the hydrogen will mean the particles are more squashed up together. This will increase the frequency of the collisions and increase the rate of reaction.

2 (a) Neutralisation / Exothermic *(1 mark)*.

(b)

Time (s)	Temperature of the reaction mixture (°C)		
	1st run	2nd run	Average
0	22	22	22.0
1	25.6	24.4	25.0
2	28.3	28.1	28.2
3	29.0	28.6	28.8
4	28.8	28.8	28.8
5	28.3	28.7	28.5

(2 marks if all correct, 1 mark for 4 or 5 correct)

(c) (28.8 – 22.0 =) 6.8 °C *(1 mark)*

Don't get caught off guard — the maximum average change is just the highest average temperature minus the lowest average temperature.

(d) Exothermic *(1 mark)* because heat is given out to the surroundings/ the temperature of the reaction mixture increases *(1 mark)*.

Page 124
Warm-Up Questions

1) Neutralisation.

2) A salt and hydrogen gas.

3) Copper nitrate and water.

4) Add the insoluble base to an acid until all the acid is neutralised and the excess base can be seen on the bottom of the flask. Then filter out the excess base and evaporate off the water to leave a pure, dry sample.

5) barium chloride + sodium sulfate → barium sulfate + sodium chloride

Exam Questions

1 (a)

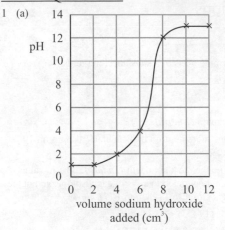

(1 mark for points plotted correctly, 1 mark for best fit curve)

(b) 7 cm³ (also accept answers between 6 and 8, depending on best fit curve at pH 7) *(1 mark)*.

(c) Because the starting pH is pH 1 *(1 mark)*.

This is the kind of question that can somehow trip you up, even if it seems obvious once you know the answer. So it's lucky you've come across it now rather than in the exam, isn't it? The pH before any alkali is added has to be the pH of the acid, and a pH of 1 means a very strong acid. See? Obvious.

(d) sodium sulfate *(1 mark)*

2 (a) It must be insoluble *(1 mark)*.

(b) silver nitrate + hydrochloric acid → silver chloride + nitric acid *(1 mark)*.

(c) First, filter the solution to remove the salt which has precipitated out *(1 mark)*. Then wash the insoluble salt *(1 mark)* and then leave it to dry on filter paper *(1 mark)*.

Page 130
Warm-Up Questions

1) It must be molten or dissolved in water.

2) Oxidation is loss of electrons and reduction is gain of electrons.

3) At the negative electrode.

4) Bromine.

5) The negative electrode.

Exam Questions

1 (a) (i) hydrogen *(1 mark)*

(ii) $2H^+ + 2e^- \rightarrow H_2$ *(1 mark)*

(b) (i) chlorine *(1 mark)*

(ii) $2Cl^- \rightarrow Cl_2 + 2e^- / 2Cl^- - 2e^- \rightarrow Cl_2$ *(1 mark)*

(iii) E.g. production of bleach / production of plastics *(1 mark)*.

(c) Sodium is more reactive than hydrogen, so sodium ions stay in solution *(1 mark)*. Hydroxide ions from water are also left behind *(1 mark)*. This means that sodium hydroxide is left in the solution *(1 mark)*.

2 (a) To lower the temperature that electrolysis can take place at *(1 mark)*. This makes it cheaper *(1 mark)*.

(b) $Al^{3+} + 3e^- \rightarrow Al$ *(1 mark)*

(c) Oxygen is made at the positive electrode *(1 mark)*. The oxygen will react with the carbon in the electrode to make carbon dioxide *(1 mark)*. This will gradually wear the electrode away *(1 mark)*.

Revision Summary for Chemistry 2b (page 131)

3 b)

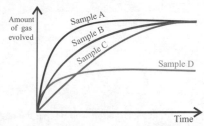

Pages 136-137
Warm-Up Questions

1) Speed

2) Acceleration — m/s², mass — kilograms (kg), weight — newtons (N)

3) $(30 - 0) \div 6 = 30 \div 6 = 5$ m/s²

4) Gravity

Exam Questions

1 (a) Because its direction is constantly changing. *(1 mark)*

(b) Acceleration = change in velocity ÷ time taken
= $(59 - 45) \div 5$
= $14 \div 5 = 2.8$ m/s²
(2 marks, allow 1 mark for correct working)

2 (a) (i) 200 m *(1 mark)*
Read the distance travelled from the graph.

(ii) $200 \div 15 = 13.3$ m/s (to 1 d.p.)
(2 marks, allow 1 mark for correct working)

(b) 13 s (allow answers from 11 s to 15 s) *(1 mark)*
The bus is stationary between about 33 and 46 seconds.

(c) The bus is travelling at constant speed (10 m/s) back towards the point it started from. *(1 mark)*

(d) E.g.

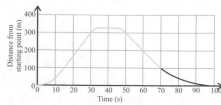

(1 mark)

3 (a) The cyclist is travelling at a constant velocity of 3 m/s. *(1 mark)*

(b) The cyclist's speed is constantly decreasing. *(1 mark)*

(c) $(3 - 0) \times (5 - 2) \div 2 = 4.5$ m *(1 mark)*
Remember, distance travelled is the area under the graph.

4 (a) Acceleration due to gravity, *g*, is lower on Mars than on Earth *(1 mark)*, because Mars has a smaller mass than Earth. *(1 mark)* So the ball's weight is less on Mars than on Earth. *(1 mark)*

(b) $3 \div 1.1 = 2.7$ (to 1 d.p.) So, the spring extends 2.7 times as far on Earth, so *g* on Earth must be 2.7 times bigger than on Mars. *(1 mark)*
$10 \div 2.7 = 3.7$ m/s² (to 1 d.p.)
(2 marks, allow 1 mark for correct working)

5 (a) Acceleration – change in velocity ÷ time taken
= $(10 - 0) \div 1 = 10$ m/s² *(1 mark)*

(b) Change in velocity = acceleration × time = $10 \times 3 = 30$ m/s
(2 marks, allow 1 mark for correct working)

(c) Assume $g = 10$ m/s².
Weight = mass × g = $0.12 \times 10 = 1.2$ N
(2 marks, allow 1 mark for correct working)

(d) None — the stone's acceleration due to gravity is determined by the mass of the Earth, not the stone. *(1 mark)*

6 All of them — everything with mass exerts a gravitational force. *(1 mark)*

Page 143
Warm-Up Questions

1) $(30 + 30) - 10 = 50$ N towards the shore

2) 0 N

3) The acceleration also doubles.

4) Against motion.

Exam Questions

1 (a) (i) 900 N – 900 N = 0 N *(1 mark)*

(ii) Parachutist A is falling at a constant (terminal) velocity. *(1 mark)*

(b) (i) Terminal velocity is reached when the force of air resistance equals the parachutist's weight. *(1 mark)*
Weight = mass × g = 70×10 *(1 mark)* = 700 N *(1 mark)*

(ii) Parachutist A would have a higher terminal velocity *(1 mark)* because he has a greater weight. *(1 mark)* This means the force of air resistance would need to be greater to balance his weight, and air resistance is greater at higher speeds. *(1 mark)*

(c) Because the parachute increases their air resistance/drag. *(1 mark)*

2 (a) The upwards force must be greater *(1 mark)* because Stefan is accelerating upwards. *(1 mark)*

(b) Assume $g = 10$ N/kg, Stefan's mass is $600 \div 10 = 60$ kg *(1 mark)*
Force = mass × acceleration = 60×2.5 *(1 mark)* = 150 N *(1 mark)*

3 (a) -500 N. *(1 mark)* If the bat exerts a force of 500 N on the ball, the ball also exerts a force of 500 N on the bat, but in the opposite direction. *(1 mark)*

(b) The ball's acceleration is greater *(1 mark)* because it has a smaller mass than the bat and receives the same force (F = ma). *(1 mark)*

Pages 149-150
Warm-Up Questions

1) The distance travelled in the time between a hazard appearing and the driver braking.

2) Braking distance

3) Because work done is a measure of energy transfer.

4) The energy an object has due to its vertical position in a gravitational field.

5) Friction as they enter the atmosphere transfers some of their kinetic energy to heat — the temperature gets so extreme that most burn up.

6) Elastic potential energy

7) The maximum force that an object can take and still extend proportionally.

Exam Questions

1 (a) (i) Accept answers between 12 and 13 m *(1 mark)*

(ii) 35 m *(1 mark)*

(iii) 35 m – 12 m = 23 m   or   35 m – 13 m = 22 m *(1 mark)*

(b) Braking distance *(1 mark)*
Using the graph, thinking distance is about 15 m and braking distance about 38 m.

(c) No, *(1 mark)* if stopping distance and speed were proportional the relationship between them would be shown by a straight line. *(1 mark)*

2 (a) $E_p = m \times g \times h = 2.5\text{ kg} \times 10\text{ N/kg} \times 1.3\text{ m} = 32.5\text{ J}$
(2 marks, allow 1 mark for correct working)

(b) $E_k = \frac{1}{2} \times m \times v^2$, so $v^2 = E_k \div (\frac{1}{2} \times m)$
$v^2 = 32.5\text{ J} \div (\frac{1}{2} \times 2.5\text{ kg})$
$v = 5.1\text{ m/s (to 1 d.p.)}$
(3 marks, allow 1 mark for correctly rearranging the equation and 1 mark for correct substitution of values into the equation)

(c) $F = k \times e$
$k = F \div e = 4\text{ N} \div 0.035\text{ m} = 114\text{ N/m (to 3 s.f.)}$
(3 marks, allow 1 mark for correctly rearranging the equation and 1 mark for correct substitution of values into the equation)

3 (a) $40\,000\text{ kg} \times 1.05\text{ m/s}^2 = 42\,000\text{ N}$
(2 marks, allow 1 mark for correct working)

(b) $42\,000\text{ N} \times 700\text{ m} = 29\,400\,000\text{ J}$
(2 marks, allow 1 mark for correct working)

(c) $29\,400\,000\text{ J} \div 29\,400\text{ N} = 1000\text{ m (1 km)}$
(2 marks, allow 1 mark for correct working)

(d) Heat/sound energy *(1 mark)*

4 (a) $\frac{1}{2} \times 2750\text{ kg} \times (12\text{ m/s})^2 = 198\,000\text{ J}$
(2 marks, allow 1 mark for correct working)

(b) The van has more energy as it has a bigger mass. *(1 mark)*

(c) $550\,000\text{ J} \div 25\text{ m} = 22\,000\text{ N}$
(2 marks, allow 1 mark for correct working)

Pages 155-156
Warm-Up Questions

1) Power is the rate at which work is done.

2) Momentum = mass × velocity $(p = m \times v)$

3) The total momentum before an event is the same as after the event.

4) Any two of, e.g. seat belts / air bags / crumple zones.

5) E.g. power of the engine, how aerodynamic the car is.

Exam Questions

1 (a) They help direct the kinetic energy of the crash *(1 mark)* away from passengers to other areas of the car. *(1 mark)*

(b) To increase the time it takes for the person to stop moving *(1 mark)* which reduces the forces acting on the chest. *(1 mark)* They also absorb some of their kinetic energy. *(1 mark)*

(c) Air flows easily over aerodynamic cars so there is less air resistance. *(1 mark)*. Cars reach their top speed when the resistive force equals the driving force *(1 mark)*. With less air resistance to overcome, aerodynamic cars can reach a higher speed before this happens. *(1 mark)*

2 (a) (i) Momentum = mass × velocity = $100 \times 6 = 600\text{ kg m/s}$ to the right
(2 marks, allow 1 mark for correct working)

(ii) $80 \times 9 = 720\text{ kg m/s}$ to the left
(2 marks, allow 1 mark for correct working)

(b) (i) Take left as positive, then the momentum of the two players is $720 - 600 = 120\text{ kg m/s}$. *(1 mark)*
The mass of the two players is $100 + 80 = 180\text{ kg}$, so the speed is $120 \div 180 = 0.67\text{ m/s}$
(2 marks, allow 1 mark for correct working)

(ii) Left *(1 mark)*
The two players travel in the direction player B was going because player B had more momentum before the collision.

3 (a) Energy transferred = power × time taken = $90\,000 \times 5$
$= 450\,000\text{ J} = 450\text{ kJ}$
(2 marks, allow 1 mark for correct working)

(b) (i) During braking, the vehicle's motor is put into reverse which slows the wheels. *(1 mark)* This motor acts as an electrical generator and converts kinetic energy into electrical energy *(1 mark)* which is stored as chemical energy in the vehicle's battery. *(1 mark)*

(ii) The energy transferred by braking is stored rather than wasted, e.g. as heat. *(1 mark)*

4 $E_p = m \times g \times h = 60 \times 10 \times 35 = 21\,000\text{ J}$
(2 marks, allow 1 mark for correct working)
Power = $E \div t = 2100 \div 50 = 420\text{ W}$
(2 marks, allow 1 mark for correct working)

5 momentum before = momentum after *(1 mark)*
$(1 \times 14\,000) = (1 \times -13\,000) + (235 \times v_2)$ *(1 mark)*
$14\,000 = 235v_2 - 13\,000$
$v_2 = (14\,000 + 13\,000) \div 235$
$= 115\text{ km/s to the right (to 3 s.f.)}$ *(1 mark)*

Page 159
Warm-Up Questions

1) Insulator

2) Positive and negative

3) Repel

4) Bad insulators

Exam Questions

1 (a) A *(1 mark)* The rod is negatively charged so would repel the negative charges in the balloon, making them move away from the rod. *(1 mark)*

(b) The negative charges in the rod attract the positive charges in the balloon. *(1 mark)* As Jane brings the rod closer to the balloon this attraction gets stronger, causing the balloon to move. *(1 mark)*

2 (a) Electrons are scraped from the cloth onto the surface. *(1 mark)*

(b) -23 *(1 mark)*

(c) E.g. metal *(1 mark)*

Page 165
Warm-Up Questions

1) Ohms, Ω

2) Potential difference = work done ÷ charge $(V = W \div Q)$

3)

4) E.g. automatic night lights / outdoor lighting / burglar detectors.

5) It decreases.

Exam Questions

1 (a) (i) Resistance = potential difference ÷ current = $1.5 \div 0.3 = 5\ \Omega$
(2 marks, allow 1 mark for correct working)

(ii) Charge = current × time = $0.3 \times 35 = 10.5\text{ C}$
(2 marks, allow 1 mark for correct working)

(b) The amount of current flowing will decrease. *(1 mark)*

(c) (i)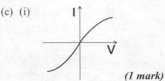
(1 mark)

(ii) As electrical charges flow through the filament some of the electrical energy is transferred into heat energy. *(1 mark)* This causes the ions in the filament to vibrate more *(1 mark)* which makes it harder for the charges to move through the filament, so the resistance increases. *(1 mark)*

2 (a) Diodes only allow current to flow in one direction. *(1 mark)*

(b) Resistance = potential difference ÷ current = $6 \div 3 = 2\ \Omega$
(2 marks, allow 1 mark for correct working)
Read the values from the graph, then use the formula $R = V \div I$.

(c) E.g. They use a smaller current. *(1 mark)*

Page 170
Warm-Up Questions

1) E.g. If you remove or disconnect one component, then the whole circuit is broken. / You can't switch components on or off independently.

2) The total resistance is the sum of all the resistances.

3) Series

4) the same

5) Parallel

Exam Questions

1 (a) Total resistance = $R_1 + R_2 + R_3 = 2 + 3 + 5 = 10\ \Omega$
   (2 marks, allow 1 mark for correct working)

   (b) The current will be 0.4 A *(1 mark)* because in a series circuit the same current flows through all parts of the circuit. *(1 mark)*

   (c) $V_3 = V - V_1 - V_2 = 4 - 0.8 - 1.2 = 2$ V
   (2 marks, allow 1 mark for correct working)

2 (a) 15 V *(1 mark)*
   Potential difference is the same across each branch in a parallel circuit.

   (b) Current = potential difference ÷ resistance = $15 \div 3 = 5$ A
   (2 marks, allow 1 mark for correct working)

   (c) $5 + 3.75 = 8.75$ A *(2 marks, allow 1 mark for correct working)*

Revision Summary for Physics 2a (page 171)

2) $a = (v - u) \div t$, $a = (14 - 0) \div 0.4 = 35$ m/s^2

7) $F = ma$, $a = F \div m = 30 \div 4 = 7.5$ m/s^2

8) Downward force of gravity on skydiver:
    $F = m \times a = 75 \times 10 = 750$ N.
    Resultant force at 80 mph:
    $F = 750 - 650 = 100$ N downwards.
    Resultant acceleration:
    $a = F \div m = 100 \div 75 = 1.33$ m/s^2

9) 120 N

12) Work done = force × distance.
     $W = 535 \times 12 = 6420$ J

13) $E_p = m \times g \times h = 4 \times 10 \times 30 = 1200$ J

14) $E_k = \frac{1}{2} \times m \times v^2$
     $E_k = \frac{1}{2} \times 78 \times 23^2 = 20\,631$ J

15) E_k just as it hits the ground = E_p at the top.   (g = 10 N/kg)
     So $E_k = m \times g \times h = 78 \times 10 \times 20 = 15\,600$ J

16) E_k transferred = work done by brakes
     $\frac{1}{2} \times m \times v^2 = F \times d$
     $\frac{1}{2} \times 1000 \times 2^2 = 395 \times d$
     $d = 2000 \div 395 = 5.1$ m
     The car would come to a stop in 5.1 m, so no, he can't avoid hitting the sheep.

18) $P = (m \times g \times h) \div t$ (g = 10 N/kg)
     $P = (78 \times 10 \times 20) \div 16.5 = 945.5$ W

24) $I = Q \div t$, so $I = 240 \div (1 \times 60) = 4$ A

28) $V = I \times R$, so $V = 2 \times 0.6 = 1.2$ V

30)a) Current is the same everywhere in the circuit and resistance adds up in a series circuit. Total resistance = $4 + 6 = 10\ \Omega$
       $I = V \div R = 12 \div 10 = 1.2$ A

   b) P.D. is shared between the bulbs. $V = I \times R = 1.2 \times 6 = 7.2$ V

   c) In parallel, the P.D. is the same over each branch of the circuit and is equal to the supply P.D., therefore the P.D. over either bulb = 12 V.

Page 180
Warm-Up Questions

1) 50 Hz

2) The neutral wire (also accept the earth wire).

3) Plastic is a good insulator.

4) Earth wire

5) Electrical energy (to kinetic energy) to heat energy.

6) E (energy) = Q (charge) × V (voltage).

Exam Questions

1 (a) (i)   brown *(1 mark)*

        (ii) blue *(1 mark)*

        (iii) green and yellow stripes *(1 mark)*

   (b) The live and neutral wires. *(1 mark)*

   (c) A fuse. *(1 mark)*

2   How to grade your answer:

       0 marks: There is no relevant information.

       1-2 marks: There is a brief description of how the earth wire and fuse protect the appliance and prevent electric shocks.

       3-4 marks: There is some description of how the earth wire and fuse protect the appliance and prevent electric shocks. The answer has a logical structure and spelling, punctuation and grammar are mostly correct.

       5-6 marks: There is a clear and detailed description of how the earth wire and fuse protect the appliance and prevent electric shocks. The answer has a logical structure and uses correct spelling, grammar and punctuation.

       Here are some points your answer may include:

       The earth wire and fuse are used to protect the circuit from being damaged by current surges.

       The metal case of the appliance is earthed using the earth wire. If the live wire touches the metal case, a huge current will flow through the live wire, through the case and then out through the earth wire.

       This surge in current melts the fuse, which breaks the circuit and cuts off the electricity supply. This isolates the whole appliance and protects the circuits and wiring in the appliance from damage.

       Isolating the appliance also makes it impossible to get an electric shock from the case.

       Shutting off the live supply also prevents fires caused by the heating effect of a large current.

3 (a) Power = current × potential difference = $0.5 \times 3 = 1.5$ W
   (2 marks, allow 1 mark for correct working)

   (b) Energy transformed = charge × potential difference = $900 \times 3 = 2700$ J
   (2 marks, allow 1 mark for correct working)

4 (a) The trace shows an AC source so cannot be from a battery / must be from mains electricity. *(1 mark)*

   (b) 20 ms *(1 mark)*
   The wave takes four divisions to repeat. 4 × 5 ms = 20 ms.

   (c) 20 ms = 0.02 s. Frequency = 1 ÷ time = $1 \div 0.02 = 50$ Hz
   (2 marks, allow 1 mark for correct working)

   (d) The amplitude (vertical height) of the wave will be decreased so the peaks and troughs will be smaller. *(1 mark)*

Page 187
Warm-Up Questions

1) Electrons

2) E.g. fallout from nuclear weapons tests / nuclear accidents / dumped nuclear waste.

3) Alpha particles

4) E.g. location and job.

5) Cosmic rays

Exam Questions

1 (a) (i)   -1 *(1 mark)*

        (ii) +1 *(1 mark)*

        (iii) 0 *(1 mark)*

   (b) Protons *(1 mark)* and neutrons *(1 mark)*

   (c) It increases by one. *(1 mark)*

   (d) It decreases by four. *(1 mark)*

(e) (i) The number of protons and neutrons in the atom. *(1 mark)*

(ii) Atom A and atom B *(1 mark)* because isotopes of the same element have the same atomic number. *(1 mark)*

(f) (i) They have opposite charge. *(1 mark)*

(ii) Alpha particles have a much greater mass. *(1 mark)*

2 (a) Most of the alpha particles went straight through the foil. *(1 mark)* But a small number of alpha particles were deflected straight back at them. *(1 mark)*

(b) E.g. Most of the atom is empty space. *(1 mark)* The nucleus of an atom is tiny *(1 mark)* and contains most of the mass *(1 mark)* and is positively charged. *(1 mark)*

Page 193
Warm-Up Questions

1) A weak alpha source is used to ionise the air between two electrodes so that a current can flow. If the alpha radiation is absorbed by smoke, the current stops and the alarm sounds.

2) Because it is ionising and can damage cells.

3) Alpha particles

4) Any two of, e.g. never look directly at the source / always handle a source with tongs / never allow the source to touch the skin / never have the source out of its lead-lined box for longer than necessary.

5) Any one of, e.g. wear lead aprons / work behind lead/concrete barriers.

Exam Questions

1 Smoke detectors *(1 mark)*

2 (a) Alpha radiation is stopped by the body's tissues and so wouldn't be detected externally. *(1 mark)* It is also strongly ionising which makes it dangerous inside the body. *(1 mark)*

(b) So that the device lasts a long time and therefore doesn't need to be replaced as often. *(1 mark)*

(c) So that the dose to the rest of the body is minimised, to reduce damage to healthy cells. *(1 mark)*

3 (a) The radiation can collide with molecules in the body's cells, causing ionisation and damaging the cell. *(1 mark)* This can then result in mutant cells dividing uncontrollably, which is cancer. *(1 mark)*

(b) It can kill cells, which causes radiation sickness if a large part of the body is affected. *(1 mark)*

4 (a) The average time taken for half of the unstable nuclei in a sample to decay / the time taken for the count rate or activity to halve. *(1 mark)*

(b) one quarter / 25% *(1 mark)*

(c) E.g. any two from: keep exposure time short / don't allow skin contact with sample / hold container at arm's length / wear protective lead clothing / put it in a lead container. *(1 mark for each)*

Page 197
Warm-Up Questions

1) E.g. uranium and plutonium.

2) It produces a lot of radioactive waste that must be carefully disposed of.

3) Clouds of dust and gas.

4) No — our Sun is a small star. Only big stars become black holes.

5) A red giant.

Exam Questions

1 (a) U-235 is bombarded with slow-moving neutrons *(1 mark)*. A U-235 nucleus captures a neutron *(1 mark)* and splits into two smaller nuclei and releases 2 or 3 neutrons *(1 mark)*. These neutrons go on to start other fissions, and so on, creating a chain reaction *(1 mark)*.

(b) The heat energy is used to heat water *(1 mark)* to drive a steam turbine and generator *(1 mark)*.

2 (a) Deuterium *(1 mark)* and hydrogen *(1 mark)*
Fission uses heavy elements, whereas nuclear fusion uses light elements.

(b) Fusion power would allow a lot of electricity to be generated from a plentiful fuel *(1 mark)* without the large amounts of waste currently produced by fission. *(1 mark)*

(c) Fusion only works at such high temperatures that it uses more energy than it can produce. *(1 mark)*

3 (a) Stars form from clouds of dust and gas which spiral in due to gravitational attraction. *(1 mark)* Gravity compresses the matter so much that intense heat develops. *(1 mark)* When the temperature gets hot enough, nuclear fusion happens and huge amounts of heat and light are emitted. *(1 mark)*

(b) The forces acting on a main sequence star are balanced, so it doesn't collapse or explode. *(1 mark)* The heat caused by nuclear fusion provides an outward force to balance the force of gravity pulling everything inwards. *(1 mark)*

(c) (i) They become unstable and eject their outer layer of dust and gases as a planetary nebula *(1 mark)* which leaves a hot, dense solid core known as a white dwarf. *(1 mark)* White dwarfs then cool to become black dwarfs. *(1 mark)*

(ii) They start to glow brightly again and undergo more fusion, and expand and contract several times. *(1 mark)* Heavier elements are formed and the star eventually explodes in a supernova. *(1 mark)* The supernova leaves behind a neutron star or a black hole. *(1 mark)*

Revision Summary for Physics 2b (page 198)

1) $f = 1 \div T$, so $f = 1 \div 0.08 = 12.5$ Hz

6) $E = P \times t$
Hair straighteners: $E = 45 \times (5 \times 60) = 13\,500$ J
Hair dryer: $E = 105 \times (2 \times 60) = 12\,600$ J
The hair straighteners use more energy.

7) $P = I \times V$, $I = P \div V$
a) $I = 1100 \div 230 = 4.8$ A, so use a 5 A fuse.
b) $I = 2000 \div 230 = 8.7$ A, so use a 13 A fuse.

8) $E = Q \times V$, $E = 530 \times 6 = 3180$ J

Exam Paper — Unit Biology 2

1 (a) (i) Number of clover Jeremy counted per m² = $(89 \times 2) - 96 = 82$ *(1 mark)*.
Mean number of buttercups per m² = $(57 + 63) \div 2 = 60$ *(1 mark)*.

(ii) $50 \times 70 = 3500$ m²
$6 \times 3500 = 21\,000$ dandelions
(2 marks for correct answer, otherwise 1 mark for correct working)
All you have to do is multiply the number of dandelions found in 1 m² by the total area of the field.

(b) E.g. they could take a larger sample size by using more quadrats / sampling more areas *(1 mark)*. They could choose the areas of the field to sample at random *(1 mark)*.

2 (a) oxygen *(1 mark)*
Remember, plants give off oxygen when they photosynthesise.

(b) The volume of gas collected would decrease because when the lamp is turned off the light intensity will decrease *(1 mark)*, so the rate of photosynthesis will decrease too *(1 mark)*.

(c) Carbon dioxide is needed for photosynthesis *(1 mark)*, so adding it to the water ensures that the rate of photosynthesis is not limited by a lack of carbon dioxide *(1 mark)*.

(d) The enzymes needed for photosynthesis work more slowly at low temperatures, so the rate of photosynthesis will be slower at low temperatures *(1 mark)*. But if the temperature is too hot, the enzymes are denatured so photosynthesis won't happen *(1 mark)*. The temperature could be controlled, for example by putting the beaker into a warm water bath to keep the temperature constant *(1 mark)*.

(e) Any three of, e.g. for respiration / for making cellulose for cell walls / for making amino acids/proteins / to store as starch / to convert into fats and oils for storage in seeds *(1 mark for each correct use)*.

3 (a) An organ is a group of tissues that work together to perform a certain function *(1 mark)*.

(b) E.g. muscular tissue *(1 mark)* — contracts to move the stomach wall and churn up food *(1 mark)*. Glandular tissue *(1 mark)* — makes/secretes digestive juices to digest food *(1 mark)*.

4 (a) Cell membrane *(1 mark)*. It controls what enters and leaves the cell *(1 mark)*.

(b) How to grade your answer:

0 marks: No relevant information is given.

1-2 marks: There is a brief description of one similarity and one difference between plant and animal cells.

3-4 marks: There is a description of two similarities and two differences between plant and animal cells. The answer has a logical structure and spelling, grammar and punctuation are mostly correct.

5-6 marks: A detailed description of three similarities and three differences between plant and animal cells is given. The answer has a logical structure and uses correct spelling, grammar and punctuation.

Here are some points your answer may include:

Similarities:

Both plant and animal cells have a nucleus, which controls the cell's activities.

Both plant and animal cells contain cytoplasm, which is where most of the cell's chemical reactions take place.

Plant cells and animal cells both have a cell membrane.

Mitochondria are found in both plant cells and animal cells.

Ribosomes are found in both plant cells and animal cells.

Differences:

Chloroplasts are present in plant cells, but not in animal cells.

Plant cells have a cell wall, but animal cells do not.

Plant cells contain a permanent vacuole, but animal cells do not.

5 (a) Each new plant would have inherited one allele for round seed coats and one allele for wrinkled seed coats *(1 mark)*. Since all the offspring had round seed coats, this allele must be dominant *(1 mark)*.

(b) (i) E.g. Parents' genotype:
Gametes' genotype:
Offspring's genotype:

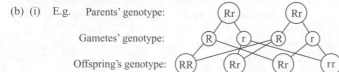

(1 mark for each correct level)

(ii) 5474 ÷ 1850 = 2.96 (to 2 d.p.), so the ratio is 2.96:1 *(2 marks for correct answer rounded to two decimal places, otherwise 1 mark for correct working)*

(iii) Because fertilisation is a random process / the genetic diagram only shows the probability *(1 mark)*.

(c) E.g. because scientists in Mendel's time had no knowledge of genes or DNA, so they did not understand the significance of his work *(1 mark)*.

6 (a) (i) As the rate of work increases Nancy's blood lactic acid concentration also increases *(1 mark)*. At higher rates of work Nancy's blood lactic acid concentration increases more quickly *(1 mark)*.

(ii) During vigorous exercise the body can't supply enough oxygen to the muscles so they start to respire anaerobically as well as aerobically *(1 mark)*. Anaerobic respiration produces lactic acid *(1 mark)*. The harder the muscles work, the more they'll resort to anaerobic respiration and the more lactic acid they'll produce *(1 mark)*.

(b) Nancy's pulse rate and breathing rate will remain high after her race *(1 mark)*. This is because after vigorous exercise the body has an oxygen debt *(1 mark)*. Her pulse rate and breathing rate remain high to help oxidise the lactic acid that has built up *(1 mark)*.

7 (a) (i) Approximately 37 °C (accept values between 35 °C and 40 °C) *(1 mark)*.

(ii) The increasing temperature causes the enzyme to change shape/denature *(1 mark)*. This means that it no longer matches the shape of the starch, so cannot catalyse its breakdown, so the time taken for the reaction to be complete increases *(1 mark)*.

(iii) E.g. proteases *(1 mark)*, lipases *(1 mark)*.

(b) Any two of: e.g. proteases are used to pre-digest proteins in some baby foods. / Carbohydrases are used to turn starch syrup into sugar syrup. / Isomerases are used to turn glucose syrup into fructose syrup. *(1 mark for each valid answer)*

(c) How to grade your answer:

0 marks: No advantages or disadvantages of using enzymes in industry are given.

1-2 marks: There is a brief description of one advantage and one disadvantage of using enzymes in industry.

3-4 marks: At least two advantages and two disadvantages of using enzymes in industry are given. The answer has a logical structure and spelling, grammar and punctuation are mostly correct.

5-6 marks: The answer gives at least three advantages and three disadvantages of using enzymes in industry. The answer has a logical structure and uses correct spelling, grammar and punctuation.

Here are some points your answer may include:

Advantages:

Enzymes speed up reactions without the need for high temperatures and pressures.

This means energy is saved, so costs are lower.

Enzymes are specific, so they only catalyse the reaction you want them to.

Enzymes work for a long time, so after the initial cost of buying, they can be continually used.

Disadvantages:

Enzymes can be expensive to produce.

Enzymes can be denatured at high temperatures.

Enzymes can be denatured by changes in pH.

Contamination of the enzyme with other substances can affect the reaction.

Exam Paper — Unit Chemistry 2

1 (a) 14 + (1 × 4) + 14 + (16 × 3) = 80 *(2 marks for correct answer, otherwise 1 mark for correct substitution)*

(b) [(14 + 14) ÷ 80] × 100 = 35% *(1 mark)*

(c) E.g. high boiling point *(1 mark)*, high melting point *(1 mark)*, dissolves easily in water *(1 mark)*, conducts electricity when melted or dissolved in water *(1 mark)*.

2 (a) The relative atomic mass of an element is the mass of one atom of that element compared with an atom of carbon-12 *(1 mark)*. It is an average value for the isotopes of that element *(1 mark)*.

(b) E.g.

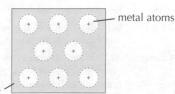

delocalised electrons   *(1 mark)*

The question asks for a labelled diagram, so if you don't label it, you don't get the mark.

(c) (i) The delocalised electrons within silver are able to move so heat is easily conducted across the metal *(1 mark)*.

(ii) The layers of atoms within silver are able to slide over each other *(1 mark)*.

(d) Particles that are 1-100 nm across *(1 mark)*.

3 (a) Any two of: e.g. reinforcing graphite in tennis rackets / lubricant coatings / drug delivery in medicines / as catalysts *(2 marks)*.

(b) (i) Each carbon atom has one delocalised (free) electron and it's these free electrons that conduct electricity *(1 mark)*.

(ii) Each carbon atom only forms three covalent bonds. This creates layers which are free to slide over each other *(1 mark)*.

(c) E.g. diamond *(1 mark)*. Each carbon atom forms four covalent bonds in a very rigid giant structure, unlike graphite *(1 mark)*. Fullerenes have carbon atoms arranged in hexagonal rings that form hollow balls or tubes, unlike in diamond *(1 mark)*.

4 (a) How to grade your answer:

    0 marks: No clear description or explanation of the properties of thermosetting or thermosoftening polymers.

    1-2 marks: Some attempt to describe the properties of thermosetting and thermosoftening polymers, but these are not explained.

    3-4 marks: The properties of thermosetting and thermosoftening polymers are described and some explanation is given. The answer has a logical structure and spelling, grammar and punctuation are mostly correct.

    5-6 marks: The properties of thermosetting and thermosoftening polymers are described and full explanations are given. The answer has a logical structure and uses correct spelling, grammar and punctuation.

Here are some points your answer may include:

Thermosoftening polymers are easy to melt.

When they cool, thermosoftening polymers harden into a new shape, so these plastics can be melted and remoulded.

Polymers are made up of lots of molecules joined together in long chains. Thermosoftening polymers don't have cross-linking between chains.

The forces between the chains in thermosoftening polymers are really easy to overcome, so it's easy to melt the plastic.

Thermosetting polymers are strong, hard and rigid.

Thermosetting polymers don't soften when they're heated.

Thermosetting polymers have crosslinks which hold the chains together in a solid structure.

(b) (i) C *(1 mark)*

    (ii) B *(1 mark)*

    (iii) Any two from: e.g. catalyst used, reaction conditions, starting materials *(2 marks)*.

5 (a) A reaction that gives out energy (usually heat) to the surroundings *(1 mark)*.

(b) E.g. measure the temperature of some water, add the solid and stir, then measure the temperature again *(1 mark)*. Repeat the experiment with other solids to determine which is the most effective. The same volume of water and mass of solid should be used for each experiment *(1 mark)*.

(c) A reaction that takes in energy (usually heat) from the surroundings *(1 mark)*.

6 How to grade your answer:

    0 marks: No advantages and disadvantages are given.

    1-2 marks: Brief description of at least one advantage and one disadvantage is given.

    3-4 marks: At least two advantages and two disadvantages are given. The answer has a logical structure and spelling, grammar and punctuation are mostly correct.

    5-6 marks: The answer gives at least three advantages and three disadvantages. The answer has a logical structure and uses correct spelling, grammar and punctuation.

Here are some points your answer may include:

Advantages:

Catalysts increase the rate of the reaction, which saves a lot of money because the plant doesn't need to operate for as long to produce the same amount of product.

A catalyst will allow the reaction to work at a much lower temperature. That reduces the energy used in the reaction (the energy cost), which can save a lot of money and also saves resources for future generations.

Catalysts never get used up in the reaction, so they can be used again and again.

Disadvantages:

Catalysts can be very expensive to buy.

Catalysts can be 'poisoned' by impurities, so they stop working. This means the reaction mixture must be kept very clean.

Catalysts often need to be removed from the product and cleaned.

7 (a) $60 \div 10 = 6$ cm^3/s *(1 mark)*

(b)

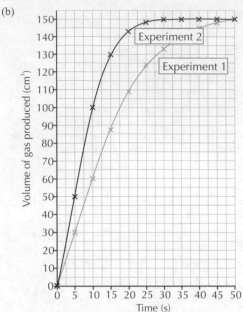

(1 mark for correctly plotted points, 1 mark for a good curve of best fit)

(c) 6-8 seconds (to collect 75 cm^3) *(1 mark)*

The total volume is 150 cm^3, so you need to read off the value from 75 cm^3 on your graph.

(d) The rate of reaction decreases as the reaction proceeds *(1 mark)*.

(e) It increases the rate of the reaction. The graph for experiment 2 has a steeper slope at the beginning. / The reaction is complete in less time *(1 mark)*.

8 (a) $2Cl^- \rightarrow Cl_2 + 2e^-$ *(1 mark)*
$2H^+ + 2e^- \rightarrow H_2$ *(1 mark)*

(b) (i) sodium hydroxide/NaOH *(1 mark)*

    (ii) E.g. the production of soap *(1 mark)*

    (iii) E.g. the production of bleach *(1 mark)* and plastics *(1 mark)*

(c) Coating of the surface of one metal with another metal using electricity *(1 mark)*.

9 (a) (i) The excess solid will just sink to the bottom of the flask *(1 mark)*.

    (ii) zinc chloride *(1 mark)* and water *(1 mark)*.

(b) E.g. using an indicator to show when the reaction's finished *(1 mark)*, add exactly the right amount of potassium hydroxide to just neutralise the hydrochloric acid *(1 mark)*. Then repeat the reaction using exactly the same volumes of alkali and acid so the salt isn't contaminated with indicator *(1 mark)*. Slowly evaporate off the water to crystallise the salt *(1 mark)*.

Exam Paper — Unit Physics 2

1 (a) (i) total momentum = 500 kg m/s + 200 kg m/s
    = 700 kg m/s to the east *(1 mark)*

    (ii) 700 kg m/s to the east
    (1 mark — must include units and direction)

(b) Momentum of Car K is $700 - 200 = 500$ kg m/s
Velocity = momentum ÷ mass = $500 \div 160 = 3.13$ m/s to the east
(3 marks for the correct speed, otherwise 1 mark for calculating the momentum of Car K, 1 mark for correct substitution. 1 mark for stating the correct direction.)

2 (a) acceleration = gradient of line = $-15 \div 7 = -2.14$ m/s² (to 2 d.p.)
(*2 marks for correct answer, otherwise 1 mark for correct substitution*)

(b) It increases (*1 mark*), as the brakes transfer the kinetic energy of wheels into heat energy (*1 mark*).

(c) E.g. they store some of the energy transferred by braking rather than wasting it (*1 mark*).

(d) E.g. driver tiredness (*1 mark*), influence of alcohol or other drugs (*1 mark*)

3 (a) work done = force × distance moved = 20 N × 300 m = 6000 J
(*2 marks for correct answer, otherwise 1 mark for correct substitution*)

(b) power = work done ÷ time taken, so
time taken = work done ÷ power = 6000 J ÷ 15 W
= 400 s
(*2 marks for correct answer, allowing follow through from part (a), otherwise 1 mark for correctly rearranging the formula or a correct substitution*)

4 (a) The air bag can change shape when a person hits it / slow a person down more gradually (*1 mark*). This absorbs some of the energy of the impact / increases the time over which the change of momentum happens which reduces the forces acting (*1 mark*).

(b) force = spring constant × extension, so
extension = force ÷ spring constant
= 13 500 N ÷ 180 000 N/m
= 0.075 m
(*3 marks for correct answer with unit, otherwise 1 mark for correct rearrangement of the formula or substitution, 1 mark for the correct numerical answer*)

5 (a) force = mass × acceleration, so
= 83 kg × 10 N/kg = 830 N
(*2 marks for correct answer, otherwise 1 mark for correct substitution*)

(b) How to grade your answer:
0 marks: There is no relevant information on the skydiver's motion.
1-2 marks: There is a brief description of the skydiver's motion.
3-4 marks: There is some description of the skydiver's motion, with brief reference to the forces acting on him. The answer has a logical structure and spelling, grammar and punctuation
5-6 marks: There is a clear and detailed description of the skydiver's motion, including details of the forces acting on him. The answer has a logical structure and uses correct spelling, grammar and punctuation.

Here are some points your answer may include:

At first, the slope of the graph is steep because he is accelerating as the force of gravity acting on him is much more than the frictional force slowing him down.

As his speed increases the friction builds up, so his acceleration is gradually reduced — shown on the graph by the gradient of the slope decreasing.

Eventually the frictional force is equal to the accelerating force and The skydiver no longer accelerates and travels at a constant velocity.

The constant velocity is shown by the flat line on the graph.

This shows that the skydiver has reached his terminal velocity.

6 (a) Circuit B has greater resistance (*1 mark*) and a smaller current (*1 mark*).

(b) Power = 3 V × 0.5 A = 1.5 W
(*2 marks for correct value with unit, otherwise 1 mark for correct substitution*)

(c) (i) A — LDR / light dependent resistor (*1 mark*)
B — thermistor (*1 mark*)

(ii) it decreases (*1 mark*)

7 (a) Alpha, because some of the radiation is stopped by the sheet of paper (*1 mark*).

(b) (i) E.g. alpha and beta radiation (*1 mark*).

(ii) The two types of radiation are deflected in opposite directions because they have opposite charges (*1 mark*). Despite having a larger charge, the alpha particles (that follow path 2) have a larger mass (*1 mark*), and so are deflected less by the electric field than the beta particles (that follow path 1) (*1 mark*).

(c) It detects background radiation (*1 mark*).

8 (a) The splitting of atomic nuclei (*1 mark*).

(b) Plutonium-239 / uranium-235 (*1 mark*)

(c) The joining together of atomic/light nuclei to form larger/heavier ones (*1 mark*).

(d) How to grade your answer:
0 marks: No advantages and disadvantages are given.
1-2 marks: Brief description of one advantage and one disadvantage.
3-4 marks: At least two advantages and two disadvantages are given. The answer has a logical structure and spelling, grammar and punctuation are mostly correct.
5-6 marks: Answer gives at least three advantages and three disadvantages. The answer has a logical structure and uses correct spelling, grammar and punctuation.

Here are some points your answer may include:

Advantages:

Much more energy is released by nuclear fusion than by nuclear fission for an equivalent mass of starting material.

Nuclear fusion does not produce radioactive waste.

There's no risk of nuclear fallout with nuclear fusion.

Hydrogen can be used as fuel for nuclear fusion — so there's no problem of fuel shortage.

Disadvantages:

Scientists have not yet found a way of getting more energy out of nuclear fusion reactors than they put in.

Nuclear fusion can only happen at very high temperatures.

The nuclear fusion reaction would need to be held in a magnetic field as the temperature would be too high for a physical container to be used.

9 (a)

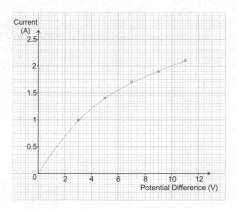

(*1 mark for correctly plotted points, 1 mark for good curve of best fit.*)

(b) The resistance of the lamp increases as the current increases (*1 mark*). The increased current causes the lamp to heat up, which makes the lattice ions of the metal filament vibrate more (*1 mark*). This leads to more collisions between lattice ions and charge-carrying electrons — increasing the electrical resistance (*1 mark*).

(c) 2 A (accept 1.95 to 2.05 A) (*1 mark*)

(d) Resistance = potential difference ÷ current
Resistance = 10 ÷ 2
Resistance = 5 Ω (*1 mark for value and 1 mark for unit. Allow follow-through from part (c)*)

Index

Index

Index